Optimization of Stochastic Systems

Topics in Discrete-Time Systems

MATHEMATICS IN SCIENCE AND ENGINEERING

A SERIES OF MONOGRAPHS AND TEXTBOOKS

Edited by Richard Bellman

University of Southern California

1. Tracy Y. Thomas. Concepts from Tensor Analysis and Differential Geometry. Second Edition. 1965
2. Tracy Y. Thomas. Plastic Flow and Fracture in Solids. 1961
3. Rutherford Aris. The Optimal Design of Chemical Reactors: A Study in Dynamic Programming. 1961
4. Joseph LaSalle and Solomon Lefschetz. Stability by Liapunov's Direct Method with Applications. 1961
5. George Leitmann (ed.). Optimization Techniques: With Applications to Aerospace Systems. 1962
6. Richard Bellman and Kenneth L. Cooke. Differential-Difference Equations. 1963
7. Frank A. Haight. Mathematical Theories of Traffic Flow. 1963
8. F. V. Atkinson. Discrete and Continuous Boundary Problems. 1964
9. A. Jeffrey and T. Taniuti. Non-Linear Wave Propagation: With Applications to Physics and Magnetohydrodynamics. 1964
10. Julius T. Tou. Optimum Design of Digital Control Systems. 1963
11. Harley Flanders. Differential Forms: With Applications to the Physical Sciences. 1963
12. Sanford M. Roberts. Dynamic Programming in Chemical Engineering and Process Control. 1964
13. Solomon Lefschetz. Stability of Nonlinear Control Systems. 1965
14. Dimitris N. Chorafas. Systems and Simulation. 1965
15. A. A. Pervozvanskii. Random Processes in Nonlinear Control Systems. 1965
16. Marshall C. Pease, III. Methods of Matrix Algebra. 1965
17. V. E. Benes. Mathematical Theory of Connecting Networks and Telephone Traffic. 1965
18. William F. Ames. Nonlinear Partial Differential Equations in Engineering. 1965
19. J. Aczél. Lectures on Functional Equations and Their Applications. 1966
20. R. E. Murphy. Adaptive Processes in Economic Systems. 1965
21. S. E. Dreyfus. Dynamic Programming and the Calculus of Variations. 1965
22. A. A. Fel'dbaum. Optimal Control Systems. 1965

MATHEMATICS IN SCIENCE AND ENGINEERING

23. A. HALANAY. Differential Equations: Stability, Oscillations, Time Lags. 1966

24. M. NAMIK OĞUZTÖRELI. Time-Lag Control Systems. 1966

25. DAVID SWORDER. Optimal Adaptive Control Systems. 1966

26. MILTON ASH. Optimal Shutdown Control of Nuclear Reactors. 1966

27. DIMITRIS N. CHORAFAS. Control System Functions and Programming Approaches. (In Two Volumes.) 1966

28. N. P. ERUGIN. Linear Systems of Ordinary Differential Equations. 1966

29. SOLOMON MARCUS. Algebraic Linguistics; Analytical Models. 1967

30. A. M. LIAPUNOV. Stability of Motion. 1966

31. GEORGE LEITMANN (ed.). Topics in Optimization. 1967

32. MASANAO AOKI. Optimization of Stochastic Systems. 1967

In preparation

A. KAUFMANN. Graphs, Dynamic Programming, and Finite Games

MINORU URABE. Nonlinear Autonomous Oscillations

A. KAUFMANN and R. CRUON. Dynamic Programming: Sequential Scientific Management

Y. SAWARAGI, Y. SUNAHARA, and T. NAKAMIZO. Statistical Decision Theory in Adaptive Control Systems

F. CALOGERO. Variable Phase Approach to Potential Scattering

J. H. AHLBERG, E. N. NILSON, and J. L. WALSH. The Theory of Splines and Their Application

HAROLD J. KUSHNER. Stochastic Stability and Control

Optimization of Stochastic Systems

Topics in Discrete-Time Systems

MASANAO AOKI
Department of Engineering
University of California
Los Angeles, California

1967
ACADEMIC PRESS New York • London

ACADEMIC PRESS INC.
111 Fifth Avenue, New York, New York 10003

United Kingdom Edition published by
ACADEMIC PRESS INC. (LONDON) LTD.
Berkeley Square House, London W.1

Library of Congress Catalog Card Number: 66-30117

PRINTED IN THE UNITED STATES OF AMERICA

To M. F. A. and C. A.

Preface

This book is an outgrowth of class notes of a graduate level seminar on optimization of stochastic systems. Most of the material in the book was taught for the first time during the 1965 Spring Semester while the author was visiting the Department of Electrical Engineering, University of California, Berkeley. The revised and expanded material was presented at the Department of Engineering, University of California, Los Angeles during the 1965 Fall Semester.

The systems discussed in the book are mostly assumed to be of discrete-time type with continuous state variables taking values in some subsets of Euclidean spaces.

There is another class of systems in which state variables are assumed to take on at most a denumerable number of values, i.e., these systems are of discrete-time discrete-space type. Although the problems associated with the latter class of systems are many and interesting, and although they are amenable to deep analysis on such topics as the limiting behaviors of state variables as time indexes increase to infinity, this class of systems is not included here, partly because there are many excellent books on the subjects and partly because inclusion of these materials would easily double the size of the book. The readers are referred to Refs. 47a, 52, 58, 63a, 74a and the books by K. L. Chung, J. G. Kemeny *et al.*, and R. S. Varga listed in the Bibliography.

Following the introductory remarks and simple one-dimensional examples to indicate the types of problems dealt with in the book, the procedures for deriving optimal Bayesian control policies for discrete-time stochastic systems are developed systematically in Chapters II through IV.

Those readers who are being exposed to the types of problems in the examples in Chapter I for the first time should glance over these examples without unduly concerning themselves with the question of how the optimal controls are derived and then come back to them after reading Chapters I and III.

Chapter II treats a class of stochastic control systems such that the complete information on the random variables in the system descriptions is available through their joint probability distribution functions.

Such systems are called purely stochastic. Chapter III treats a class of stochastic systems in which the joint probability distribution functions of the random variables are parametrized by unknown parameters in known parameter spaces. Such systems are called parameter adaptive.

Chapter IV presents the most general formulation of optimal Bayesian optimization problems in the book and is a generalization of the material in Chapters II and III. Advanced readers may go directly to Chapter IV to see the general mathematical formulation used. The material in Chapters II and III is included primarily for pedagogical purposes.

Since optimal control problems often involve estimation problems as subproblems, and since the topic is of interest in its own right, Chapter V is devoted to discussions of estimation problems of linear and nonlinear systems.

Chapter VI concerns the convergence questions in Bayesian optimization method and includes material on stochastic observability of systems. Some of the material in this chapter is relevant to learning systems.

Chapter VII presents approximations in control and estimation problems and current topics such as various suboptimal estimation schemes and construction of suboptimal control policies for adaptive systems.

Control problems discussed are mostly of finite duration, N. The behaviors of systems as $N \to \infty$ are only touched upon in Chapters VIII and IX.

Chapter VIII briefly describes the question of stability of stochastic systems. The last section of Chapter VI and this chapter constitute material on the quantitative aspects of discrete-time systems. Needless to say, the concept of optimal controls is meaningful only when the resultant system behaviors are stable. Implicit in this is the assumption that there is at least one control policy which makes the expected value of the criterion function finite. Although this point becomes important when the control problems with infinite duration are discussed, the stability question is considered primarily as an application of martingales discussed in Chapter VI.

This and some other topics not contained in previous chapters are mentioned in Chapter IX and some future problems are also suggested.

All my work on stochastic control systems included here has been supported by the Office of Naval Research. I am particularly grateful to Professor G. Estrin who has supported and encouraged my work in this area for many years since I was a graduate student, to Professor R. Bellman who introduced me to problems of optimization and suggested writing the book, to Professors Zadeh and Desoer who gave me the opportunity to visit the University of California, Berkeley and to give a seminar, and to Professors A. V. Balakrishnan and C. T. Leondes for their support of the seminar conducted at the University of California, Los Angeles. The book has been improved materially as the results of discussion with D. D. Sworder, R. E. Mortensen, A. R. Stubberud, and J. R. Huddle.

I want to express my sincere thanks and appreciation to my teachers, colleagues, and students for their help in preparing the book.

The following charts are included as an aid for those readers who wish to follow particular topics of interest.

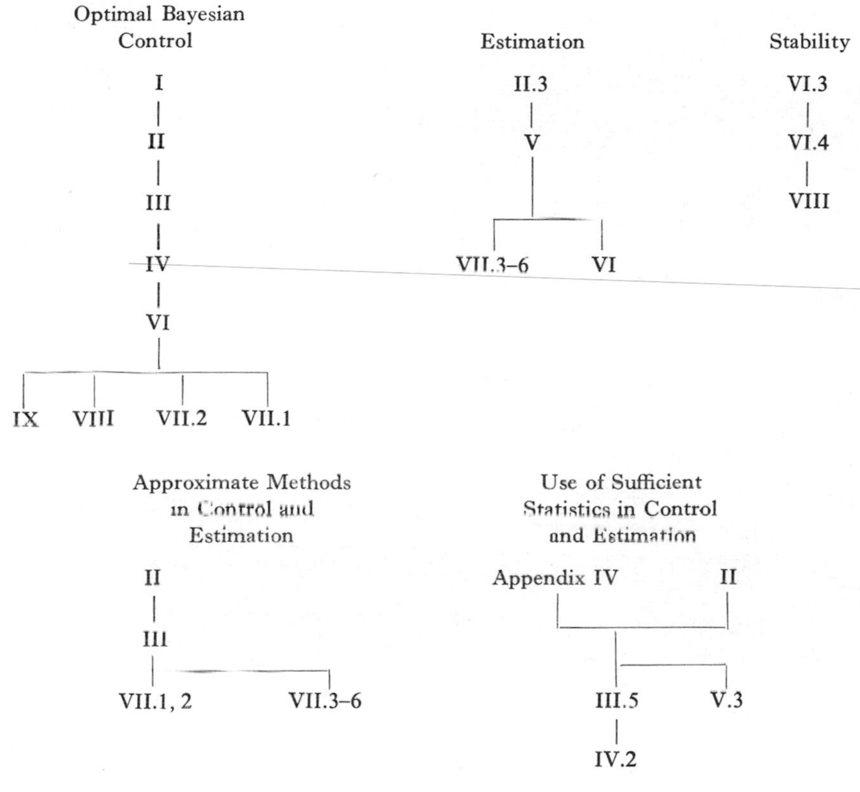

Los Angeles, California
December, 1966

MASANAO AOKI

Contents

Optimization of Stochastic Systems

Topics in Discrete Time Systems

Chapter I

Introduction

1. Introduction

There is a wide range of engineering problems in which we want to control physical equipment or ensembles of such equipment. These problems may range from a relatively simple problem of controlling a single piece of equipment, such as a motor, to a very complex one of controlling a whole chemical plant. Moreover, we want to control them in the best, or nearly best, possible manner with respect to some chosen criterion or criteria of optimality. These criteria are usually referred to as the performance indices, or criterion functions (functionals), etc.

In each of these control problems, we are given a physical system (a plant) that cannot be altered, and a certain amount of key information on the plant and the nature of the control problems.

The information on control problems may be classified loosely into four somewhat interrelated classes[57]*:

(1) requirements on over-all control systems to be synthesized,

(2) characteristics of plants,

(3) characteristics of the controllers to be used, and

(4) permissible interactions between the controllers and the plants.

The first class of information will include such things as the desired responses of the plants which may be given indirectly by the performance indices or directly in terms of the desired outputs of the plants, such as the requirement that outputs of plants follow inputs exactly.

* Superscript numbers refer to the references at the end of this book.

In the second class will be included descriptions of the dynamical behaviors of given plants. For example, plants may be governed by linear or nonlinear ordinary differential equations, difference equations, or by partial differential equations, the last being the case for distributed parameter systems. This class may also include information available on plant parameters and on random disturbances affecting the plant behavior, such as plant time-constant values, probability distribution functions of random noises acting on the outputs of plants, or random variations of some plant characteristics, and so on.

Available controllers may be limited in amplitude or in total energy available for control purposes. Controllers to be used may be capable of storing certain amounts of information fed into them. Their complexities may also be constrained. For example, for some reason we may want to use only linear controllers, or we may want to limit their complexities by allowing no more than a specified number of components, such as integrators and so on. This information is given by the third class.

Finally, the fourth class may include specifications on the types of feasible measurements to be performed on plants, on the ways actuators can influence plant behaviors, and generally on the way information on the states of plants is fed back to the controllers and descriptions of the class of inputs the controllers are expected to handle, etc.

The natures and difficulties of optimal control problems, therefore, vary considerably, depending on the kinds of available information in each of these four categories.

The theory of optimal control has reached a certain level of maturity, and we now possess such theoretical tools as Pontryagin's maximum principle,[114] dynamic programming,[20–22] functional analysis,[91] RMS filtering and prediction theory,[44,98] etc., in addition to the classical control theory, to synthesize optimal control systems, *given* the necessary information for the problems.

However, one major shortcoming of these theoretical tools is that they assume "perfect" information for the problems to be solved. Namely, for such theories to be applicable one needs information such as the equation for a system to be controlled, the mechanism by which the system is observed, the statistical properties of internally and externally generated noises affecting system performance, if any, the criterion of performance, and so on.

In other words, when all pertinent information on the structures, parameter values, and/or nature of random disturbances affecting the system performances are available, the problem of optimally controlling such systems can, in principle, be solved. Such a theory of optimal control might be termed as the theory of optimal control under perfect information.

In reality, the "perfect information" situation is never true, and one needs a theory of control which allows acceptable systems to be synthesized even when one or more pieces of key information required by the current optimal control theory are lacking.

This book is intended as an attempt to offer partial answers to the defects of "perfect information" optimal control theories. It primarily discusses optimal control problems with varying assumptions on items in Classes 2 and 4, and with relatively standard assumptions on items in Classes 1 and 3.

The main objective of the present book, therefore, may be stated as the unified investigation of optimal stochastic control systems including the systems where some information needed for optimal controller synthesis is missing and is to be obtained during the actual controlling of the systems.

In this book we are concerned with *closed-loop* optimal control policies of stochastic and adaptive control systems. More detailed discussion on the nature of optimal controls is found in Section 1 of Chapter II.

Although closed-loop control policies and open-loop control policies are equivalent in deterministic systems, they are quite different in systems involving random elements of some kinds.[99] For an elementary discussion of this point see, for example, S. Dreyfus.[49] Further discussions are postponed until Section 1, A of Chapter II.

Whatever decision procedures controllers employ in supplying the missing information must, of course, be evaluated by the consequences reflected in the qualities of control in terms of the stated control objectives or chosen performance indices. Statistical decision theory[29,115] will have a large part to play in synthesizing optimal controllers.

Papers on the theoretical and computational aspects of optimal stochastic and adaptive control problems began to appear about 1960.[3,21,55,60,61] In particular, in a series of four papers on dual control theory, Fel'dbaum recognized the importance of statistical decision theory.[55]

The major part of the present book is concerned with the question of how to derive optimal Bayesian control policies for discrete-time control systems. The derivation is somewhat different from that of Fel'dbaum, however, and is partly based on the method suggested by Stratonovich.[130] For similar or related approaches see Refs. 2, 54, 105a, 124, 132, 133, 141.

2. Preliminary Examples

In order to introduce the topics of the next three chapters and to illustrate the kinds of problems encountered there, very simple examples of optimal control problems are discussed in this section without showing in detail how the indicated optimal controls are derived, before launching into detailed problem formulations and their solutions. These simple examples will also be convenient in comparing the effects on the complexities of optimal control policies of various assumptions on the systems.

The readers are recommended to verify these optimal controls after becoming familiar with the materials in Chapters II and III.

The plant we consider in these examples is described by the first-order scalar difference equation

$$x_{i+1} = ax_i + bu_i, \qquad u_i \in (-\infty, \infty), \quad 0 \leqslant i \leqslant N-1 \tag{1}$$

where x, a, b, and u are all taken to be scalar quantities. The criterion function is taken to be

$$J = x_N^2$$

That is, a final value control problem of the first-order system is under consideration. We will consider only nonrandomized control policies in the following examples. The questions of randomized controls versus nonrandomized controls will be discussed in the next chapter. For the purpose of comparison, a deterministic system is discussed in Example 1 where the plant parameters a and b are assumed to be known constants. Later this assumption is dropped and the optimal control of System (1) will be discussed (Examples 2, 5–7) where a and/or b are assumed to be random variables. The effects on the form of control of random disturbances on the plant and observation errors will be discussed in Examples 3 and 4.

In all examples the control variable u is taken to be unconstrained. Optimization problems, where the magnitude of the control variable is constrained, are rather complex and are discussed in Ref. 45, for example.

A. Operations with Conditional Probabilities

Before beginning the discussion of examples, let us list here some of the properties of conditional probabilities[58] (or probability densities when they exist) that are used throughout this book. These are given for probability density functions. Analogous relations are valid in terms of probabilities. Some definitions, as well as a more detailed discussion of expectations, conditional expectations, and other useful facts and theorems in the theory of probabilities, are found in Appendix I, at the end of this book.

There are three basic operations on conditional probability density functions that are used constantly. The first of these is sometimes referred to as the chain rule:

$$p(a, b \mid c) = p(b \mid c)\, p(a \mid b, c) \tag{2}$$

Equation (2) is easily verified from the definition of conditional probability densities.

The second operation is the integrated version of (2):

$$p(a \mid c) = \int p(b \mid c)\, p(a \mid b, c)\, db \tag{3}$$

This operation is useful when it is easier to compute $p(b \mid c)$ and $p(a \mid b, c)$ than to compute $p(a \mid c)$ directly. For example, consider a system with a plant equation

$$x_{i+1} = F(x_i\, , \xi_j\, , \alpha) \tag{4}$$

where α is a random system parameter. Assuming that $p(\alpha \mid x_i)$ is available, this formula is used to compute $p(x_{i+1} \mid x_i)$, since $p(x_{i+1} \mid x_i\, , \alpha)$ is easily obtained from the plant equation (4) if the probability density $p(\xi_i)$ is assumed known.

The last of the three basic operations is used to compute certain conditional probability densities when it is easier to compute those conditional probability densities where some of the variables and the conditioning variables are interchanged. This is known as Bayes' formula:

$$p(a \mid b, c) = \frac{p(a \mid b)\, p(c \mid a, b)}{\int p(a \mid b)\, p(c \mid a, b)\, da} \tag{5}$$

or its simpler version

$$p(a \mid b) = \frac{p(a)\, p(b \mid a)}{\int p(a)\, p(b \mid a)\, da} \tag{6}$$

The Bayes formula is used, for example, to compute $p(x_i \mid y_i)$ given $p(y_i \mid x_i)$ where y_i is the observed value of x_i .

In this book the notation $E(\cdot)$ is used for the expectation operation. A detailed discussion of the $E(\cdot)$ operation can be found in Appendix I. This is a linear operation so that, given two random variables X and Y with finite expectations and two scalar quantities a and b,

$$E(aX + bY) = a\,E(X) + b\,E(Y) \tag{7}$$

This formula is also valid when $E(X)$ and/or $E(Y)$ is infinite when the right-hand side of (7) is well defined.

Another useful formula is

$$E(X^2) = [E(X)]^2 + \text{var}\,X \tag{8}$$

where var X is the variance of X which is defined to be

$$\text{var}\,X = E(X - EX)^2 \tag{9}$$

B. Example 1. Deterministic Control System

Suppose we have a scalar deterministic control system described by the difference equation (1) with a and b known and observed by

$$y_i = x_i\,, \qquad 0 \leqslant i \leqslant N - 1 \tag{10}$$

Such a system is drawn schematically in Fig. 1.1. Equation (10) shows that the state of the system is observed exactly. That is, the control system of Example 1 is deterministic, completely specified, and its state is exactly measured. This final control problem has a very simple optimal control policy. Since

$$J = x_N{}^2 = (ax_{N-1} + bu_{N-1})^2$$

clearly an optimal control variable at time $N - 1$, denoted by u_{N-1}^*, is given by

$$u_{N-1}^* = -ax_{N-1}/b \tag{11}$$

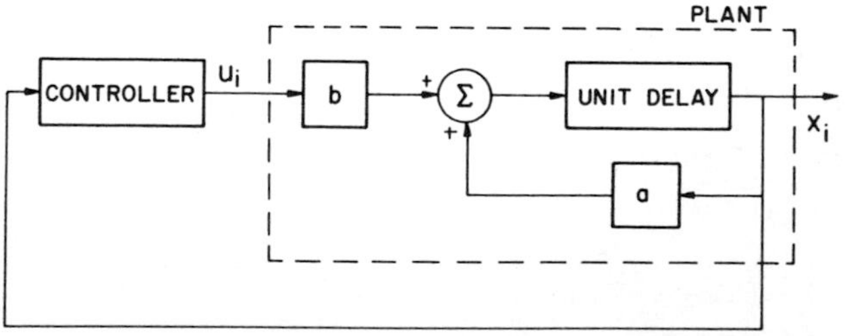

Fig. 1.1. System with deterministic plant and with exact measurement. a, b are known constants.

$u_0{}^*, u_1{}^*, \ldots, u_{N-2}^*$ are arbitrary, and $\min J = 0$. Actually in this example we can choose any one or several of the N control variables $u_0, u_1, \ldots, u_{N-1}$ appropriately to minimize J. For the purpose of later comparisons we will consider the policy given by (11) and choose $u_i{}^* = -ax_i/b$, $i = 0, 1, \ldots, N-1$.

From (11) we see that this optimal control policy requires, among other things, that (i) a and b of (1) be exactly known, and that (ii) x_{N-1} be exactly observable as indicated by (10). When both of these assumptions are not satisfied, the optimal control problem of even such a simple problem is no longer trivial.

Optimal control problems without Assumptions (i) and/or (ii) will be discussed later. Now let us discuss the optimal control problem of a related stochastic system where the plant time-constant a of (1) is assumed to be a random variable.

C. Example 2. Stochastic Control System: System with Random Time Constant

Consider a discrete-time control system

$$x_{i+1} = a_i x_i + bu_i\,, \qquad u_i \in (-\infty, \infty) \tag{12}$$

$$x_0 \quad \text{given}$$

$$y_i = x_i\,, \qquad 0 \leqslant i \leqslant N-1 \tag{13}$$

where $\{a_i\}$ is a sequence of independently and identically distributed random variables with *known* mean θ and *known* variance σ^2. This system is a slight modification of the system of Example 1. It is given schematically in Fig. 1.2. The criterion function is still the same $x_N{}^2$. Since x_N

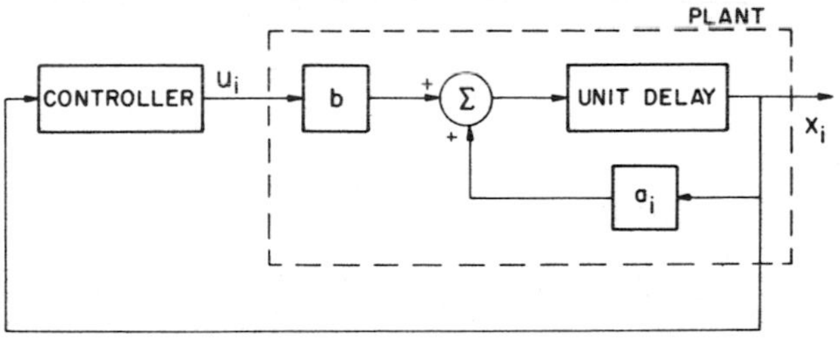

Fig. 1.2. System with random plant and with exact measurement. a_i are independently and identically distributed random variable with known mean and variance; b is a known constant.

is a random variable now, an optimal control policy is a control policy which minimizes the expected value of J, EJ.

Consider the problems of choosing u_{N-1} at the $(N-1)$th control stage. Since

$$Ex_N^2 = E[E(x_N^2 \mid x_0, x_1, \ldots, x_{N-1}, u_0, u_1, \ldots, u_{N-1})] \tag{14}$$

where the outer expectation operation is taken with respect to the random variables x_0, x_1, x_{N-1},* Ex_N^2 is minimized by minimizing the inner conditional expectation with respect to u_{N-1} for every possible collection of $x_0, \ldots, x_{N-1}, u_0, \ldots, u_{N-1}$. Now

$$\begin{aligned} E(x_N^2 \mid x_0, \ldots, x_{N-1}, u_0, \ldots, u_{N-1}) &= E(a_{N-1}x_{N-1} + bu_{N-1})^2 \\ &= (\theta x_{N-1} + bu_{N-1})^2 + \sigma^2 x_{N-1}^2 \end{aligned} \tag{15}$$

where u_{N-1} is taken to be some definite (i.e., nonrandom) function of $x_0, x_1, \ldots, x_{N-1}$. In obtaining the last expression in (15), use is made of the basic formula of the expectation operations (7) and (8). From (15),

$$u_{N-1}^* = -\theta x_{N-1}/b \tag{16}$$

and

$$\min_{u_{N-1}} E(x_N^2 \mid x_0, \ldots, x_{N-1}, u_0, \ldots, u_{N-1}) = \sigma^2 x_{N-1}^2 \tag{17}$$

By assumption, σ is a known constant. Therefore, the problem of choosing u_{N-2} is identical to that of choosing u_{N-1}. Namely, instead of choosing u_{N-1} to minimize Ex_N^2, u_{N-2} is now chosen to minimize $\sigma^2 E(x_{N-1}^2)$. Thus it is generally seen that each control stage can be optimized separately with

$$u_i^* = -\theta x_i/b, \qquad 0 \leqslant i \leqslant N-1 \tag{18}$$

and

$$\min_{u_0, \ldots, u_{N-1}} EJ = \sigma^{2N} x_0^2 \tag{19}$$

This problem can also be treated by a routine application of dynamic programming.[20] Define

$$I_{N-n}(x) = \min_{u_n, \ldots, u_{N-1}} E(x_N^2 \mid x_n = x \text{ at time } n) \tag{20}$$

---

* Since only nonrandomized closed-loop control policies are under consideration, $u_0, \ldots, u_{N-1}$ are some definite functions of $x_0, \ldots, x_{N-1}$ for any given control policy.

$I_{N-n}(x)$ is the expected value of x_N^2 starting from x at time n employing an optimal sequence of controls $u_n ,..., u_{N-1}$. Then, invoking the principle of optimality, I_{N-n} satisfies the functional equation

$$I_{N-n}(x_n) = \min_{u_n} E(I_{N-n-1}(x') \mid x_n) \tag{21}$$

where

$$x' = a_n x_n + b u_n$$

To solve (21), it is easily seen that $I_{N-n}(x_n)$ is quadratic in x_n ; therefore, put

$$I_{N-n}(x_n^2) = Q_{N-n} x_n^2 + \mu_{N-n} , \qquad 0 \leqslant n \leqslant N \tag{22}$$

where Q's and μ's are to be determined. Since $I_0(x_N) = x_N^2$, we have

$$Q_0 = 1, \qquad \mu_0 = 0 \tag{23}$$

From (21)–(23) one obtains

$$Q_n = \sigma^{2n} \tag{24}$$

$$\mu_n = 0, \qquad 0 \leqslant n \leqslant N \tag{25}$$

therefore

$$\min_{u_0,\ldots,u_{N-1}} E x_N^2 = \sigma^{2N} x_0^2$$

with

$$u_i^* = -\theta x_i / b, \qquad 0 \leqslant i \leqslant N-1 \tag{26}$$

Comparing (18) with (11) of the previous example, one notices that $u_0 , u_1 ,..., u_{N-2}$ are no longer arbitrary and the mean θ is regarded as "a" of the deterministic system.

If you consider a system associated with (12) where the random variable a_i is replaced by its expected value θ, then we have a deterministic system

$$x_{i+1} = \theta x_i + b u_i$$

with

$$y_i = x_i , \qquad i = 0, 1,..., N-1$$

If you consider a control problem with this plant equation replacing the original system (12), then from (11) the optimal control policy for this associated system is such that

$$u_{N-1}^* = -\theta x_{N-1} / b$$

which turns out to be identical with the optimal control at time $N - 1$ for the original system (12). This is an example of applying what is known as the certainty equivalence principle,[49,136a] where a given stochastic system is replaced by a corresponding deterministic system by substituting expected values for random variables. Sometimes optimal control policies for the deterministic system thus obtained are also optimal for the original stochastic systems.

The detailed discussion of this principle is deferred until Chapter II, Section 2.

Systems involving randomness of one sort or another are called stochastic to distinguish them from deterministic control systems. The adjective "purely" is used to differentiate stochastic systems with known probability distribution functions or moments, such as mean and variance, from stochastic systems in which some of the key statistical information is lacking, or incomplete. Such systems will be called adaptive to differentiate them from purely stochastic systems. The system of this section is therefore a simple example of a purely stochastic control system. One can go a step further in this direction and consider an adaptive system, for example, by assuming that the mean θ is random with a given a priori distribution for θ. Before doing this, let us go back to the basic system of Example 1 and add random disturbances to the state variable measurement (10) and/or to the plant equation (1).

D. Example 3. Stochastic Control System: System with Noisy Observation

Let us now assume that the observations of state variables are noisy. Figure 1.3 is the schematic diagram of this system. Later, in Example 4 of this section, as well as in Chapters III and IV, we will consider

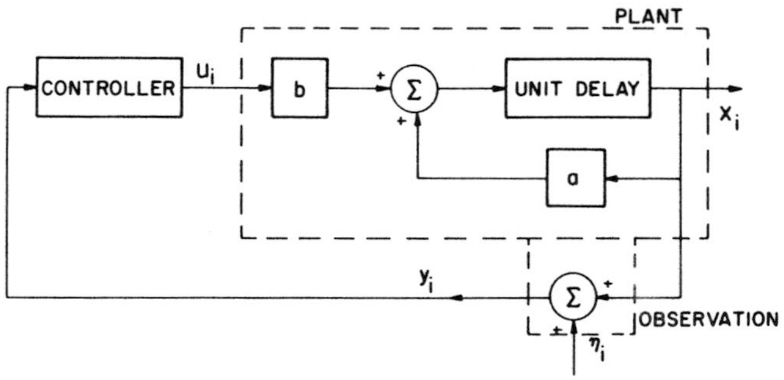

Fig. 1.3. System with deterministic plant and with noisy measurement. a, b are known constants, and η_i are measurement noises.

several such examples which show that the optimal control problems with noisy observations are substantially more difficult than those with exact state variable observations.

In this example, the plant parameters a and b are still assumed given, but instead of (10) we now assume that

$$y_i = x_i + \eta_i, \qquad 0 \leqslant i \leqslant N-1 \tag{27}$$

where η_i is the noise in the observation mechanism (observation error random variable of the system at time i). Its first and second moments are assumed given. Otherwise, the system is that of Example 1. Note that it is no longer possible to say as we did in Example 1 that the control variable of (11) is optimal, since what we know at time $N-1$ is the collection $y_{N-1}, y_{N-2}, \ldots, y_0$ rather than that of $x_{N-1}, x_{N-2}, \ldots, x_0$; i.e., x_{N-1} is not available for the purpose of synthesizing control variable u_{N-1}. We must now consider closed-loop control policies where u_i is some deterministic function of the current and past observations on the system state variable and of past employed controls. That is, the control is taken to be

$$u_i = \phi_i(y_0, y_1, \ldots, y_i, u_0, \ldots, u_{i-1})$$

and the function $\phi_0, \phi_1, \ldots, \phi_{N-1}$ must be chosen to minimize EJ. Control policies are discussed in Section 1, A, Chapter II.

Denote the conditional mean and variance of x_i by

$$E(x_i \mid y_0, \ldots, y_i) = \mu_i \tag{28}$$

and

$$\operatorname{var}(x_i \mid y_0, \ldots, y_i) = \sigma_i^2, \qquad 0 \leqslant i \leqslant N-1 \tag{29}$$

Then, from (7), (9), (28), and (29),

$$\begin{aligned} E(x_N^2 \mid y_0, \ldots, y_{N-1}, u_0, \ldots, u_{N-1}) &\\ = E[(ax_{N-1} + bu_{N-1})^2 \mid y_0, \ldots, y_{N-1}, u_0, \ldots, u_{N-1}] &\\ = (a\mu_{N-1} + bu_{N-1})^2 + a^2\sigma_{N-1}^2 & \qquad (30) \end{aligned}$$

By choosing u_{N-1} to minimize (30) for given $y_0, \ldots, y_{N-1}, u_0, \ldots, u_{N-1}$, Ex_N^2 is minimized, since

$$Ex_N^2 = E[E(x_N^2 \mid y^{N-1}, u^{N-1})] \tag{31}$$

where the outer expectation is with respect to all possible y^{N-1} and u^{N-1}, where the notation y^{N-1} is used for $y_0, \ldots, y_{N-1}$ and u^{N-1} for $u_0, \ldots, u_{N-1}$.

If σ_{N-1} is independent of u_{N-1}, then

$$\begin{aligned} u_{N-1}^* &= -a\mu_{N-1}/b \\ &= -a\,E(x_{N-1} \mid y^{N-1})/b, \qquad u_0, \ldots, u_{N-2} \ \text{arbitrary} \end{aligned} \tag{32}$$

is optimal in the sense that this control policy minimized EJ, and

$$\min_{u_{N-1}} E(J \mid y^{N-1}, u^{N-1}) = a^2\sigma_{N-1}^2 \tag{33}$$

Note that the problem of choosing u_{N-1} optimally is reduced to that of estimating x_{N-1} given y^{N-1} by the conditional mean μ_{N-1}. Later we will see how to generate such estimates using additional assumptions on the observation noises. See, for example, Section 3, Chapter II, and Section 2, Chapter III.

Note also that one of the effects of noisy observations is to increase the minimal EJ value by some positive constant value proportional to the variance of the noise.

E. Example 4. Stochastic Control System: System with Additive Plant Noise

The system to be considered next is that of Example 1, with random disturbances added to the plant equation:

$$x_{i+1} = ax_i + bu_i + \xi_i, \qquad u_i \in (-\infty, \infty), \quad 0 \leqslant i \leqslant N-1 \tag{34}$$

x_0 given

$$y_i = x_i, \qquad 0 \leqslant i \leqslant N-1 \tag{35}$$

where ξ_i are independent with

$$E(\xi_i) = 0 \tag{36}$$

$$E(\xi_i^2) = \sigma_i^2, \qquad 0 \leqslant i \leqslant N-1 \tag{37}$$

See Fig. 1.4 for the schematic diagram.

Proceeding as in Example 2,

$$E(x_N^2 \mid x^{N-1}, u^{N-1}) = (ax_{N-1} + bu_{N-1})^2 + \sigma_{N-1}^2 \tag{38}$$

since

$$E(x_N \mid x_{N-1}, u_{N-1}) = ax_{N-1} + bu_{N-1}$$

and

$$\operatorname{var}(x_N \mid x_{N-1}, u_{N-1}) = \sigma_{N-1}^2$$

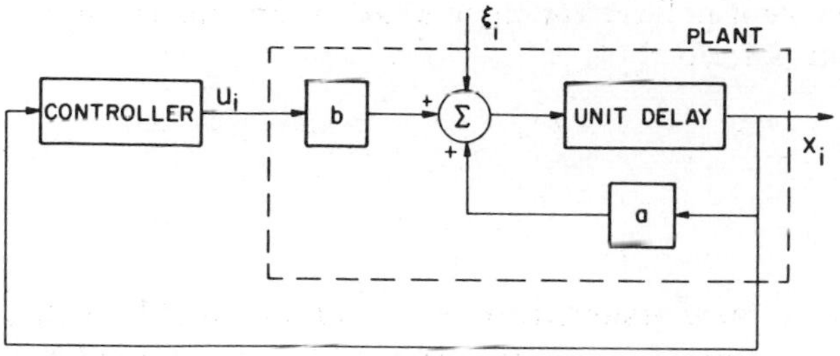

Fig. 1.4. System with deterministic plant, with additive random plant disturbances, and with exact measurement. a, b are known constants, and ξ_i are random disturbances on the plant.

because the conditional probability density $p(x_N \mid x_{N-1}, u_{N-1})$ is given by that of ξ_{N-1} with $\xi_{N-1} = x_N - ax_{N-1} - u_{N-1}$. From (38), the optimal policy is given by

$$u_{N-1}^* = -ax_{N-1}/b \tag{39}$$

since σ_{N-1} is a constant independent of u_{N-1}. Observe that the random disturbance in the plant equation has an effect on EJ similar to that of the disturbance in the observation equation. In both cases the minimum of $E(J \mid y^{N-1})$ is increased by an amount proportional to the variance of the disturbances. Since the mean of ξ_i is zero, the system of Example 1 is the deterministic system obtained from the system of Example 4 by replacing ξ_i by its mean, i.e., by applying the certainty equivalence principle to the system. Comparing (11) with (39), the optimal control policy for this system is seen to be identical with that of Example 1.

Comparing Example 3 with Example 4, the optimal control policy for Example 4 is seen to be simpler. In Example 3 it is necessary to compute μ's, whereas the optimal control policy for Example 4 is the same as that of Example 1.

As this example indicates, it is typically more difficult to obtain optimal control policies for systems with noisy state vector observations than with exact state vector measurements.

F. Example 5. Stochastic Control System: System with Unknown Time Constant

In Examples 1, 3, and 4, it is essential that the plant time-constant a be known exactly since it appears explicitly in the expressions for optimal control policies for these systems. In this example, we consider the system described by

$$x_{i+1} = ax_i + bu_i , \qquad u_i \in (-\infty, \infty) \tag{40}$$

$$y_i = x_i + \eta_i \tag{41}$$

$$J = x_N^2 \tag{42}$$

where "a" is now assumed to be a random variable with known mean and variance and where η's are assumed to be independent. It is further assumed that "a" is independent of η's and that

$$E(a) = \alpha \tag{43}$$

$$\text{var}(a) = \sigma_1^2 \tag{44}$$

where α and σ_1 are assumed known.

One may interpret the value of the time-constant "a" as a sample from a common distribution function with known mean and variance. Such a situation may arise when the plant under consideration is one of the many manufactured in which, due to the manufacturing tolerances, the time-constant of the plant is known to have a statistical distribution with known mean and variance. The noise in the observation (41) prevents the determination of "a" exactly by measuring the state variables at two or more distinct time instants.

This problem is a simple example of plant parameter adaptive control systems. Later we consider another parameter adaptive system, in Section H (Example 7).

In Example 3, we have derived the optimal control policy when a is a known constant. There we have

$$u_{N-1}^* = -a\mu_{N-1}/b$$

In this example a is not known exactly. In Examples 1 and 3, by comparing (11) and (32) we see that the only change in u_{N-1} when the observations are noisy is to replace x_{N-1} by its conditional mean value μ_{N-1}. In Example 2, where the time constant is chosen independently from the common distribution at each time instant, the time-constant a in the optimal control of (11) has been replaced by the mean value in the optimal control of (18). Therefore, it is not unreasonable to expect that

$$u_{N-1} = -\alpha_{N-1}\mu_{N-1}/b \tag{45}$$

is optimal where the random variable a is replaced by its a posteriori mean value

$$\alpha_{N-1} \triangleq E(a \mid y^{N-1})$$

The control of (45) is *not* optimal. Namely, the optimal control policy for Example 5 cannot be derived by applying the certainty equivalence principle mentioned in Examples 2 and 4.

To obtain the optimal control at time $N - 1$, compute

$$\begin{aligned} E(x_N^2 \mid y^{N-1}, u^{N-1}) &= \int x_N^2 \, p(x_N \mid y^{N-1}, u^{N-1}) \, dx_N \\ &= \int x_N^2 \, p(x_N \mid x_{N-1}, u_{N-1}, a) \\ &\quad \times p(x_{N-1}, a \mid y^{N-1}, u^{N-1}) \, dx_N \, dx_{N-1} \, da \\ &= \int (a x_{N-1} + b u_{N-1})^2 \\ &\quad \times p(x_{N-1}, a \mid y^{N-1}, u^{N-1}) \, dx_{N-1} \, da \end{aligned} \tag{46}$$

where the probability densities are assumed to exist. Denoting

$$\widehat{ax}_{N-1} = E(a x_{N-1} \mid y^{N-1}, u^{N-1})$$

and

$$\Sigma_{N-1}^2 = \operatorname{var}(a x_{N-1} \mid y^{N-1}, u^{N-1})$$

(46) can be expressed as

$$E(x_N^2 \mid y^{N-1}, u^{N-1}) = (\widehat{ax}_{N-1} + b u_{N-1})^2 + \Sigma_{N-1}^2$$

Therefore, assuming that Σ_{N-1}^2 is independent of u_{N-1}, the optimal control at time $N - 1$ is given by

$$u_{N-1}^* = -\widehat{ax}_{N-1}/b$$

By the chain rule, we can write

$$p(x_{N-1}, a \mid y^{N-1}, u^{N-1}) = p(a \mid y^{N-1}, u^{N-1}) \, p(x_{N-1} \mid a, y^{N-1}, u^{N-2})$$

In Chapter II, we will show that if the observation noises are Gaussian then the conditional probability density function of x_{N-1}, given a, y^{N-1}, and u^{N-2}, is Gaussian, and that its conditional mean satisfies the recursion equation

$$\mu_{N-1} = a\mu_{N-2} + b u_{N-2} + K_{N-1}[y_{N-1} - a\mu_{N-2} - b u_{N-2}]$$

where $\mu_i = E(x_i \mid a, y^i, u^{i-1})$ and where K_{N-1} is a constant independent of y's and u's. We will also show that the conditional variance of x_{N-1}, given a, y^{N-1}, and u^{N-2}, is independent of y's and u's.

The conditional mean and the variance of x_{N-1}, however, are some nonlinear functions of a. Therefore,

$$\widehat{ax}_{N-1} \neq E(x_{N-1} \mid a, y^{N-1}, u^{N-2})\, E(a \mid y^{N-1}, u^{N-1})$$

showing that the control given by (45) is not optimal. We will take up the questions of computing the optimal control policies for systems with random parameters in Chapter III.

G. Example 6. Stochastic Control System: System with Unknown Gain

In Examples 1–4 we see that their optimal control policies have the common structure that the random or the unknown quantities are replaced by their (a posteriori) mean values; i.e., the certainty equivalent principle yields the optimal control policies for these examples. The optimal control policy in Example 5, however, does not have this structure.

As another example of the latter nature let us consider a stochastic control system

$$x_{i+1} = ax_i + bu_i + \xi_i, \qquad u_i \in (-\infty, \infty) \tag{47}$$

$$x_0 \text{ given}$$

$$y_i = x_i, \qquad 0 \leqslant i \leqslant N-1 \tag{48}$$

where a is a known constant but where b is now assumed to be a random variable, independent of ξ's with finite mean and variance. The schematic diagram of this system is also given by Fig. 1.4. The plant disturbance ξ's are assumed to be independently and identically distributed random variables with

$$E(\xi_i) = 0 \tag{49}$$

$$\operatorname{var}(\xi_i) = \Sigma_0^2, \qquad 0 \leqslant i \leqslant N-1 \tag{50}$$

According to the certainty equivalence principle, in order to obtain u_{N-1}^*, we consider the deterministic plant

$$x_N = ax_{N-1} + b_{N-1}u_{N-1} \tag{51}$$

where

$$b_{N-1} \triangleq E(b \mid x^{N-1}) \tag{52}$$

From (11), the optimal u_{N-1} for the system (51) is given by

$$u_{N-1} = -ax_{N-1}/b_{N-1} \tag{53}$$

With this control, the conditional expected value of J, i.e., the contribution to EJ from the last control stage, is given by

$$E(x_N^2 \mid x^{N-1}, u^{N-1}) = E\left[\left(ax_{N-1} - \frac{b}{b_{N-1}} ax_{N-1} + \xi_{N-1}\right)^2 \Big| x^{N-1}\right]$$

$$= \frac{\sigma_{N-1}^2 (ax_{N-1})^2}{b_{N-1}^2} + \Sigma_0^2 \tag{54}$$

where

$$\sigma_{N-1}^2 = \operatorname{var}(b \mid x^{N-1})$$

Let us try another control variable

$$u_{N-1} = -\frac{b_{N-1}}{b_{N-1}^2 + \sigma_{N-1}^2} (ax_{N-1}) \tag{55}$$

With this control,

$$E(x_N^2 \mid x^{N-1}, u^{N-1}) = E\left[\left(ax_{N-1} - \frac{bb_{N-1}}{b_{N-1}^2 + \sigma_{N-1}^2} ax_{N-1} + \xi_{N-1}\right)^2 \Big| x^{N-1}\right]$$

$$= \frac{\sigma_{N-1}^2}{b_{N-1}^2 + \sigma_{N-1}^2} (ax_{N-1})^2 + \Sigma_0^2 \tag{56}$$

Comparing (54) and (56), we see the optimal control for the deterministic system (51) is not optimal since the control variable of (55) is better. This is only one of the many subtle points that arise in optimal control of stochastic systems. In Chapter III we will show how to derive such a policy in a routine manner.

H. Example 7. Stochastic Control System: Random Time-Constant System with Unknown Mean

In Example 2, the random time-constants $\{a_i\}$ are assumed to have known means. Now, we assume the mean is *unknown*. The system is described by

$$x_{i+1} = a_i x_i + bu_i, \qquad u_i \in (-\infty, \infty) \tag{57}$$

$$y_i = x_i \tag{58}$$

where a_i's are independently and identically distributed Gaussian random variables with mean θ and variance σ^2, where σ is assumed known but θ is assumed to be a random variable.

It is convenient to introduce a notation $\mathscr{L}(\cdot)$ to denote the distribution of a random variable. Using this notation, it is assumed that

$$\mathscr{L}(a_i) = N(\theta, \sigma^2) \tag{59}$$

where σ is given and where $N(a, b)$ is a standard notation for a normal distribution with mean a and variance b. The unknown mean θ is assumed to have the a priori distribution

$$\mathscr{L}_0(\theta) = N(\theta_0, \sigma_0^2)$$

with θ_0 and σ_0 given.

This type of control problem, which is stochastic but not purely stochastic, is called adaptive or more precisely parameter-adaptive to distinguish it from purely stochastic problems. If, instead of assuming that the mean of a is known in Example 5, we assume that the mean is a random variable with given a priori distribution, then we obtain another example of adaptive control system. The optimal control policy for parameter adaptive control systems are discussed in Section 3, Chapter III.

I. Example 8. System with Unknown Noise

Most parts of this book are concerned with a class of control policies known as closed-loop Bayes control policies.[29]

Loosely speaking, the Bayesian approach to the optimal control problems requires the assumption of a priori probability distribution functions for the unknown parameters. These distribution function are updated by the Bayes rule, given controls and state vector measurements up to the current time.

The Bayes approach is examined in some detail in Chapter VI.

The min-max approach does not assume the probability distribution functions for the unknown parameters. In Chapter IX, we will briefly discuss min-max control policies[29] and their relationship with Bayes control policies.

As an illustration, consider a system with perfect observation:

$$x_1 = ax_0 + u_0 + \xi_0$$
$$y_0 = x_0 \text{ given}$$

where it is assumed that a is known and that ξ_0 is a random variable with

$$\xi_0 = \begin{cases} \theta_1 & \text{with probability } p \\ \theta_2 & \text{with probability } 1 - p \end{cases}$$

where θ_1 and θ_2 are given, $\theta_1 > \theta_2$.

The criterion function is taken to be

$$J = x_1^2 = (ax_0 + u_0 + \xi_0)^2$$

Since J is a function of u_0 as well as p we write it as $J(p, u)$. The expected value of J is given as

$$EJ = p(ax_0 + u_0 + \theta_1)^2 + (1 - p)(ax_0 + u_0 + \theta_2)^2$$

Therefore, the control given by

$$u_0^* = -[ax_0 + p\theta_1 + (1 - p)\theta_2]$$

minimizes EJ:

$$\gamma_1^* \triangleq \min_{u_0} EJ = p(1 - p)(\theta_1 - \theta_2)^2$$

Note that γ_1^* is maximized when $p = \frac{1}{2}$. When p is known, the control u_0 is called the optimal Bayes control for the problem. If p is not given, u_0^* cannot be obtained. Let us look for the control which makes J independent of θ_1 or θ_2. Namely, consider $\hat{u}_0$ given by

$$\hat{u}_0 = -\left[ax_0 + \frac{\theta_1 + \theta_2}{2}\right]$$

Then

$$J(1, \hat{u}_0) = J(0, \hat{u}_0) = \left(\frac{\theta_1 - \theta_2}{2}\right)^2$$

Thus, if $\hat{u}_0$ is employed, x_1^2 is the same regardless of p values.

Such a control policy is called an equalizer control policy.[58a,133] The value of J is seen to be equal to γ_1^* when $p = \frac{1}{2}$.

In other words, the control $\hat{u}_0$ minimizes the criterion function for the worst possible case $p = \frac{1}{2}$. Therefore $\hat{u}_0$ may be called the min-max control since it minimizes the maximal possible EJ value. Comparing $\hat{u}_0$ and u_0^*, $\hat{u}_0$ is seen to be the optimal Bayes control for $p = \frac{1}{2}$.

For this example, an equalizer control policy is a min-max control policy, which is equal to the optimal Bayes control policy for the worst possible a priori distribution function for the unknown parameter θ.

It is known that the above statements are true generally when the unknown parameter θ can take on only a finite number of possible values. When θ can take an infinite number of values, similar but weaker statements are known to be true. See Chapter IX, Section 2 of this book or Ferguson[58a] and Sworder,[133] for details.

Chapter II

Optimal Bayesian Control of General Stochastic Dynamic Systems

In this chapter, we develop a systematic procedure for obtaining optimal control policies for discrete-time stochastic control systems, i.e., for systems where the random variables involved are such that they all have known probability distribution functions, or at least have known first, second, and possibly higher moments.

Stochastic optimal control problems for discrete-time linear systems with quadratic performance indices have been discussed in literature under the assumptions that randomly varying systems parameters and additive noises in the plant and/or in the state variable measurements are independent from one sampling instant to the next.[67,80] The developments there do not seem to admit any ready extensions to problems where the independence assumption is not valid for random system parameters, nor to problems where distribution functions for noises or the plant parameters contain unknown parameters.

In this chapter, a method will be given to derive optimal control policies which can be extended to treat a much larger class of optimal control problems than those mentioned above, such as systems with unknown parameters and dependent random disturbances. This method can also be extended to cover problems with unknown parameters or random variables with only partially known statistical properties. Thus, we will be able to discuss optimal controls of parameter adaptive systems without too much extra effort.

The method to be discussed[14,15] partly overlaps those discussed by other investigators, notably that of Fel'dbaum.[55] Although the method presented here is essentially its equivalent,[105a] the present method is believed to be more concise and less cumbersome to apply to control problems. For example, the concept of sufficient statistics[73] are incorporated in the method and some assumptions on the systems which lead to simplified formulations are explicitly pointed out.[15,16] The evaluations of various expectation operations necessary in deriving optimal control policies are all based on recursive derivations of certain conditional probabilities or probability densities. As a result, the expositions are simpler and most formulas are stated recursively which are easier to implement by means of digital computers.

1. Formulation of Optimal Control Problems

A. Preliminaries

In this section, purely stochastic problems are considered. Namely, all random variables involved are assumed to have known probability densities and no unknown parameters are present in the system dynamics or in the system observation mechanisms.

We consider a control system described by

$$x_{k+1} = F_k(x_k, u_k, \xi_k), \qquad u_k \in U_k, \quad k = 0, 1, ..., N-1 \tag{1}$$

where $p_0(x_0)$ is given and observed by

$$y_k = G_k(x_k, \eta_k), \qquad k = 0, 1, ..., N \tag{2}$$

and where x_k is an n-dimensional state vector at kth time instant, u_k is a p-dimensional control vector at the kth time instant, U_k is the set in the p-dimensional Euclidean vector space and is called the admissible set of controls, ξ_k is a q-dimensional random vector at the kth time instant, y_k is an m-dimensional observation vector at the kth time instant, and η_k is an r-dimensional random vector at the kth time instant.

The functional forms of F_k and G_k are assumed known for all k. Figure 2.1 is the schematic diagram of the control system.

The vectors ξ_k and η_k are the random noises in the system dynamics and in the observation device, or they may be random parameters of the system. In this chapter, they are assumed to be mutually independent, unless stated otherwise.

Their probability properties are assumed to be known completely. The problem of optimal controls with imperfect probability knowledge will be discussed in the next chapter.

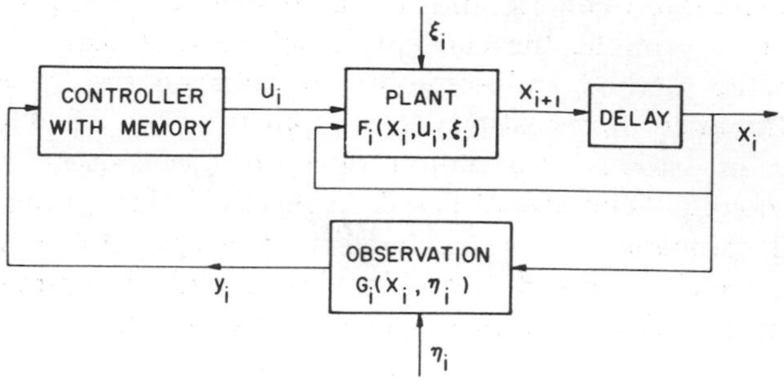

Fig. 2.1. Schematic diagram of general stochastic control system.

From now on, Eq. (1) is rcferred to as the plant equation and Eq. (2) is referred to as the state variable observation equation or simply as the observation equation.

The performance index is taken to be

$$J = \sum_{k=1}^{N} W_k(x_k, u_{k-1}), \qquad W_k \geqslant 0 \tag{3}$$

This form of performance index is fairly general. It contains the performance indices of final-value problems, for example, by putting $W_i = 0, i = 1,..., N - 1$ and taking W_N to be a function of x_N only. We use a notation u^k to indicate the collection $u_0, u_1, ..., u_k$. Similarly x^k stands for the collection $x_0, x_1, ..., x_k$.

Although in the most general formulation the set of admissible control at time k, U_k, will depend on x^k and u^{k-1}, U_k is assumed in this book to be independent of x^k, u^{k-1}.

a. *Optimal Control Policy*

One of our primary concerns in the main body of this book is the problem of deriving optimal control policies, in other words, obtaining the methods to control dynamic systems in such a way that some chosen numbers related to system performances are minimized. Loosely speaking, a control policy is a sequence of functions (mappings) which generates a sequence of control actions $u_0, u_1, ...$ according to some rule. The class of control policies to be considered throughout this book is that of closed-loop control policies, i.e., control policies such that the control u_k at time k is to depend only on the past and current observations y^k and on the past control sequences u^{k-1} which are assumed to be also observed. A nonrandomized closed-loop control policy for an N-stage control process is a sequence of N control actions u_i, such that each u_i takes value in the set of admissible control U_i, $u_i \in U_i$, $0 \leqslant i \leqslant N-1$, depending on the past and current observations on the system $y_0, y_1, \ldots, y_{i-1}, y_i$ and on the past control vectors $u_0, \ldots, u_{i-1}$. Since past controls $u_0, \ldots, u_{i-1}$ really depend on $y_0, \ldots, y_{i-1}$, u_i depends on $y_0, \ldots, y_{i-1}, y_i$.* Thus a control policy $\phi(u)$ is a sequence of functions (mappings) $\phi_0, \phi_1, \ldots, \phi_{N-1}$ such that the domain of ϕ_i is defined to be the collection of all points

$$y^i = (y_0, \ldots, y_i), \qquad \text{with} \quad y_j \in Y_j, \quad 0 \leqslant j \leqslant 1$$

where Y_j is the set in which the jth observation takes its value, and such that the range of ϕ_i is U_i. Namely, $u_i = u_i(y^i, u^{i-1}) = \phi_i(y^i) \in U_i$.† When the value of u_i is determined uniquely from y^i, u^{i-1}, that is when the function ϕ_i is deterministic, we say a control policy is nonrandomized. When ϕ_i is a random transformation from y^i, u^{i-1} to a point in U_i, such that ϕ_i is a probability distribution on U_i, a control policy is called randomized.

A nonrandomized optimal control policy, therefore, is a sequence of mappings from the space of observable quantities to the space of control vectors; in other words, it is a sequence of functions which assigns definite values to the control vectors, given all the past and current observations, in such a way that the sequence minimizes the expected value of J.

From (3), using $E(\cdot)$ to denote the expectation operation, the expected value of J is evaluated as

$$EJ = E\left(\sum_{k=1}^{N} W_k\right)$$

$$= \sum_{1}^{N} R_k$$

where

$$R_k \triangleq E(W_k)$$

Essentially, the method of Fel'dbaum[55] consists in evaluating $E(W_k)$ by

$$E(W_k) = \int W_k(x_k, u_{k-1})\, p(x^k, y^{k-1}, u^{k-1})\, dx^k\, dy^{k-1}\, du^{k-1}$$

---

* For the sake of convenience, initially available information on the system is included in the initial observation.

† $u_0 = u_0(y_0) = \phi_0(y_0), \ldots, u_i = u_i(y^i, u^{i-1}) = u_i(y^i, \phi_0(y_0), \ldots, \phi_{i-1}(y^{i-1})) = \phi_i(y^i)$.

where $dx^k \triangleq dx_0\, dx_1 \cdots dx_k$, $dy^{k-1} \triangleq dy_0 \cdots dy_{k-1}$, and $du^{k-1} \triangleq du_0 \cdots du_{k-1}$, and writing $p(x^k, y^{k-1})$ in terms of more elementary probability densities related to (1) and (2).

Since we do not follow his method directly, we will not discuss it any further in this chapter. However, in order to give the readers some feeling for and exposure to his method, we give, as an example in Section 6, his method of the treatment of a particular class of parameter adaptive systems.

The other method, to be developed fully in this and later chapters, evaluates not R_k directly but the conditional mean of W_k,

$$E(W_k \mid y^{k-1}, u^{k-2}) = \int W_k(x_k, u_{k-1})\, p(x_k, u_{k-1} \mid y^{k-1}, u^{k-2})\, dx_k\, du_{k-1} \quad (4)$$

and generates

$$p(x_k \mid y^k, u^{k-1}) \quad \text{and} \quad p(y_{k+1} \mid y^k, u^k), \qquad 0 \leqslant k \leqslant N-1$$

recursively. See (21) and (22) for the significance of these expressions.

b. *Notations*

It may be helpful to discuss the notations used in the book here. In the course of our discussions, it will become necessary to compute various conditional probability densities such as $p(x_{i+1} \mid y^i)$. As mentioned before, we are interested in obtaining optimal closed-loop control policies; i.e., the class of control policies to be considered is such that the ith control variable u_i is to be a function of the past and current observable quantities only, i.e., of y^i and u^{i-1} only, $0 \leqslant i \leqslant N-1$. If nonrandomized control policies are used,* then at time i, when the ith control u_i is to be determined as a function of y^i as $u_i = \phi_i(y^i)$, it is the functional form of ϕ_i that is to be chosen optimally, assuming ϕ^{i-1} are known. In other words, ϕ_i depends on ϕ^{i-1}. Note that even though the function ϕ_i is fixed, $\phi_i(y^i)$ will be a random variable prior to time i since y^i are random variables. It will be shown in the next section that these ϕ's are obtained recursively starting from ϕ_{N-1} on down to ϕ_0. Therefore, ϕ_i is expressed as a function of $\phi_0, \ldots, \phi_{i-1}$, which is yet to be determined. Therefore, it is sometimes more convenient to express $u_i = \phi_i(y^i)$ as $u_i = u_i(u^{i-1}, y^i)$, whereby the dependence of u_i on past controls $\phi_0, \ldots, \phi_{i-1}$ is explicitly shown by a notational abuse of using u_j for ϕ_j, $0 \leqslant j \leqslant i$. Since u_i is taken to be a measurable function of y^i,

$$p(\cdot \mid y^i) = p(\cdot \mid y^i, u^i)$$

* It is shown later on that we need consider only the class of nonrandomized closed-loop control policies in obtaining optimal Bayesian control policies.

Of course, one must remember that $p(\cdot \mid y^i, u^i)$ is a function of u_i, among others, which may yet be determined as a function of y^i (or equivalently of u^{i-1} and y^i). To make this explicit, sometimes a subscript ϕ_i is used to indicate the dependence of the argument on the form of the past and current control, e.g.,

$$p_{\phi_i}(x_{i+1} \mid x_i, y^i) = p(x_{i+1} \mid x_i, u_i = \phi_i(y^i)).$$

When randomized control policies are used, the situation becomes more complicated since it is the probability distribution on U_i that is to be specified as a function of u^{i-1} and y^i; i.e., a randomized control policy is a sequence of mappings $\phi_0, \phi_1, \ldots, \phi_{N-1}$ such that ϕ_i maps the space of observed state vectors y^i into a probability distribution on U_i. A class of nonrandomized control policies is included in the class of randomized control policies since a nonrandomized control policy may be regarded as a sequence of probability distributions, each of which assigns probability mass 1 to a point in U_i, $0 \leqslant 1 \leqslant N-1$. The question of whether one can really find optimal control policies in the class of nonrandomized control policies is discussed, for example, in Ref. 3.

For randomized control policies,

$$p(y_{i+1} \mid y^i) = \int p(y_{i+1} \mid u_i, y^i)\, p(u_i \mid y^i)\, du_i$$

hence $p(y_{i+1} \mid y^i)$ is a functional depending on the form of the density function of u_i, $p(u_i \mid y^i)$. When u_i is nonrandomized, $p(y_{i+1} \mid y^i)$ is a functional depending on the value of u_i and we write

$$p_{\phi_i}(y_{i+1} \mid y^i) = [\,p(y_{i+1} \mid y^i)]_{u_i=\phi_i(y^i)} = p(y_{i+1} \mid y^i, u_i = \phi_i(y^i))$$

or simply $p(y_{i+1} \mid y^i, u_i)$.

The variables u_i or u^i are sometimes dropped from expressions such as $p(\cdot \mid y^i, u_i)$ or $p(\cdot \mid y^i, u^i)$ where no confusion is likely to occur.

Let

$$p_{\phi^{i-1}}(x^i, y^{i-1})\, d(x^i, y^{i-1}) \tag{5}$$

be the joint conditional probability that the sequence of the state vectors and observed vectors will lie in the elementary volume $dx_0 \cdots dx_i$ $dy_0 \cdots dy_{i-1}$ around x^i and y^{i-1}, given a sequence of control specified by ϕ^{i-1}, where the notation

$$\begin{aligned} d(x^i, y^{i-1}) &= d(x_0, \ldots, x_i, y_0, \ldots, y_{i-1}) \\ &\triangleq dx_0 \cdots dx_i\, dy_0 \cdots dy_{i-1} \end{aligned} \tag{6}$$

is used to indicate the variables with respect to which the integrations are carried out.

Let

$$p(y_k \mid x_k)\, dy_k \tag{7}$$

be the conditional probability that the observation at time k lies in the elementary volume dy_k about y_k, given x_k. Finally, let

$$p_0(x_0)\, dx_0 \tag{8}$$

be the probability that the initial condition is in the elementary volume about x_0. Various probability density functions in (5), (7), and (8) are assumed to exist. If not, they must be replaced by Stieltjes integral notations.

B. Derivation of Optimal Control Policies

We will now derive a general formula to obtain optimal control policies. At this point, we must look for optimal control policies from the class of closed-loop randomized control policies.

a. *Last Stage*

Consider the last stage of control, assuming y^{N-1} have been observed and u^{N-2} have been determined somehow, and that only the last control variable u_{N-1} remains to be specified. Since u_{N-1} appears only in W_N, EJ is minimized with respect to u_{N-1} by minimizing EW_N with respect to u_{N-1}. Since

$$R_N = E(W_N) = E[E(W_N \mid y^{N-1}, u^{N-2})] \tag{9}$$

where the outer expectation is with respect to y^{N-1} and u^{N-2}, R_N is minimized if $E(W_N \mid y^{N-1}, u^{N-2})$ is minimized for every y^{N-1} and u^{N-2}.

One can write

$$E(W_N \mid y^{N-1}, u^{N-2}) = \int W_N(x_N, u_{N-1})\, p(x_N, u_{N-1} \mid y^{N-1}, u^{N-2})\, d(x_N, u_{N-1}) \tag{10}$$

By the chain rule, the probability density in (10) can be written as

$$p(x_N, u_{N-1} \mid y^{N-1}, u^{N-2}) = p(u_{N-1} \mid y^{N-1}, u^{N-2}) \times p(x_N \mid u^{N-1}, y^{N-1}) \tag{11}$$

where

$$p(x_N \mid u^{N-1}, y^{N-1}) = \int p(x_N \mid x_{N-1}, u^{N-1}, y^{N-1}) \times p(x_{N-1} \mid u^{N-1}, y^{N-1})\, dx_{N-1} \tag{12}$$

If the ξ's and η's are mutually independent and for each k, i.e., if $\xi_0, \xi_1, \ldots, \xi_{N-1}, \eta_0, \ldots, \eta_{N-1}$ are all independent, then, from Eqs. (1) and (2),

$$\begin{aligned} p(x_{i+1} \mid x_i, y^i, u^i) &= p(x_{i+1} \mid x_i, u_i) \\ p(y_i \mid x^i, y^{i-1}, u^{i-1}) &= p(y_i \mid x_i), \qquad 0 \leqslant i \leqslant k-1 \end{aligned} \tag{13}$$

We will use Eq. (13) throughout this section. Developments are quite similar when this Markov property[58] does not hold. One merely uses the left-hand side of Eq. (13). See Section 2 of Chapter IV for more general discussions of the Markov property.

In particular, in (12),

$$p(x_N \mid x_{N-1}, u^{N-1}, y^{N-1}) = p(x_N \mid x_{N-1}, u_{N-1})$$

and

$$p(x_{N-1} \mid u^{N-1}, y^{N-1}) = p(x_{N-1} \mid y^{N-1}, u^{N-2}) \tag{14}$$

since u_{N-1} affects x_N but not x_{N-1}. Define

$$p(u_{N-1} \mid y^{N-1}, u^{N-2}) \triangleq p_{N-1}(u_{N-1})$$

Therefore, if one assumes that (14) is available, then (10) can be written as

$$E(W_N \mid y^{N-1}, u^{N-2}) = \int \lambda_N p_{N-1}\, du_{N-1} \tag{15}$$

where

$$\lambda_N \triangleq \int W_N(x_N, u_{N-1})\, p(x_N \mid x_{N-1}, u_{N-1}) \times p(x_{N-1} \mid y^{N-1}, u^{N-2})\, d(x_N, x_{N-1}) \tag{16}$$

In (16), the probability density $p(x_N \mid x_{N-1}, u_{N-1})$ is obtainable from the known probability density function for ξ_{N-1} and the plant equation (1) under appropriate assumptions on (1). See for example Eq. (27).

The second probability density in (16), $p(x_{N-1} \mid y^{N-1}, u^{N-2})$, is not generally directly available. It will be shown in the next section how it can be generated. For the moment assume that it is available.

Thus λ_N is in principle computable as a function of y^{N-1} and u^{N-1}, hence its minimum with respect to u_{N-1} can in principle be found. Denote this minimizing u_{N-1} by u_{N-1}^*. Define

$$\min_{\rho_{N-1}} E(W_N \mid y^{N-1}) = \gamma_N{}^* \tag{17}^\dagger$$

Thus, the minimization of EW_N with respect to ρ_{N-1} is accomplished by that of $E(W_N \mid y^{N-1}, u^{N-2})$, which is achieved by taking $\rho_{N-1} = \delta(u_{N-1} - u_{N-1}^*)$. Since λ_N is a function of y^{N-1} and u^{N-1}, u_{N-1}^* is obtained as a function of y^{N-1} and u^{N-2} as desired. See Fig. 2.2 for illustrations of random and nonrandom control policies and the corresponding values of the conditional expectation of W_N.

In Eq. (15) the expression $\rho_{N-1}(u_{N-1})$ represents a probability density function of $u_{N-1} \in U_{N-1}$, where the functional form of the density function depends on the history of observation or on y^{N-1}. The functional form of ρ_{N-1} specifies the probability $\rho_{N-1}(u_{N-1})\, du_{N-1}$ with which a control in the neighborhood of a point u_{N-1} is used in the last control stage.

However, we have seen that this generality is not necessary, at least for the last control u_{N-1}, and we can actually confine our search for the optimal u_{N-1} to the class of nonrandomized control policies; i.e., the value of the optimal control vector u_{N-1} will actually be determined, given y^{N-1}, and it is not that merely the form of the probability density will be determined. We can see by similar arguments that the u_i are all nonrandomized, $0 \leqslant i \leqslant N-1$. Thus, we can remove u_{N-1} from

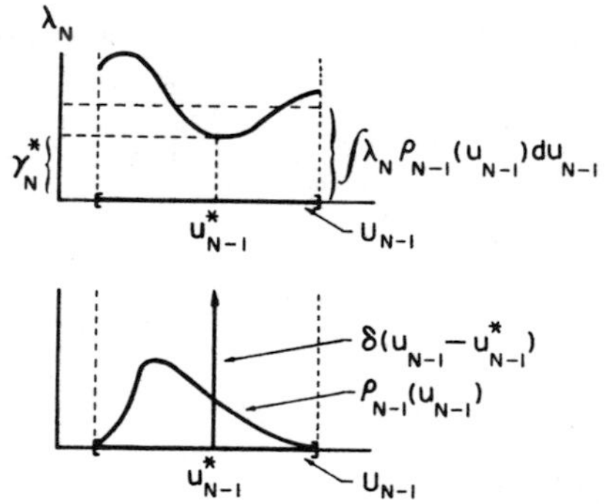

Fig. 2.2. $E(W_N \mid y^{N-1})$ versus u_{N-1}.

† If u_{N-1}^* is not unique, then the following arguments must be modified slightly. By choosing any one control which minimizes λ_N and concentrating the probability mass one there, a nonrandomized control still results.

the probability density function in Eq. (11) and we can deal with $p(x_N \mid y^{N-1})$ with the understanding that u_{N-1} is uniquely determined by y^{N-1}.

Figure 2.3 illustrates this fact schematically for scalar control variable. A typical $\rho_{N-1}(u)$ may have a form like Fig. 2.3(a), where U_{N-1} is taken to be a closed interval. Optimal ρ_{N-1}, however, is given by Fig. 2.3(b).

A nonrandomized control is such that a point in U_{N-1} is taken with probability 1. If U_{N-1} consists of Points A, B, and C for two-dimensional control vectors, as shown in Fig. 2.4(a), then there are three possible nonrandomized u_{N-1}, i.e., u_{N-1} given by Point A, Point B, or Point C, whereas a neighborhood of any point in Triangle ABC typically may be chosen with a randomized control policy with probability $\rho_{N-1}(u)\, du$, where du indicates a small area about u in Triangle ABC. This is shown in Fig. 2.4(b).

b. *Last Two Stages*

Putting aside, for the moment, the question of how to evaluate $p(x_{N-1} \mid y^{N-1})$, let us proceed next to the consideration of optimal control

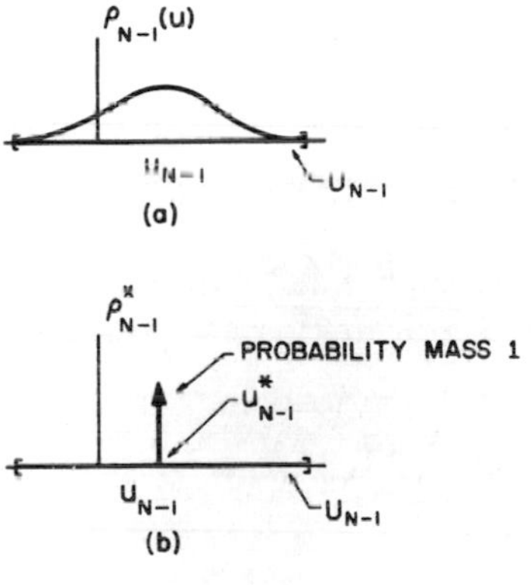

Fig. 2.3. Schematic representation of randomized and nonrandomized control.

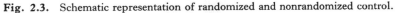

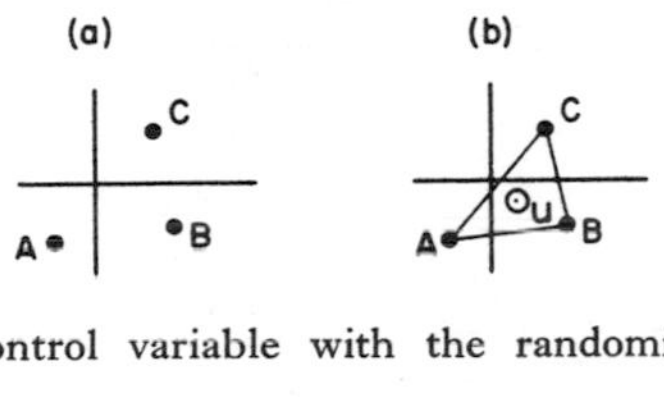

Fig. 2.4. Admissible control variable with the randomized and nonrandomized control policies.

policies for the last two stages of the process. Assume that y^{N-2} and u^{N-3} are given. The control variable u_{N-2} appears in W_{N-1} and W_N. Since

$$E[W_{N-1}(x_{N-1}, u_{N-2}) + W_N(x_N, u_{N-1})] = E[E(W_{N-1} + W_N \mid y^{N-2}, u^{N-3})]$$

where the outer expectation is with respect to y^{N-2}, and since a choice of certain u_{N-2} transforms the problem into the last stage situation just considered, EJ is minimized by choosing u_{N-2} such that it minimizes $E(W_{N-1} + W_N \mid y^{N-2}, u^{N-3})$ for every y^{N-2} and by following this u_{N-2} by u^*_{N-1}. Analogous to (15) we have

$$E(W_{N-1} \mid y^{N-2}, u^{N-3}) = \int \lambda_{N-1} \rho_{N-2}\, du_{N-2} \tag{18}$$

where

$$\rho_{N-2}(u_{N-2}) = p(u_{N-2} \mid y^{N-2}, u^{N-3})$$

and where

$$\lambda_{N-1} \triangleq \int W_{N-1}(x_{N-1}, u_{N-2})\, p(x_{N-1} \mid x_{N-2}, u_{N-2}) \times p(x_{N-2} \mid y^{N-2}, u^{N-3})\, d(x_{N-1}, x_{N-2}) \tag{19}$$

Also

$$E(W_N \mid y^{N-2}, u^{N-3}) = E[E(W_N \mid y^{N-1}, u^{N-2}) \mid y^{N-2}, u^{N-3}]$$

since $y^{N-2} \subset y^{N-1}$. This is seen also from

$$p(\cdot \mid y^{N-2}, u^{N-3}) = \int p(\cdot \mid y^{N-1}, u^{N-2})\, p(y_{N-1} \mid y^{N-2}, u^{N-2}) \times \rho(u_{N-2}) d(y_{N-1}, u_{N-2})$$

where use is made of the elementary operations (1) and (2) discussed in Chapter I.

The optimal ρ_{N-2} is such that it minimizes $E(W_{N-1} + W_N{}^*)$ where the asterisk on W_N is to indicate that u^*_{N-1} is used for the last control. Now,

$$\begin{aligned}
\min_{\rho_{N-2}} E(W_{N-1} + W_N{}^* \mid y^{N-2}, u^{N-3}) &= \min_{\rho_{N-2}} [E(W_{N-1} \mid y^{N-2}, u^{N-3}) \\
&\qquad + E(W_N{}^* \mid y^{N-2}, u^{N-3})] \\
&= \min_{\rho_{N-2}} E[W_{N-1} \\
&\qquad + E(W_N{}^* \mid y^{N-1}, u^{N-2}) \mid y^{N-2}, u^{N-3}] \\
&= \min_{\rho_{N-2}} E[W_{N-1} \\
&\qquad + \gamma_N{}^* \mid y^{N-2}, u^{N-3}] \\
&= \min_{\rho_{N-2}} \int \Big[\lambda_{N-1} \\
&\qquad + \int \gamma_N{}^*\, p(y_{N-1} \mid u^{N-2}, y^{N-2})\, dy_{N-1}\Big] \\
&\qquad \times \rho_{N-2}\, du_{N-2}
\end{aligned} \tag{20}$$

where it is assumed that $p(y_{N-1} \mid u^{N-2}, y^{N-2})$ is available. Defining γ_{N-1} by

$$\gamma_{N-1} = \lambda_{N-1} + \int \gamma_N^* \, p(y_{N-1} \mid y^{N-2}, u^{N-2}) \, dy_{N-1}$$

Eq. (20) is written as

$$\min_{\rho_{N-2}} E(W_{N-1} + W_N^* \mid y^{N-2}, u^{N-3}) = \min_{\rho_{N-2}} \int \gamma_{N-1} \rho_{N-2} \, du_{N-2}$$

Comparing this with Eq. (15), it is seen that the optimal control is such that $\rho_{N-2}^* = \delta(u_{N-2} - u_{N-2}^*)$, where u_{N-2}^* is u_{N-2} which minimizes γ_{N-1}, and the control at $(N-2)$th stage is also nonrandomized.

c. *General Case*

Generally, $E(\sum_{k+1}^N W_i)$ is minimized by minimizing $E(\sum_{k+1}^N W_i \mid y^k, u^{k-1})$ with respect ρ_k for each y^k, u^{k-1} and following it with $\rho_{k+1}^*, \ldots, \rho_{N-1}^*$. It should now be clear that arguments quite similar to those employed in deriving ρ_{N-1}^* and ρ_{N-2}^* can be used to determine ρ_k^*. Define

$$\gamma_k = \lambda_k + \int \gamma_{k+1}^* \, p(y_k \mid y^{k-1}, u^{k-1}) \, dy_k, \qquad 1 \leqslant k \leqslant N \tag{21}$$

$$\gamma_{N+1}^* = 0$$

where $p(y_k \mid y^{k-1}, u^{k-1})$ is assumed available and where λ_k is given, assuming $p(x_{k-1} \mid y^{k-1}, u^{k-2})$ is available, by

$$\lambda_k = \int W_k(x_k, u_{k-1}) \, p(x_k \mid x_{k-1}, u_{k-1}) \, p(x_{k-1} \mid y^{k-1}, u^{k-2}) \, d(x_k, x_{k-1}), \qquad 1 \leqslant k \leqslant N \tag{22}$$

Then optimal control at time $k-1$, u_{k-1}^*, is u_{k-1}, which minimizes γ_k:

$$\min_{u_{k-1}} \gamma_k = \gamma_k^*, \qquad 1 \leqslant k \leqslant N \tag{23}$$

By computing γ_k recursively, optimal control variables are derived in the order of $u_{N-1}^*, u_{N-2}^*, \ldots, u_0^*$. Once the optimal control policy is derived, these optimal control variables are used, of course, in the order of time $u_0^*, u_1^*, \ldots, u_{N-1}^*$. The conditional probability densities assumed available in connection with (21) and (22) are derived in Section 1,C.

At each time k, $u_0^*, \ldots, u_{k-1}^*$ and $y_0, \ldots, y_k$ are no longer random but *known*. Therefore, u_k^* is determined definitely since

$$u_k^* = \phi_k(u_0^*, \ldots, u_{k-1}^*, y_0, \ldots, y_k)$$

and ϕ_k is given as a deterministic function.

From (22), $\lambda_k = 0$ if $W_k = 0$. Therefore, if we have a final value problem, then $\lambda_k = 0, k = 1, 2, \ldots, N-1$ and, from (21), γ_k's are simply obtained by repeated operations of minimization with respect to u's and integrations with respect to y's.

From (21) and (23) we have

$$\begin{aligned}\gamma_k^* &= \min \gamma_k \\ &= \min_{u_{k-1}} \left[\lambda_k + \int \gamma_{k+1}^* p(y_k \mid y^{k-1}, u^{k-1})\, dy_k\right]\end{aligned}$$

This is precisely the statement of the principle of optimality[20] applied to this problem where

$$\gamma_k^* = \min_{u_{k-1}, \ldots, u_{N-1}} E[W_k + W_{k+1} + \cdots + W_N \mid y^{k-1}]$$

To see this simply, let us assume that the state vectors are perfectly observable, i.e.,

$$y_i = x_i, \qquad 0 \leqslant i \leqslant N-1$$

Then, the key relation (21) reads

$$\gamma_k^*(x^{k-1}, u^{k-2}) = \min_{u_{k-1}}[\lambda_k + E(\gamma_{k+1}^* \mid x^{k-1}, u^{k-1})]$$

which is the result of applying the principle of optimally to

$$\gamma_k^* = \min_{u_{k-1}, \ldots, u_{N-1}} E[W_k + \cdots + W_N \mid x^{k-1}]$$

We have the usual functional equation of the dynamic programming if the $\{x_k\}$-process is a first-order Markov sequence, for example, if ξ_k's are all independent. Then

$$\gamma_k^*(x_{k-1}) = \min_{u_{k-1}}[\lambda_k(x_{k-1}, u_{k-1}) + E(\gamma_{k+1}^*(x_k) \mid x_{k-1}, u_{k-1})]$$

When the observations are not perfect, then the arguments of γ_k^* are generally y^{k-1} and u^{k-2}. Thus the number of the arguments changes with k. γ_N^* is computed as a function of y^{N-1} and u^{N-2} and, at step k, y_k in γ_{k+1}^* is integrated out and the presence of u_{k-1} is erased by the minimization operation on u_{k-1} to obtain γ_k^* as a function of y^{k-1} and u^{k-2}. As we will discuss in Section 3, when the information in (y^k, u^{k-1}) is replaceable by that in quantities called sufficient statistics,[73] s_k, and when s_k satisfies a certain condition, then the recursion relation for the general noisy observation case also reduces to the usual functional equation of dynamic programming

$$\gamma_k^*(s_{k-1}) = \min_{u_{k-1}}[\lambda_k(s_{k-1}, u_{k-1}) + E(\gamma_k^*(s_k) \mid s_{k-1}, u_{k-1})]$$

where s_k satisfies the relation

$$s_k = \psi(s_{k-1}, y_k, u_{k-1})$$

for some function ψ. For detail, the reader is referred to Sections II, 3 and IV,2. Similar observations are valid for recurrence equations in later chapters.

C. Derivation of Certain Conditional Probability Densities

Equations (21)–(23) constitute a recursive solution of optimal control policies. One must evaluate γ's recursively and this requires that the conditional densities $p_\phi(x_i \mid y^i)$ and $p_\phi(y_{i+1} \mid y^i)$ or, equivalently, $p(x_i \mid y^i, u^{i-1})$ and $p(y_{i+1} \mid y^i, u^i)$ are available.* We have noted, also, that these conditional densities are not readily available in general.

The general procedure for deriving such densities are developed in Chapters III and IV.

To indicate the method, let us derive these densities under the assumption that noise random vectors ξ's and η's are mutually independent and independent for each time.

Consider a conditional density $p(x_{i+1}, y_{i+1} \mid y^i, u^i)$.

By the chain rule, remembering that we are interested in control policies in the form of $u_i = \phi_i(y^i, u^{i-1})$, $0 \leqslant i \leqslant N-1$,

$$p(x_{i+1}, y_{i+1} \mid y^i, u^i) = p(y_{i+1} \mid y^i, u^i)\, p(x_{i+1} \mid y^{i+1}, u^i).$$

We can write, using (13),

$$\begin{aligned} &p(x_i, x_{i+1}, y_{i+1} \mid y^i, u^i) \\ &\quad = p(x_i \mid y^i, u^{i-1})\, p(x_{i+1} \mid x_i, y^i, u^i)\, p(y_{i+1} \mid x_i, x_{i+1}, y^i, u^i) \\ &\quad = p(x_i \mid y^i, u^{i-1})\, p(x_{i+1} \mid x_i, u_i)\, p(y_{i+1} \mid x_{i+1}) \end{aligned} \tag{24}$$

---

* Alternately, one can just as easily generate $p(x_{i+1} \mid y^i, u^i)$ and $p(y_{i+1} \mid y^i, u^i)$ recursively. They are related by

$$p(x_{i+1} \mid y^i, u^i) = \int p(x_{i+1} \mid x_i, u_i)\, p(x_i \mid y^i, u^{i-1})\, dx_i$$

Thus, from (24),

$$
\begin{aligned}
p(x_{i+1}, y_{i+1} \mid y^i, u^i) &= \int p(x_i, x_{i+1}, y_{i+1} \mid y^i, u^i)\, dx_i \\
&= \int p(x_i \mid y^i, u^{i-1})\, p(x_{i+1} \mid x_i, u_i) \\
&\quad \times p(y_{i+1} \mid x_{i+1})\, dx_i
\end{aligned}
\tag{25}
$$

Hence

$$
\begin{aligned}
p(x_{i+1} \mid y^{i+1}, u^i) &= \frac{p(x_{i+1}, y_{i+1} \mid y^i, u^i)}{p(y_{i+1} \mid y^i, u^i)} \\
&= \frac{\int p(x_i \mid y^i, u^{i-1})\, p(x_{i+1} \mid x_i, u_i)\, p(y_{i+1} \mid x_{i+1})\, dx_i}{\int (\text{numerator})\, dx_{i+1}}
\end{aligned}
\tag{26}
$$

where the denominator of (26) gives $p(y_{i+1} \mid y^i, u^i)$ and where $p(x_{i+1} | x_i, u_i)$ and $p(y_i \mid x_i)$ are obtainable from the plant and observation equations and the density functions for ξ_i and η_i.

The recursion formula is started from $p(x_0 \mid y_0)$, which may be computed by the Bayes formula

$$
p(x_0 \mid y_0) = \frac{p_0(x_0)\, p(y_0 \mid x_0)}{\int p_0(x_0)\, p(y_0 \mid x_0)\, dx_0}
$$

where $p_0(x_0)$ is assumed available as a part of the a priori information on the system.

Equation (26) is typical in that the recursion formulas for $p(x_i \mid y^i, u^{i-1})$ and $p(y_{i+1} \mid y^i, u^i)$ generally have this structure for general stochastic and adaptive control problems in later chapters.

In the numerator of Eq. (26), $p(x_{i+1} \mid x_i, u_i)$ is computed from the plant equation and the known density function for ξ_i and $p(y_{i+1} \mid x_{i+1})$ is computed from the observation equation and the known density function for η_i. The first factor $p(x_i \mid y^i, u^{i-1})$ is available from the previous stage of the recursion formula. With suitable conditions[73,109b]

$$
p(x_{i+1} \mid x_i, u_i) = p(\xi_i) | J_\xi |
$$

and

$$
p(y_i \mid x_i) = p(\eta_i) | J_\eta |
\tag{27}
$$

where J_ξ and J_η are appropriate Jacobians and where the plant and the observation equations are solved for ξ_i and η_i, respectively, and substituted in the right-hand sides.

When ξ's and η's enter into Eqs. (1) and (2) additively, then the probability densities in Eq. (26) can be obtained particularly simply from the probability densities for ξ's and η's. See Ref. 1 for multiplicative random variable case. For example, if Eqs. (1) and (2) are

$$x_{k+1} = F_k(x_k, u_k) + \xi_k$$
$$y_k = G_k(x_k) + \eta_k$$

then

$$|J_\xi| = |J_\eta| = 1$$

and

$$\xi_k = x_{k+1} - F_k(x_k, u_k)$$

and

$$\eta_k = y_k - G_k(x_k)$$

are substituted in the right-hand sides of Eq. (27). Thus, if

$$p(\xi_i) = \frac{1}{(2\pi)^{1/2}\sigma_1} \exp\left(-\frac{\xi_i^2}{2\sigma_1^2}\right) \quad \text{and} \quad p(\eta_i) = \frac{1}{(2\pi)^{1/2}\sigma_2} \exp\left(-\frac{\eta_i^2}{2\sigma_2^2}\right)$$

then

$$p(x_{i+1} \mid x_i, u_i) = \frac{1}{(2\pi)^{1/2}\sigma_1} \exp\left[-\frac{1}{2\sigma_1^2}[x_{i+1} - F_i(x_i, u_i)]^2\right]$$

and

$$p(y_i \mid x_i) = \frac{1}{(2\pi)^{1/2}\sigma_2} \exp\left[-\frac{1}{2\sigma_2^2}(y_i - G_k(x_i))^2\right]$$

Equation (26) indicates clearly the kind of difficulties we will encounter time and again in optimal control problems.

Equation (26) can be evaluated explicitly by analytical methods only in a special class of problems. Although this special class contains useful problems of linear control systems with Gaussian random noises as will be discussed in later sections of this chapter, in a majority of cases, Eq. (26) cannot be integrated analytically. We must resort either to numerical evaluation, to some approximate analytical evaluations of Eq. (26), or to both. Numerical integrations of Eq. (26) are nontrivial by any means since the probability density function $p(x_i \mid y^i, u^{i-1})$ will not be any well-known probability density in general, cannot be represented conveniently analytically, and hence must be stored numerically. See Appendix IV at the end of this book and Chapter III for additional details. Also see Ref. 73a.

In order to synthesize u_i^*, it is necessary to compute $p(x_i \mid y^i, u^{i-1})$ by (26) and then to compute λ_{i+1}, to generate $p(y_{i+1} \mid y^i, u^i)$, to evaluate $E(\gamma_{i+2}^* \mid y^i, u^i)$, to obtain γ_{i+1}, and finally to minimize γ_{i+1} with respect to u_i.

Note that the controller must generally remember y^i and u^{i-1} at time i in order to generate u_i^*.

Although some of the information necessary to compute u_i can be precomputed, i.e., generated off-line, all these operations must generally be done on the real-time basis if the control problem is the real-time optimization problem.

If k sampling times are needed to perform these operations, one must then either find the optimal control policy from the class of control policies such that

$$u_i = \phi_i(y^{i-k}, u^{i-1}), \qquad i = k, k+1, \ldots, N-1$$

where u_0^* through u_{k-1}^* must be chosen based on the a priori information only, or use approximations so that all necessary computations can be performed within one sampling time. In practice we may have to consider control policies with the constraints on the size of the memory in the controller and/or we may be forced to use control policies as functions of several statistical moments (such as mean or variance) instead of the probability density functions and generate these statistics recursively. For example, u_i^* may have to be approximated from the last few observations and controls, say y_{i-1}, y_i, u_{i-2}, and u_{i-1}.

The problems of suboptimal control policies[11,78] are important not only from the standpoint of simple engineering implementations of optimal control policies but also from the standpoint of approximately evaluating Eq. (26). The effects of any suboptimal control policies on the system performance need be evaluated carefully either analytically or computationally, for example, by means of Monte Carlo simulations of system behaviors.

We will return to these points many times in the course of this book, in particular in Chapter VII, where some approximation techniques are discussed.

2. Example. Linear Control Systems with Independent Parameter Variations

A. Introduction

As an application of the optimal control formulation given in Sections 1,B and 1,C, the optimal control policy for a linear stochastic sampled-data control system with a quadratic performance index will be derived. We assume that system parameters are independent random variables, that systems are subject to external disturbances, and that the state vector measurements are noisy. These random disturbances are all assumed to have known means and covariances. Specializations of this general problem by dropping appropriate terms lead to various stochastic optimal control problems, such as the optimal control of a deterministic plant with noisy state vector measurements, the optimal control of random plant with exact state vector measurements, and so on. Scalar cases of such systems have been discussed as Examples 2-4 of Chapter I. This type of optimal control problem has been analyzed by means of dynamic programming.[67,80] The key step in such an analysis is, of course, the correct application of the principle of optimality to derive the functional equation.

By the method of Section 1,B the correct functional equations will result naturally without invoking the principle of optimality explicitly. Consider the sampled-data control system of Fig. 2.5, where the state vector of the system satisfies the difference equation (28a), where the system output vector is given by (28b), and where the observation equation is given by (33):

$$x_{k+1} = A_k x_k + B_k u_k + \xi_k \tag{28a}$$

where $p_0(x_0)$ is assumed given,

$$c_k = M_k x_k \tag{28b}$$

where

x_k is an n-vector (state vector),
A_k is an $n \times n$ matrix,
B_k is an $n \times p$ matrix,

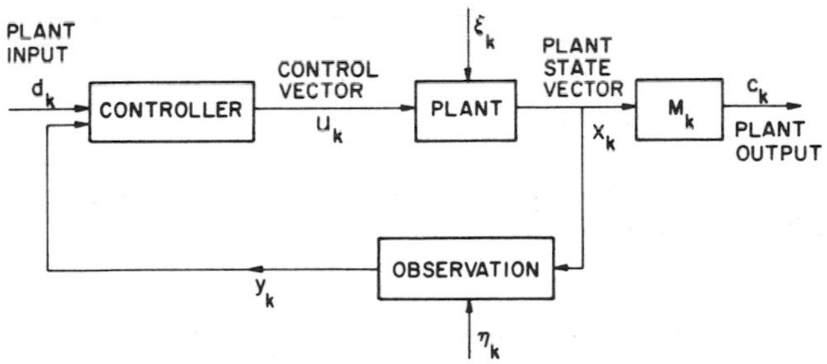

Fig. 2.5. System with linear random plant, with additive plant disturbances, and with noisy measurement. The sequence of imput signals d_i are generated by Eq. (34).

u_k is a p-vector (control vector), $u_k \in U_k$, where U_k is a subset of E_p (p-dimensional Euclidean space) and is called an admissible set of controls,

ξ_k is an n-vector (noise vector),

c_k is an s-vector (output vector), and

M_k is an $s \times n$ matrix.

In (28a), A_k, B_k, and ξ_k are generally random variables, which are assumed to be independent for each k. The $\{\xi_k\}$ random variables are also assumed to be independent of $\{A_k\}$ and of $\{B_k\}$. The independence assumption on ξ_k for each k can be weakened somewhat by introducing another random variable v_k such that

$$\xi_{k+1} = C_k \xi_k + D_k v_k, \qquad k = 0, 1, ..., N - 1 \tag{29}$$

where C_k is a known $(n \times n)$ matrix, D_k is a known $(n \times q)$ matrix, v_k is a q-vector, and v_k is a random variable assumed to be independent for each k, and independent of A's and B's at all times. Equation (29) is introduced to handle random disturbances on the system which is not independent in k but which may be derived from another stochastic process $\{v_k\}$ which has the desirable property of being independent for each k.*

This type of noises is not more general, since by augmenting the state vector x_k with ξ_k, Eqs. (28) and (29) can be combined to give an equation similar to Eq. (28) with an independent random variable as a forcing term. Let

$$z_k = \begin{pmatrix} x_k \\ \xi_k \end{pmatrix}$$

then

$$z_{k+1} = S_k z_k + T_k u_k + \delta_k \tag{30}$$

where

$$S_k = \begin{pmatrix} A_k & I_k \\ 0 & C_k \end{pmatrix}, \qquad T_k = \begin{pmatrix} B_k \\ 0 \end{pmatrix}, \qquad \delta_k = \begin{pmatrix} 0 \\ D_k \end{pmatrix} v_k$$

and where z_k is the generalized (or augmented) state vector.† The random noise in (30), δ_k, is independent for each k and of random variables S_k

* The noises ξ's are analogous to those generated by white noise through a linear shaping filter in continuous time processes. See for example Ref. 98.

† See Chapter IV for more systematic discussions of the idea of augmented state vectors.

and T_k for all k. Thus, it is seen that, by augmenting the original equation for the system state vector by another equation describing the noise generation mechanism, it is possible to treat certain classes of dependent noises by the augmented state equation, Eq. (30), on which only independent noises act.

Thus, it is no loss of generality to discuss Eq. (28) with independent ξ_k for this class.

Assume that the control problem is to make the system output follow the desired output sequence $\{d_k\}$ as closely as possible, measured in terms of the performance index J:

$$J = \sum_{1}^{N} W_k(e_k, u_{k-1}), \qquad W_k \geqslant 0 \tag{31}$$

where W_k is a functional which assigns a real number to each pair of an error vector $e_k \triangleq d_k - c_k$ and u_{k-1}.

For example, W_k may be a quadratic form in e_k:

$$W_k = e_k' V_k e_k \triangleq \| e_k \|^2_{V_k} \tag{32}$$

where V_k is a positive symmetric $(s \times s)$ matrix, and a prime denotes a transpose. The feedback is assumed to consist of

$$y_k = H_k x_k + \eta_k \tag{33}$$

where y_k is an m vector (observation vector); i.e., the controller does not observe x_k directly but receives y_k where η_k is the random observation error.

In most control situations, the desired output sequence $\{d_n\}$ is a sampled sequence of a solution to some linear differential equation on which some noise is possibly superimposed.

Assume that $\{d_k\}$ is generated by

$$\begin{aligned} g_{k+1} &= F_k g_k + G_k \zeta_k \\ d_k &= \tilde{H}_k g_k \end{aligned} \tag{34}$$

where

g_k is an m' vector,
F_k is an $(m' \times m')$ matrix,
G_k is an $(m' \times r)$ matrix,
ζ_k is an r-dimensional random vector independent for each k, and
$\tilde{H}_k$ is an $(s \times m')$ matrix.

Since most deterministic signals are solutions of linear differential or difference equations or can be approximated by such solutions, the class of desired output sequences described by (34) is fairly large. It is possible to combine Eqs. (28) and (34) into a single equation.

Define

$$X_k = \begin{pmatrix} x_k \\ g_k \end{pmatrix} \quad \text{and} \quad \theta_k = \begin{pmatrix} \xi_k \\ \zeta_k \end{pmatrix} \tag{35}$$

Then

$$X_{k+1} = \Phi_k X_k + \Psi_k u_k + \Xi_k \theta_k \tag{36}$$

where

$$\Phi_k = \begin{pmatrix} A_k & 0 \\ 0 & F_k \end{pmatrix}, \qquad \Psi_k = \begin{pmatrix} B_k \\ 0 \end{pmatrix}, \qquad \Xi_k = \begin{pmatrix} I & 0 \\ 0 & G_k \end{pmatrix}$$

and the generalized output of the system is given by

$$\tilde{c}_k = L_k X_k \tag{37}$$

where

$$\tilde{c}_k = \begin{pmatrix} c_k \\ d_k \end{pmatrix} \quad \text{and} \quad L_k = \begin{pmatrix} M_k & 0 \\ 0 & \tilde{H}_k \end{pmatrix}$$

The performance index for systems described by (36) can be expressed as a quadratic from in X by defining a new V_k appropriately when W's are quadratic in (31). For example, since

$$\begin{aligned} e_k &= d_k - c_k \\ &= \tilde{H}_k g_k - M_k x_k \\ &= (-M_k\,, \tilde{H}_k) X_k \end{aligned}$$

the quadratic form $(e_k' V_k e_k)$ becomes

$$W_k = X_k' \begin{pmatrix} -M_k' \\ \tilde{H}_k' \end{pmatrix} V_k(-M_k\,, \tilde{H}_k)\, X_k$$

Letting the new V_k be

$$\begin{pmatrix} -M_k' \\ \tilde{H}_k' \end{pmatrix} V_k(-M_k\,, H_k)$$

one can write $(X_k' V_k X_k)$ instead of $(e_k' V_k e_k)$, where the new V_k again is positive symmetric with dimension $(m' + n)$.* Thus, by suitably

---

* For those not familiar with operating with partitioned matrices, see for example Gantmacher.[63a]

augmenting the state equation for the plant, it is possible to incorporate the mechanisms for dependent noises and/or input signals and the control problems can be taken to be the regulator problem, i.e., that of bringing the (augmented) state vector to the origin in the state space. Since we are interested in closed-loop control policies, the control at the kth sampling instant is assumed to depend only on the initially available information plus y^k and u^{k-1} and on nothing else.

We see from the above discussions that the problem formulation of this section with the system of (28) observed by (33) is not as restrictive as it may appear at first and is really a very general formulation of linear control systems with quadratic performance indices. It can cover many different control situations (for example, by regarding (28) as the state equation for the augmented systems). With this in mind, we will now discuss the regulator problem of the original system (28).

In the development that follows, W_k of the performance index is taken, for definiteness, to be

$$W_k = x_k' V_k x_k + u_{k-1}' P_{k-1} u_{k-1}$$

B. Problem Statement

Having given a general description of the nature of the problem, we are ready to state the problem more precisely. The problem is to find a control policy u^{N-1} such that it minimizes the expected value of the performance index

$$EJ$$

where $u_i \in U_i$, $0 \leqslant i \leqslant N-1$, and where the performance index is given by

$$J = \sum_1^N x_k' V_k x_k + \sum_0^{N-1} u_k' P_k u_k \tag{38}$$

where V_k's and P_k's are symmetric positive matrices, and where the system's dynamics is given by

$$x_{k+1} = A_k x_k + B_k u_k + \xi_k, \qquad k = 0, 1, \ldots, N-1 \tag{39a}$$

where $p_0(x_0)$ is given and where A_k, B_k, and ξ_k are random variables with

$$E(\xi_i) = 0, \qquad E(\xi_i \xi_j) = Q_i \delta_{ij}, \qquad i = 0, 1, \ldots, N-1 \tag{39b}$$

It is assumed that ξ_k's are independent of all (A_k, B_k), that ξ_k and (A_k, B_k) are independent for each k, and the system is observed by

$$y_k = H_k x_k + \eta_k, \qquad k = 0, 1, ., N-1 \tag{40}$$

where $E(\eta_k) = 0$, $E(\eta_k \eta_k') = R_k$, and for simplicity of exposition η_k is assumed independent for each k and of all other random variables ξ_k and (A_k, B_k), $k = 0, 1,\ldots, N-1$. R's and Q's are assumed known. The situation where ξ's and η's are not independent can be treated also. See for example Section 3,E.

We have seen in the previous section that this problem statement can cover situations with dependent noise, input signal dynamics, and others by considering Eq. (39) as the equation for the augmented state vectors, if necessary. Various conditional probability density functions and moments are all assumed to exist in the following discussions.

C. One-Dimensional Example

Before launching into the derivations of the optimal control policy for the problem, let us examine its simpler version of the one-dimensional problem so that various steps involved in arriving at the optimal control policy are made clear. In this way, we will avoid getting lost when we deal with general vector cases.

The one dimensional problem is given with the plant equation

$$x_{i+1} = \alpha_i x_i + \beta_i u_i + \xi_i, \qquad 0 \leqslant i \leqslant N-1, \quad u_i \in (-\infty, \infty) \tag{41}$$

and the observation equation

$$y_i = x_i + \eta_i, \qquad 0 \leqslant i \leqslant N-1 \tag{42}$$

where α_i, β_i, ξ_i, and η_i, $0 \leqslant i \leqslant N-1$, are assumed to be independent random variables.

It is assumed that

$$E(\alpha_i) = a_i \tag{43a}$$

$$E(\beta_i) = b_i \tag{43b}$$

$$E(\xi_i) = E(\eta_i) = 0, \qquad 0 \leqslant i \leqslant N-1 \tag{43c}$$

and that the random variables all have finite variances. Take J to be

$$J = x_N^2 \tag{44}$$

Then, according to the development in Section 1,B, in order to obtain u_{N-1}^*, one must compute

$$\begin{aligned}\gamma_N \triangleq \lambda_N &= E(x_N^2 \mid y^{N-1}) \\ &= \int x_N^2\, p(x_N \mid \alpha_{N-1}, \beta_{N-1}, \xi_{N-1}, x_{N-1}, u_{N-1}) \\ &\quad \times p(\alpha_{N-1}, \beta_{N-1}, \xi_{N-1}, x_{N-1} \mid y^{N-1}) \\ &\quad \times d(x_N, x_{N-1}, \alpha_{N-1}, \beta_{N-1}, \xi_{N-1}) \\ &= \int (\alpha_{N-1}x_{N-1} + \beta_{N-1}u_{N-1} + \xi_{N-1})^2 \\ &\quad \times p(\alpha_{N-1}, \beta_{N-1}, \xi_{N-1}, x_{N-1} \mid y^{N-1}) \\ &\quad \times d(x_{N-1}, \alpha_{N-1}, \beta_{N-1}, \xi_{N-1}) \end{aligned} \tag{45}$$

By the independence assumption, one has, in (45),

$$p(\alpha_i, \beta_i, \xi_i, x_i \mid y^i) = p(\alpha_i)\, p(\beta_i)\, p(\xi_i)\, p(x_i \mid y^i), \qquad 0 \leqslant i \leqslant N-1 \tag{46}$$

and

$$\begin{aligned}\gamma_N = \int & [(a_{N-1}x_{N-1} + b_{N-1}u_{N-1})^2 + \sigma_{N-1}^2 x_{N-1}^2 + \Sigma_{N-1}^2 u_{N-1}^2 + q_{N-1}^2] \\ & \times p(x_{N-1} \mid y^{N-1})\, dx_{N-1}\end{aligned} \tag{47}$$

where

$$\operatorname{var}(\alpha_i) = \sigma_i^2 \tag{48a}$$

$$\operatorname{var}(\beta_i) = \Sigma_i^2 \tag{48b}$$

$$\operatorname{var}(\xi_i) = q_i^2, \qquad 0 \leqslant i \leqslant N-1 \tag{48c}$$

Let

$$E(x_i \mid y^i) = \mu_i \tag{49a}$$

and

$$\operatorname{var}(x_i \mid y^i) = \Delta_i^2, \qquad 0 \leqslant i \leqslant N-1 \tag{49b}$$

These μ's and Δ's may be computed explicitly with the additional assumptions on the random variables. For example, if these random variables are all assumed to be Gaussian, then they can be computed as in the examples of Section 3. From (47)–(49),

$$\begin{aligned}\gamma_N = {} & (a_{N-1}\mu_{N-1} + b_{N-1}u_{N-1})^2 + \sigma_{N-1}^2\mu_{N-1}^2 + \Sigma_{N-1}^2 u_{N-1}^2 + q_{N-1}^2 \\ & + \Delta_{N-1}^2(a_{N-1}^2 + \sigma_{N-1}^2)\end{aligned} \tag{50}$$

Assuming μ_i and Λ_i are independent of u_i, γ_N is minimized with respect to u_{N-1} to give

$$u_{N-1}^* = -\Lambda_{N-1}\mu_{N-1} \tag{51}$$

where

$$\Lambda_{N-1} = \frac{a_{N-1}b_{N-1}}{\Sigma_{N-1}^2 + b_{N-1}^2} \tag{52}$$

and

$$\begin{aligned} \min_{u_{N-1}} \gamma_N &= \gamma_N^* \\ &= I_1\mu_{N-1}^2 + \rho_1 \end{aligned} \tag{53}$$

where

$$I_1 \triangleq \frac{\Sigma_{N-1}^2}{\Sigma_{N-1}^2 + b_{N-1}^2} a_{N-1}^2 + \sigma_{N-1}^2 \tag{54a}$$

and

$$\rho_1 \triangleq q_{N-1}^2 + \Lambda_{N-1}^2(a_{N-1}^2 + \sigma_{N-1}^2) \tag{54b}$$

The expression for γ_N^* can be put slightly differently, retaining the conditional expectation operation $E(\cdot \mid y^{N-1})$ in the expression for γ_N^*.
In this alternate form, (47) can be written as

$$\gamma_N^* = E[I_1x_{N-1}^2 + \nu_1 \mid y^{N-1}] \tag{55}$$

where

$$\nu_1 = q_{N-1}^2 + \frac{a_{N-1}^2b_{N-1}^2}{b_{N-1}^2 + \Sigma_{N-1}^2}\Lambda_{N-1}^2 \tag{56}$$

One can easily check that Eqs. (53) and (55) give the same value for γ_N^* since

$$\begin{aligned} E[I_1x_{N-1}^2 + \nu_1 \mid y^{N-1}] &= I_1\mu_{N-1}^2 + \Delta_{N-1}^2 I_1 + \nu_1 \\ &= I_1\mu_{N-1}^2 + \rho_1 \end{aligned}$$

Having obtained some insight into the problem, we will treat the general case next.

D. Optimal Control Policy

As discussed in Section 1,B, in order to determine the optimal control policy for problem one must first compute λ_k, $1 \leqslant k \leqslant N$:

$$\begin{aligned} \lambda_k &= E(W_k \mid y^{k-1}, u^{k-2}) \\ &= \int W_k\, p(x_k \mid y^{k-1}, u^{k-2})\, dx_k \end{aligned} \tag{57a}$$

where

$$p(x_k \mid y^{k-1}, u^{k-2}) = \int p(x_k \mid x_{k-1}, u_{k-1}, A_{k-1}, B_{k-1}, \xi_{k-1}) \times p(x_{k-1}, A_{k-1}, B_{k-1}, \xi_{k-1} \mid y^{k-1}, u^{k-2}) \times d(x_{k-1}, A_{k-1}, B_{k-1}, \xi_{k-1}) \tag{57b}$$

By the independence assumptions of the random variables A_i, B_i, ζ_i, and η_i, $0 \leqslant i \leqslant N-1$, one can write

$$p(x_{k-1}, A_{k-1}, B_{k-1}, \xi_{k-1} \mid y^{k-1}, u^{k-2}) = p(x_{k-1} \mid y^{k-1})\, p(A_{k-1}, B_{k-1})\, p(\xi_{k-1}) \tag{58}$$

Therefore,

$$\lambda_k = \int [x_k' V_k x_k + u_{k-1}' P_{k-1} u_{k-1}] \times p(x_k \mid x_{k-1}, u_{k-1}, A_{k-1}, B_{k-1}, \xi_{k-1}) \times p(x_{k-1} \mid y^{k-1}, u^{k-2})\, p(A_{k-1}, B_{k-1})\, p(\xi_{k-1}) \times d(x_k, x_{k-1}, A_{k-1}, B_{k-1}, \xi_{k-1}) \tag{59}$$

To obtain u_{N-1}^*, λ_N is evaluated first. Since the mean of ξ_{N-1} is zero by Assumption (39b), the contribution of $(x_N' V_N x_N)$ to λ_N is given by

$$\begin{aligned}
&\int (x_k' V_N x_N)\, p(x_N \mid x_{N-1}, u_{N-1}, A_{N-1}, B_{N-1}, \xi_{N-1})\, p(x_{N-1} \mid y^{N-1}) \\
&\qquad \times p(A_{N-1}, B_{N-1})\, p(\xi_{N-1})\, d(x_N, x_{N-1}, A_{N-1}, B_{N-1}, \xi_{N-1}) \\
&= \int [(A_{N-1}x_{N-1} + B_{N-1}u_{N-1})' V_N (A_{N-1}x_{N-1} + B_{N-1}u_{N-1}) + E_\xi(\xi' V_N \xi)] \\
&\qquad \times p(A_{N-1}, B_{N-1})\, p(x_{N-1} \mid y^{N-1})\, d(x_{N-1}, A_{N-1}, B_{N-1})
\end{aligned} \tag{60}$$

where E_ξ is the expectation operation with respect to ξ. Denoting by a bar the expectation operation with respect to the random variables A and B, we have, from (39b), (59), and (60),

$$\begin{aligned}
\lambda_N = &\int [x_{N-1}' \overline{(A_{N-1}' V_N A_{N-1})}\, x_{N-1} + 2\, u_{N-1}' \overline{(B_{N-1}' V_N A_{N-1})}\, x_{N-1} \\
&+ u_{N-1}' (P_{N-1} + \overline{B_{N-1}' V_N B_{N-1}})\, u_{N-1}]\, p(x_{N-1} \mid y^{N-1})\, dx_{N-1} \\
&+ \operatorname{tr}(V_N Q_{N-1})
\end{aligned} \tag{61}$$

By minimizing (61) with respect to u_{N-1}, the optimal u_{N-1} is given by

$$u_{N-1}^* = -\Lambda_{N-1} \mu_{N-1} \tag{62}$$

where

$$\Lambda_{N-1} = [P_{N-1} + \overline{B_{N-1}V_N B_{N-1}}]^+ \overline{B'_{N-1}V_N A_{N-1}} \tag{63}$$

and where

$$\mu_{N-1} = E(x_{N-1} \mid y^{N-1}) \tag{64}$$

In (63), the superscript plus denotes the pseudoinverse. The pseudoinverse is discussed in Appendix II at the end of this book. If the inverse exists, for example, if P_{N-1} is assumed to be positive definite, then the pseudoinverse coincides, of course, with the inverse. See Appendix A and B at the end of this chapter for further discussion of the pseudoinverse and its applications to minimizations of quadratic forms.

Substituting (62) into (61) and making use of (B.9) in Appendix B,

$$\begin{aligned}\gamma_N{}^* &= \min_{u_{N-1}} \lambda_N \\ &= E[x'_{N-1} I_1 x_{N-1} + \nu_1 \mid y^{N-1}]\end{aligned} \tag{65}$$

where

$$I_1 \triangleq \overline{A'_{N-1}V_N A_{N-1}} - \pi_1 \tag{66a}$$

$$\pi_1 = \overline{A'_{N-1}V_N B_{N-1}}\,(P_{N-1} + \overline{B'_{N-1}V_N B_{N-1}})^+ \overline{B'_{N-1}V_N A_{N-1}} \tag{66b}$$

and

$$\nu_1 = \operatorname{tr}(V_N Q_{N-1}) + E[(x_{N-1} - \mu_{N-1})'\pi_1(x_{N-1} - \mu_{N-1}) \mid y^{N-1}] \tag{66c}$$

The first term in Eq. (66c) is independent of x_{N-1} and y^{N-1} by assumption on ξ_{N-1}. The second term will be independent of past controls if the estimation error $(x_{N-1} - \mu_{N-1})$ has a conditional covariance matrix independent of x_{N-1} and y^{N-1}, for example, if $x_{N-1} - \mu_{N-1}$ is normally distributed (see Section 2,F). To obtain u^*_{N-2}, we compute

$$\begin{aligned}\gamma_{N-1} &= \lambda_{N-1} + E(\gamma_N{}^* \mid y^{N-2}) \\ &= E[x'_{N-1}V_{N-1}x_{N-1} + u'_{N-2}P_{N-2}u_{N-2} \mid y^{N-2}] + E(\gamma_N{}^* \mid y^{N-2}) \\ &= E[x'_{N-1}(V_{N-1} + I_1)\, x_{N-1} + u'_{N-2}P_{N-2}u_{N-2} + \nu_1 \mid y^{N-2}]\end{aligned} \tag{67}$$

where use is made of the property of the conditional expectation

$$E[E(\cdot \mid y^{N-1})\, y^{N-2}] = E(\cdot \mid y^{N-2}) \tag{68}$$

We encountered this relation earlier in Section 1,B. Proceeding as before, noting that now $(V_{N-1} + I_1)$ corresponds to V_N, P_{N-2} to P_{N-1}, etc., the development from (60) to (66) is repeated to give

$$\gamma_{N-1}^* = E[x'_{N-2} I_2 x_{N-2} + \nu_2 \mid y^{N-2}] \tag{69}$$

and

$$u_{N-2}^* = -\Lambda_{N-2} \mu_{N-2} \tag{70}$$

where

$$\mu_{N-2} = E(_{N-2} \mid y^{N-2}) \tag{71}$$

and where

$$I_2 \triangleq \overline{A'_{N-2}(V_{N-1} + I_1)A_{N-2}} - \pi_2 \tag{72a}$$

$$\pi_2 \triangleq \overline{A'_{N-2}(V_{N-1} + I_1)B_{N-2}}\,(P_{N-2} + \overline{B'_{N-2}(V_{N-1} + I_1)B_{N-2}})^+ \times \overline{B'_{N-2}(V_{N-1} + I_1)A_{N-2}} \tag{72b}$$

$$\Lambda_{N-1} \triangleq [P_{N-2} + \overline{B'_{N-2}(V_{N-1} + I_1)B_{N-2}}]^+ \,\overline{B'_{N-2}(V_{N-1} + I_1)A_{N-2}} \tag{72c}$$

and

$$\nu_2 \triangleq \nu_1 + \operatorname{tr}[(V_{N-1} + I_1)Q_{N-2}] + E[(x_{N-2} - \mu_{N-2})' \times \pi_2(x_{N-2} - \mu_{N-2}) \mid y^{N-2}] \tag{72d}$$

In general,

$$\gamma_{i+1}^* = E[x_i' I_{N-i} x_i + \nu_{N-i} \mid y^i], \qquad 0 \leqslant i \leqslant N - 1 \tag{73}$$

and

$$u_i^* = -\Lambda_i \mu_i, \qquad 0 \leqslant i \leqslant N - 1 \tag{74a}$$

where

$$\mu_i \triangleq E(x_i \mid y^i) \tag{74b}$$

and where

$$I_{N-i} \triangleq \overline{A_i'(V_{i+1} + I_{N-i-1})A_i} - \pi_{N-i} \tag{75a}$$

$$\pi_{N-i} \triangleq \overline{A_i'(V_{i+1} + I_{N-i-1})B_i}\,[P_i + \overline{B_i'(V_{i+1} + I_{N-i-1})B_i}]^+ \times \overline{B_i'(V_{i+1} + I_{N-i-1})A_i} \tag{75b}$$

$$\Lambda_i \triangleq [P_i + \overline{B_i'(V_{i+1} + I_{N-i-1})B_i}]^+ \,\overline{B_i'(V_{i+1} + I_{N-i-1})A_i} \tag{75c}$$

and

$$\nu_{N-i} \triangleq \nu_{N-i-1} + \operatorname{tr}[(V_{i+1} + I_{N-i-1})Q_i] + E[(x_i - \mu_i, \pi_{N-i}(x_i - \mu_i)) \mid y^i] \tag{75d}$$

When μ_i's are computed explicitly as a function of y^i and u^{i-1}, Eqs. (73)–(75d) solve the proposed problem completely. Equations (74) and (75) show that the feedback coefficients Λ are computable before the control process begins, i.e., off-line since they do not depend on the previous control vectors nor on the observation vectors. Note also that Λ's are not random. Computations of μ's generally must be done on-line. They are computed later in Section 3 with the additional assumptions that the noise are all Gaussian random vectors. Figure 2.6 shows the configuration of the optimal control system. In terms of μ, (73) can also be written as

$$\gamma_{i+1}^* = \mu_i' I_{N-i} \mu_i + \rho_{N-i} \tag{76a}$$

where

$$\rho_{N-i} = \nu_{N-i} + \operatorname{tr}(I_{N-i} \Sigma_i) \tag{76b}$$

and where

$$\Sigma_i = E[(x_i - \mu_i)(x_i - \mu_i)' \mid y^i] \tag{76c}$$

is the conditional covariance matrix of x_i.

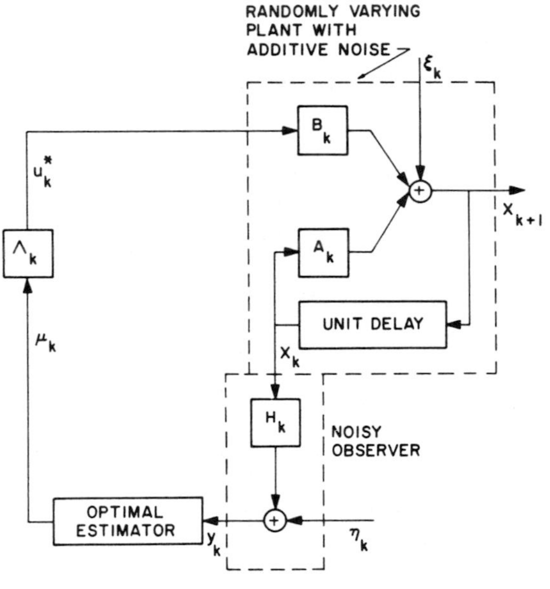

Fig. 2.6. Optimal controller for the stochastic system of Fig. 2.5 with noisy state vector measurement. See Fig. 2.8 for the schematic diagram of the optimal estimator. $\Lambda_k = -[P_k + \overline{B_k'(V_{k+1} + I_{N-k-1})B_k}]^\dagger \; \overline{B_k'(V_{k+1} + I_{N-k-1})A_k}$; $\{I_i\}$, $i = 1, \ldots, N$ generated by Eq. (75).

When the state vectors can be observed exactly, $E(x_i \mid y^i)$ reduces to x_i and the term $E[(x_i - \mu_i)' \pi_i(x_i - \mu_i) \mid y^i]$ vanishes in the equation for ν_i. Replacing μ_i by x_i in (62)–(76), the optimal control vectors with the exact state vector measurements are given by

$$u_i^* = -\Lambda_i x_i, \qquad 0 \leqslant i \leqslant N-1 \tag{77}$$

where Λ_i is the same as before and is given by (75c) and

$$\gamma_{i+1}^* = x_i' I_{N-i} x_i + \tilde{\nu}_{N-i} \tag{78}$$

where

$$\tilde{\nu}_{N-i} = \tilde{\nu}_{N-i-1} + \operatorname{tr}[(V_{i+1} + I_{N-i-1})Q_i] \tag{79a}$$

with

$$\tilde{\nu}_1 = \operatorname{tr}(V_N Q_{N-1}) \tag{79b}$$

Figure 2.7 is the optimal control system configuration with no observation noises. Thus, as already observed in connection with a simple system of Example 4 of Chapter 1, the effect of additive noise ξ to the system is merely to increase γ^* by $\tilde{\nu}$.

When the performance index is given by

$$J = \sum_1^N x_k' V_k x_k \tag{80}$$

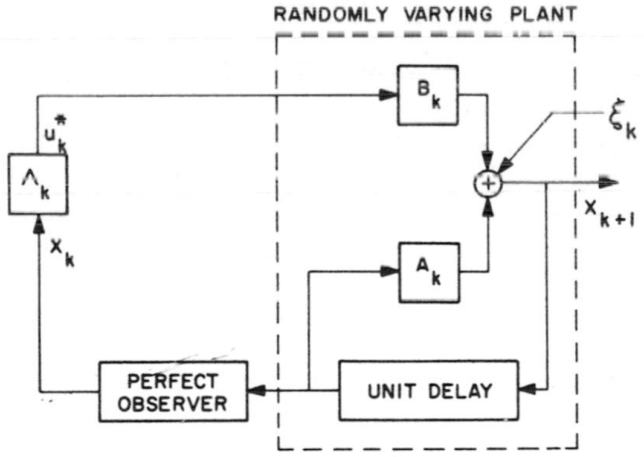

Fig. 2.7. Optimal controller for the stochastic system of Fig. 2.5 when the state vector measurement is exact. $\Lambda_k = -[P_k + \overline{B_k'(V_{k+1} + I_{N-k-1})B_k}]^\dagger \overline{B_k'(V_{k+1} + I_{N-k-1})A_k}$; $\{I_i\}$, $i = 1, ..., N$, generated by Eq. (75).

rather than by (38), the recursion formula for γ^* is obtained by putting all P_i equal to zero. Then, from (75c), the optimal control policy with the new performance index of (80) is given by (74a) and (75c) with $P_i \equiv 0$. In particular,

$$u^*_{N-1} = -(\overline{B'_{N-1} V_N B_{N-1}})^+ \, \overline{B'_{N-1} V_N A_{N-1}} \, E(x_{N-1} \mid y^{N-1}) \tag{81}$$

and

$$I_1 = \overline{A'_{N-1} V_N A_{N-1}} - \overline{A'_{N-1} V_N B_{N-1}} \, (\overline{B'_{N-1} V_N B_{N-1}})^+ \, (\overline{B'_{N-1} V_N A_{N-1}}) \tag{82}$$

Unlike the previous problem, where $P_i \neq 0$, this problem permits a certain simplification and one can write

$$I_1 = \overline{\Psi_1' V_N \Psi_1} \tag{83}$$

where

$$\Psi_1 = A_{N-1} - B_{N-1}(\overline{B'_{N-1} V_N B_{N-1}})^+ \, (\overline{B'_{N-1} V_N A_{N-1}}) \tag{84}$$

Generally, with $P_i = 0$, $0 \leqslant i \leqslant N-1$,

$$I_i = \overline{\Psi_i'(V_{N-i+1} + I_{i-1})\Psi_i} \tag{85}$$

where

$$\Psi_i = A_{N-i} - B_{N-i}(\overline{B_{N-i}(V_{N-i+1} + I_{i-1})B_{N-i}})^+ \times \overline{B_{N-i}(V_{N-i+1} + I_{i-1})A_{N-i}} \tag{86}$$

Equations (74) and (75), which define recursively the optimal feedback control coefficients and the optimal criterion function values, can be put in a little more transparent forms when the system parameters A's and B's are deterministic and ξ's and η's are the only random variables.

From (74a) and (75c), we write Λ_i as

$$\Lambda_i = N_i A_i \tag{74a-1}$$

where

$$N_i \triangleq (P_i + B_i' L_{N-i-1} B_i)^+ B_i' L_{N-i-1} \tag{74a-2}$$

and where we give a symbol L_{N-i} to $V_i + I_{N-i}$ for ease of reference.

Defining J_i by

$$I_{N-i} \triangleq A_i' J_i A_i \tag{75a-1}$$

we have from (75a) and (75b)

$$J_i = L_{N-i-1}(I - B_i N_i) \tag{75a-2}$$

and

$$L_{N-i} = V_i + A_i' J_i A_i \tag{75a-3}$$

The recursion formulas (74a-2), (75a-2), and (75a-3) for N's, J's and L's are initiated by putting $I_0 = 0$ or equivalently $J_N = 0$. Then from (75a-3)

$$L_0 = V_N$$

From (74a-1) and (74a-2)

$$\begin{aligned} \Lambda_{N-1} &= N_{N-1} A_{N-1} \\ &= (P_{N-1} + B'_{N-1} V_N B_{N-1})^+ B'_{N-1} V_N A_{N-1} \end{aligned}$$

which is in agreement with (63), taking note of the fact that A_{N-1} and B_{N-1} are now deterministic by assumption.

By using (75a-2), we have

$$J_{N-1} = L_0(I - B_{N-1} N_{N-1})$$

and from (75a-3)

$$L_1 = V_{N-1} + \Lambda'_{N-1} J_{N-1} \Lambda_{N-1}$$

Now, N_{N-2}, J_2, and L_2 etc. are determined in the orders indicated.

Later in Section 3 of this chapter as well as in Chapter V, we will encounter a similar set of recursion equations in expressions for conditional means and conditional covariance matrices of certain Gaussian random sequences. We will postpone the discussions of the significance of this similarity until then.

E. Certainty Equivalence Principle

If we consider a plant with nonrandom plant parameters and if ξ's and η's are the only random variables in the system, then the bars over the expressions for Λ_i, I_i, and π_i in (75) can be removed. Since these quantities are independent of the plant noise process $\{\xi_i\}$, and of the observation noise process $\{\eta_i\}$, they are identical to the ones derived for a deterministic plant with no random input and with exact state vector measurements. As observed earlier in connection with (58), (66), (74), and (75), $\{\xi_i\}$ and $\{\eta_i\}$ processes affect only ν_i and $E(x_i \mid y^i)$. Since the optimal control vectors are specified fully when $E(x_i \mid y^i)$ are given, the problem of optimal control is separated into two parts: the estimation of the state vectors, given a set of observation data; and the determination of proper feedback coefficients, $\{\Lambda_i\}$, which can be done from the corresponding deterministic plant.

If A's are random but B's are deterministic in the plant equation, then Λ_i, I_i, and π_i are the same as the ones for the equivalent deterministic plant

$$x_{i+1} = \bar{A}_i x_i + B_i u_i$$

The procedure to obtain control policies for stochastic systems by considering the optimal control policies for the related deterministic systems where the random variables are replaced by their expected values, is called the certainty equivalence principle.[49,136a] One may speak of a modified certainty equivalence principle when the random variables are replaced with some functions of their statistical moments. For systems with random A's and deterministic B's, their optimal certainty equivalent control policies are the optimal control policies for the same class of stochastic systems with $y_i = x_i$, i.e., when the x_i are observed exactly and when $E(\xi_i) = 0$, $0 \leqslant i \leqslant N-1$, or if $y_i \neq x_i$, then x_i is replaced by $E(x_i \mid y^i)$. When A's and B's are both random, the optimal certainty equivalent control policies are optimal control policies for the deterministic system with the plant equation

$$x_{i+1} = \bar{A}_i x_i + \bar{B}_i u_i$$

For example, with

$$J = \sum_1^N [x_i' V_i x_i + u_{i-1}' P_{i-1} u_{i-1}]$$

$$u_i^* = -[P_i + \bar{B}_i'(V_{i+1} + I_{N-i})\bar{B}_i]^+ \bar{B}_i'(V_{i+1} + I_{N-i})\bar{A}_i E(x_i \mid y^i)$$

where

$$\begin{aligned} I_{N-i} = \bar{A}_i'(V_{i+1} + I_{N-i-1})\bar{A}_i - \bar{A}_i'(V_{i+1} + I_{N-i-1}) \\ \times \bar{B}_i[P_i + \bar{B}_i'(V_{i+1} + I_{N-i-1})\bar{B}_i]^+ \\ \times \bar{B}_i'(V_{i+1} + I_{N-i-1})\bar{A}_i \end{aligned}$$

Since

$$\overline{B_i'(V_{i+1} + I_{N-i-1})B_i} \neq \bar{B}_i'(V_{i+1} + I_{N-i-1})\bar{B}_i$$

the optimal certainty equivalent control policy is not optimal for this class of stochastic control systems.

F. Gaussian Random Variables

It has been assumed in connection with Eq. (74) that quantities

$$E[((x_i - \mu_i)' \pi_{N-i}(x_i - \mu_i)) \mid y^i], \qquad 0 \leqslant i \leqslant N$$

are independent of x_i and y^i.

Two sufficient conditions for this to be true are:

(a) All random variables in the problem have a joint Gaussian distribution.
(b) The plant and observation equations are all linear.

This will be shown by computing the conditional error covariance matrix $E[(x_i - \mu_i)'(x_i - \mu_i) \mid y^i]$ explicitly under Assumptions (a) and (b) in the next section, Section 3.

See Appendix III at the end of this book for brief expositions of Gaussian random variables.

3. Sufficient Statistics

We have seen in previous sections that u_k is generally a function of y^k and not just of y_k. From (21) and (22) of Section 1,B, we note that this dependence of u_k on y^k occurs through $p(x_k \mid y^k)$ and $p(y_{k+1} \mid y^k, u^k)$ in computing γ's. Intuitively speaking, if a vector s_k, a function of y^k, exists such that $p(x_k \mid y^k) = p(x_k \mid s_k)$, then the dependence of u_k on past observation is summarized by s_k and optimal u_k will be determined, given s_k and perhaps y_k without the need of additional knowledge of y^{k-1}. Such a function of observations is called a sufficient statistic.[73] See also Appendix IV.

We discuss two simple one-dimensional examples first. Those readers who are familiar with matrix operations and Gaussian random variables may go directly to Section 3, C.

A. One Dimensional Example 1

To show that such a function exists and to see how it helps simplify the control problem solution, consider a scalar control system with a plant equation

$$x_{i+1} = a_i x_i + b_i u_i + \xi_i, \qquad 0 \leqslant i \leqslant N-1, \quad u_i \in (-\infty, \infty) \tag{87}$$

and the observation equation

$$y_i = h_i x_i + \eta_i, \qquad h_i \neq 0, \quad 0 \leqslant i \leqslant N-1 \tag{88}$$

Take as the performance index a quadratic form in x and u,

$$J = \sum_1^N (v_i x_i^2 + t_{i-1} u_{i-1}^2), \qquad v_i > 0, \quad t_{i-1} > 0 \tag{89}$$

where a_i and b_i are known deterministic plant parameters and where ξ's and η's are assumed to be independent Gaussian random variables with

$$E(\xi_i) = E(\eta_i) = 0, \qquad 0 \leqslant i \leqslant N-1 \tag{90a}$$

$$E(\xi_i^2) = q_i^2 > 0, \qquad 0 \leqslant i \leqslant N-1 \tag{90b}$$

$$E(\eta_i^2) = r_i^2 > 0, \qquad 0 \leqslant i \leqslant N-1 \tag{90c}$$

$$E(\xi_i \eta_j) = 0, \qquad \text{all } i \text{ and } j \tag{90d}$$

Assume also that x_0 is Gaussian, independent of ξ's and η's with mean α and variance σ^2. This system is a special case of the class of systems discussed in Section 2. Now

$$p(x_0 \mid y_0) = \frac{p(x_0)\, p(y_0 \mid x_0)}{\int p(x_0)\, p(y_0 \mid x_0)\, dx_0} = \text{const} \exp\left(-\frac{(x_0 - \mu_0)^2}{2\sigma_0^2}\right) \tag{91}$$

where

$$\mu_0 = (\alpha/\sigma^2 + h_0 y_0/r_0^2)/(1/\sigma^2 + h_0^2/r_0^2) \tag{92a}*$$

$$1/\sigma_0^2 = 1/\sigma^2 + h_0^2/r_0^2 \tag{92b}$$

From (26) of Section 1,C,

$$p(x_{i+1} \mid y^{i+1}) = \frac{\int p(x_i \mid y^i)\, p(x_{i+1} \mid x_i, u_i)\, p(y_{i+1} \mid x_{i+1})\, dx_i}{p(y_{i+1} \mid y^i)} \tag{93}$$

From (88), (90a), and (90c),

$$p(y_i \mid x_i) = \text{const} \exp\left(-\frac{(y_i - h_i x_i)^2}{2r_i^2}\right) \tag{94}$$

From (87), (90a), and (90b),

$$p(x_{i+1} \mid x_i, u_i) = \text{const} \exp\left(-\frac{(x_{i+1} - a_i x_i - b_i u_i)^2}{2q_i^2}\right) \tag{95}$$

We will now show by mathematical induction on i that

$$p(x_i \mid y^i, u^{i-1}) = \text{const} \exp\left(-\frac{(x_i - \mu_i)^2}{2\sigma_i^2}\right) \tag{96}$$

holds for all $0 \leqslant i \leqslant N-1$ with appropriately chosen μ_i and σ_i. This relation is satisfied for $i = 0$ by (91). Substituting (94)–(96) into (93) and carrying out the integration with respect to x_i,

$$p(x_{i+1} \mid y^{i+1}) = \text{const} \exp\left(-\frac{(x_{i+1} - \mu_{i+1})^2}{2\sigma_{i+1}^2}\right)$$

* If $p(x_0) = \delta(x_0 - \alpha)$, i.e., if we are absolutely sure of the value of x_0, then $E(x_0 \mid y_0) = \alpha$, i.e., the measurement y_0 does not change our mind about $x_0 = \alpha$.

where

$$\mu_{i+1} = a_i\mu_i + b_iu_i + K_{i+1}[y_{i+1} - h_{i+1}(a_i\mu_i + b_iu_i)] \tag{97}$$

where

$$K_{i+1} = \frac{h_{i+1}(q_i^2 + a_i^2\sigma_i^2)}{h_{i+1}^2(q_i^2 + a_i^2\sigma_i^2) + r_{i+1}^2} \tag{98a}$$

and where

$$1/\sigma_{i+1}^2 = h_{i+1}^2/r_{i+1}^2 + 1/(q_i^2 + a_i^2\sigma_i^2)$$

$$= \frac{h_{i+1}^2(q_i^2 + a_i^2\sigma_i^2) + r_{i+1}^2}{r_{i+1}^2(q_i^2 + a_i^2\sigma_i^2)} \tag{98b}$$

Thus (96) is established for all $i = 0, 1,...$ Note that μ_i and σ_i^2 in (96) are the conditional mean and variance of x_i, respectively, given y^i and u^{i-1}. K_{i+1} can also be expressed as $K_{i+1} = \sigma_{i+1}^2 h_{i+1}/r_{i+1}^2$. Equation (96) shows that (μ_i, σ_i^2) are sufficient statistics and contain all information carried by (y^i, u^{i-1}). Equation (97) shows that the equation satisfied by the sufficient statistic μ_i is composed of two parts: the first part is the same as the dynamic equation of the plant, and the second part constitutes a correction term proportional to $y_{i+1} - h_{i+1}(a\mu_i + bu_i)$ which may be interpreted as the difference between the actual observed value of x_{i+1} and the predicted value of the observation based on the estimate μ_i of x_i, $h_{i+1}(a\mu_i + bu_i)$. Note that y^i and u^{i-1} are replaced by μ_i and σ_i^2 and that σ's are computed from the knowledge of the noise variance and are constants independent of the observations and controls. In other words, σ's can be generated off-line.

We are now ready to determine u_{N-1}^*. As usual we first compute from (87), (89), (90), and (96):

$$\begin{aligned}
\lambda_N &= E(W_N \mid y^{N-1}) \\
&= \int (v_N x_N^2 + t_{N-1}u_{N-1}^2)\, p(x_N \mid y^{N-1})\, dx_N \\
&= \int (v_N x_N^2 + t_{N-1}u_{N-1}^2)\, p(x_N \mid x_{N-1}, u_{N-1}) \\
&\quad \times p(x_{N-1} \mid y^{N-1})\, d(x_N, x_{N-1}) \\
&= \int [v_N(a_{N-1}x_{N-1} + b_{N-1}u_{N-1})^2 + v_N q_{N-1}^2 + t_{N-1}u_{N-1}^2] \\
&\quad \times p(x_{N-1} \mid y^{N-1})\, dx_{N-1} \\
&= D_N + t_{N-1}u_{N-1}^2 + v_N(a_{N-1}\mu_{N-1} + b_{N-1}u_{N-1})^2
\end{aligned} \tag{99}$$

where

$$D_N = v_N(q_{N-1}^2 + a_{N-1}^2\sigma_{N-1}^2) \tag{100}$$

Minimization of (99) with respect to u_{N-1} gives

$$u_{N-1}^* = -\Lambda_{N-1}\mu_{N-1} \tag{101}$$

where

$$\Lambda_{N-1} = \frac{v_N b_{N-1} a_{N-1}}{t_{N-1} + v_N b_{N-1}^2} \tag{102}$$

Substituting (101) into (99) gives

$$\gamma_N{}^* = C_N + T_N \mu_{N-1}^2 \tag{103}$$

where

$$T_N = \frac{v_N t_{N-1} a_{N-1}^2}{(t_{N-1} + v_N b_{N-1}^2)} \tag{104a}$$

$$C_N = D_N \tag{104b}$$

To compute u_{N-2}^*, one must compute γ_{N-1}. λ_{N-1} is given by computations similar to (99):

$$\lambda_{N-1} = D_{N-1} + t_{N-2}u_{N-2}^2 + v_{N-1}(a_{N-2}\mu_{N-2} + b_{N-2}u_{N-2})^2 \tag{105}$$

The probability density $p(y_{N-1} \mid y^{N-2})$, necessary to evaluate $E(\gamma_N{}^* | y^{N-2})$, is given from (88) and (96) by the Gaussian probability density with mean $h_{N-1}(a_{N-2}\mu_{N-2} + b_{N-2}u_{N-2})$ and variance

$$h_{N-1}^2(a_{N-2}^2\sigma_{N-2}^2 + q_{N-2}^2) + r_{N-1}^2 .$$

From (97) and (103), $\gamma_N{}^*$ is seen to depend on y_{N-1} only through μ_{N-1}, since μ_{N-2} are functions of y^{N-2} and u^{N-3}. We have

$$E(\mu_{N-1} \mid y^{N-2}) = a_{N-2}\mu_{N-2} + b_{N-2}u_{N-2} \tag{106}$$

and

$$\operatorname{var}(\mu_{N-1} \mid y^{N-2}) = K_{N-1}^2[h_{N-1}^2(a_{N-2}^2\sigma_{N-2}^2 + q_{N-2}^2) + r_{N-1}^2] \tag{107}$$

Therefore, from (103), (106), and (107),

$$E(\gamma_N{}^* \mid y^{N-2}) = C_N + T_N\{(a_{N-2}\mu_{N-2} + b_{N-2}u_{N-2})^2 + K_{N-1}^2[h_{N-1}^2(a_{N-2}^2\sigma_{N-2}^2 + q_{N-2}^2) + r_{N-1}^2]\} \tag{108}$$

From (105) and (108)

$$\gamma_{N-1} = \lambda_{N-1} + E(\gamma_N^* \mid y^{N-2})$$

$$= C_{N-1} + t_{N-2}u_{N-2}^2 + (v_{N-1} + T_N)(a_{N-2}\mu_{N-2} + b_{N-2}u_{N-2})^2 \quad (109)$$

where

$$C_{N-1} = D_{N-1} + C_N + T_N K_{N-1}^2[h_{N-1}^2(a_{N-2}^2\sigma_{N-2}^2 + q_{N-2}^2) + r_{N-1}^2] \quad (110)$$

Therefore, by minimizing (109) with respect to u_{N-2},

$$u_{N-2}^* = -\Lambda_{N-2}\mu_{N-2}$$

where

$$\Lambda_{N-2} = \frac{(v_{N-1} + T_N)b_{N-2}a_{N-2}}{t_{N-2} + (v_{N-1} + T_N)b_{N-2}^2}$$

and

$$\gamma_{N-1}^* = C_{N-1} + T_{N-1}\mu_{N-1}^2$$

where

$$T_{N-1} = \frac{(v_{N-1} + T_N)t_{N-2}a_{N-2}^2}{t_{N-2} + (v_{N-1} + T_N)b_{N-2}^2}$$

The above process is perfectly general and one has

$$u_i^* = -\Lambda_i u_i \quad (111a)$$

where

$$\Lambda_i = \frac{(v_{i+1} + T_{i+2})b_i a_i}{t_i + (v_{i+1} + T_{i+2})b_i^2}, \qquad 0 \leqslant i \leqslant N-1, \quad T_{N+1} = 0 \quad (111b)$$

$$\gamma_i^* = C_i + T_i\mu_i^2 \quad (111c)$$

where

$$C_i = D_i + C_{i+1} + T_{i+1}K_i^2[h_i^2(a_{i-1}^2\sigma_{i-1}^2 + q_{i-1}^2) + r_i^2] \quad (111d)$$

$$C_{N+1} = 0$$

$$D_i = v_i(q_{i-1}^2 + a_{i-1}^2\sigma_{i-1}^2), \qquad 1 \leqslant i \leqslant N \quad (111e)$$

and

$$T_i = \frac{(v_i + T_{i+1})t_{i-1}a_{i-1}^2}{t_{i-1} + (v_i + T_{i+1})b_{i-1}^2}, \qquad T_{N+1} = 0, \quad 1 \leqslant i \leqslant N \quad (111f)$$

When $t_i = 0$, $1 \leqslant i \leqslant N-1$, in (89), from (111b), $\Lambda_0 = a_0/b_0$, and, from (111a), $a_0\mu_0 + b_0u_0^* = 0$. More generally, $\Lambda_i = a_i/b_i$ and $a_i\mu_i + b_iu_i^* = 0$ for all $0 \leqslant i \leqslant N-1$. Therefore, from (97),

$$\mu_i = K_i y_i, \qquad 0 \leqslant i \leqslant N-1$$

and, from (111a),

$$u_i^* = -\Lambda_i K_i y_i\,, \qquad 0 \leqslant i \leqslant N-1$$
$$= -a_i K_i y_i / b_i$$

is the optimal policy for the system with the plant equation (87) and the observation equation (88) and the criterion function $J = \sum_1^N v_i x_i^2$; i.e., with this criterion function u_i^* is proportional to y_i More discussions on this point are found in Section 3,D.

B. One-Dimensional Example 2

As a special case of the above example, consider a system

$$x_{i+1} = ax_i + bu_i\,, \qquad b \neq 0, \quad u_i \in (-\infty, \infty) \tag{112}$$

$$y_i = x_i + \eta_i\,, \qquad 0 \leqslant i \leqslant N-1 \tag{113}$$

where a and b are known constants and where η's are independent random variables with $E(\eta_i) = 0$, $\operatorname{var}(\eta_i) = r_i^2$, $0 \leqslant i \leqslant N-1$, and where x_0 is a random variable independent of everything else.

This is the system discussed as Example 3 of Chapter I, with $J = x_N^2$. There we have obtained the optimal control policy in terms of the statistics

$$E(x_i \mid y^i) = \mu_i \quad \text{and} \quad \operatorname{var}(x_i \mid y^i) = \sigma_i^2, \quad 0 \leqslant i \leqslant N$$

without indicating how they may be computed.

With the additional assumption that x_0 and η's are Gaussian,

$$\mathscr{L}(x_0) = N(\alpha, \sigma^2), \qquad \mathscr{L}(\eta_i) = N(0, r_i^2), \qquad 0 \leqslant i \leqslant N-1$$

the result of Example 1 of this chapter can be used to compute these statistics. Namely, μ's and σ's are sufficient and can be computed as

$$\mu_i = a\mu_{i-1} + bu_{i-1} + K_i[y_i - (a\mu_{i-1} + bu_{i-1})], \qquad 1 \leqslant i \leqslant N-1 \tag{114a}$$

$$\mu_0 = [\alpha/\sigma^2 + y_0/r_0^2]/(1/\sigma^2 + 1/r_0^2) \tag{114b}$$

$$K_i = \sigma_i^2/r_i^2, \qquad 0 \leqslant i \leqslant N-1 \tag{114c}$$

$$1/\sigma_i^2 = 1/r_i^2 + 1/(a^2\sigma_{i-1}^2), \qquad 1 \leqslant i \leqslant N-1 \tag{114d}$$

$$1/\sigma_0^2 = 1/\sigma^2 + 1/r_0^2 \tag{114e}$$

When J is given, λ_i is computable since $p(x_i \mid y^i)$ is known as a Gaussian probability density function with the conditional mean μ_i

and the conditional variance σ_i^2. The conditional probability density $p(y_{i+1} \mid y^i, u^i)$ needed to compute $E(\gamma_{i+2}^* \mid y^i)$ is obtained analogous to $p(\mu_{N-1} \mid y^{N-2})$ given by (106) and (107) or independently as follows.

From Eq. (113),

$$x_i = y_i - \eta_i$$

hence

$$\mu_i = E(x_i \mid y^i) = y_i - E(\eta_i \mid y^i)$$

or

$$E(\eta_i \mid y^i) = y_i - \mu_i$$

Similarly

$$\operatorname{var}(\eta_i \mid y^i) = \operatorname{var}(x_i \mid y^i) = \sigma_i^2$$

From Eqs. (112) and (113),

$$y_{i+1} = ay_i + bu_i + \eta_{i+1} - a\eta_i$$

where y_{i+1} is a Gaussian random variable since it is a linear combination of Gaussian random variables. Now

$$\begin{aligned} E(y_{i+1} \mid y^i, u^i) &= ay_i + bu_i + E(\eta_{i+1} \mid y^i) - aE(\eta_i \mid y^i) \\ &= ay_i + bu_i - a(y_i - \mu_i) \\ &= a\mu_i + bu_i \end{aligned} \tag{115}$$

because

$$E(\eta_{i+1} \mid y^i) = E(\eta_{i+1}) = 0$$

Also

$$[y_{i+1} - (a\mu_i + bu_i)]^2 = [-a(\eta_i - y_i + \mu_i) + \eta_{i+1}]^2$$

hence

$$\operatorname{var}(y_{i+1} \mid y^i, u^i) = a^2\sigma_i^2 + r_{i+1}^2 \tag{116}$$

Equations (115) and (116) determine $p(y_{i+1} \mid y^i, u^i)$ completely.

The reader is asked to compare the effectiveness of the optimal closed-loop control policy for the system of Example 2 with that of the optimal open-loop control policy (i.e., the controls are function of y_0 only) with a quadratic criterion function. What difference do these two policies make in the values of $E(J \mid y_0)$?

C. Example 3. Uncorrelated Gaussian Noises

The above examples can be extended to a system with a vector difference equation as the plant equation

$$x_{i+1} = A_i x_i + B_i u_i + \xi_i \tag{117}$$

and the vector observation equation

$$y_i = H_i x_i + \eta_i \tag{118}$$

where x_0 is assumed to be a Gaussian random variable with $E(x_0) = a$, $\text{cov}(x_0) = \Sigma_0$, where ξ's and η's are Gaussian random variables independent of x_0 with

$$\begin{aligned} E(\xi_i) &= 0 \\ E(\eta_i) &= 0 \\ E(\xi_i \xi_j{}') &= \delta_{ij} Q_i \\ E(\eta_i \eta_j{}') &= \delta_{ij} R_i \\ E(\xi_i \eta_j{}') &= 0 \qquad \text{for all } i \text{ and } j \end{aligned} \tag{119}$$

where Q_i and R_i are assumed to be positive definite. The last assumption on the independence of ξ's of η's is made to simplify computations and can easily be removed with some additional complications in the derivations. This is indicated in Section 3,E.

To derive optimal control policies, one must first compute

$$\lambda_i = \int W_i(x_i, u_{i-1})\, p(x_i \mid y^{i-1}, u^{i-1})\, dx_i, \qquad 1 \leqslant i \leqslant N \tag{120}$$

where

$$p(x_i \mid y^{i-1}) = \int p(x_i \mid x_{i-1}, u_{i-1})\, p(x_{i-1} \mid y^{i-1}, u^{i-2})\, dx_{i-1} \tag{121}$$

where $p(x_{i-1} \mid y^{i-1}, u^{i-2})$ is computed recursively by (26) of Section 1,C. Actually, one could just as well derive the recursion relation for $p(x_{i+1} \mid y^i)$ rather than for $p(x_i \mid y^i)$. See (149) in Section 3,E for derivation.

The recursion process is initiated by computing

$$p(x_0 \mid y_0) = \frac{p_0(x_0)\, p(y_0 \mid x_0)}{p(y_0)} \tag{122}$$

where by assumption

$$p_0(x_0) = \text{const} \exp(-\tfrac{1}{2} \| x_0 - a \|^2_{\Sigma_0^{-1}}) \tag{123}$$

and where the notation $\| z \|_S^2 \triangleq z'Sz$ is used. From (119),

$$p(y_0 \mid x_0) = \text{const} \exp(-\tfrac{1}{2} \| y_0 - H_0 x_0 \|^2_{R_0^{-1}}) \tag{124}$$

From (123), $p(x_0 \mid y_0)$ is seen to be a Gaussian:

$$p(x_0 \mid y_0) = \text{const} \exp(-\tfrac{1}{2} \| x_0 - \mu_0 \|^2_{\Gamma_0^{-1}}) \tag{125}$$

where

$$\Gamma_0^{-1} = \Sigma_0^{-1} + H_0{}'R_0^{-1}H_0 \tag{126}$$

and

$$\mu_0 = \Gamma_0(H_0{}'R_0^{-1}y_0 + \Sigma_0^{-1}a) \tag{127}$$

The detail is carried out in Appendixes C and D at the end of this chapter. See also Refs. 84–86, 141.

Assume that $p(x_i \mid y^i)$ has also a Gaussian density:

$$p(x_i = x \mid y^i) = \text{const} \exp(-\tfrac{1}{2} \| x - \mu_i \|^2_{\Gamma_i^{-1}}) \tag{128}$$

where $\mu_i \triangleq E(x_i \mid y^i)$ and $\Gamma_i \triangleq \text{cov}(x_i \mid y^i)$. The variable μ_i is therefore the conditional mean and Γ_i is the conditional covariance matrix of x_i, given the past and current observation $y_0, \ldots, y_i$. This is certainly true for $i = 0$ from (125). From (26),

$$\begin{aligned} p(x_{i+1} \mid y^{i+1}) &= \text{const} \int p(x_i \mid y^i)\, p(x_{i+1} \mid x_i, u_i)\, p(y_{i+1} \mid x_{i+1})\, dx_i \\ &= \text{const} \int \exp(-\tfrac{1}{2} E_i)\, dx_i \end{aligned} \tag{129}$$

where

$$E_i = \| x_i - \mu_i \|^2_{\Gamma_i^{-1}} + \| x_{i+1} - A_i x_i - B_i u_i \|^2_{Q_i^{-1}} + \| y_{i+1} - H_{i+1} x_{i+1} \|^2_{R_{i+1}^{-1}} \tag{130}$$

since

$$p(x_{i+1} \mid x_i, u_i) = \text{const} \exp(-\tfrac{1}{2} \| x_{i+1} - A_i x_i - B_i u_i \|^2_{Q_i^{-1}})$$

and

$$p(y_i \mid x_i) = \text{const} \exp(-\tfrac{1}{2} \| y_i - H_i x_i \|^2_{R_{i+1}^{-1}})$$

After carrying out the integration, which is shown in detail in Appendix C, one has

$$p(x_{i+1} \mid y^{i+1}) = \text{const} \exp(-\tfrac{1}{2} \| x_{i+1} - \mu_{i+1} \|^2_{\Gamma_{i+1}^{-1}}) \tag{131}$$

where

$$\begin{aligned} \mu_{i+1} &= A_i\mu_i + B_i u_i + \Gamma_{i+1} H_{i+1}' R_{i+1}^{-1}[y_{i+1} - H_{i+1}(A_i\mu_i + B_i u_i)] \\ &= \Gamma_{i+1}(Q_i + A_i \Gamma_i A_i{}')^{-1}(A_i\mu_i + B_i u_i) \\ &\quad + \Gamma_{i+1} H_{i+1}' R_{i+1}^{-1} y_{i+1} \end{aligned} \tag{132a}$$

and where

$$\begin{aligned}\Gamma_{i+1}^{-1} &= H'_{i+1}R_{i+1}^{-1}H_{i+1} + Q_i^{-1} - Q_i^{-1}A_i(\Gamma_i^{-1} + A_i'Q_i^{-1}A_i)^{-1}A_i'Q_i^{-1} \\ &= H'_{i+1}R_{i+1}^{-1}H_{i+1} + (Q_i + A_i\Gamma_iA_i')^{-1} \qquad (132b)\end{aligned}$$

This completes the mathematical induction on i and Eq. (128) has been established for $i = 0, 1,\ldots$. Figure 2.8 shows a schematic diagram of a filter which generates μ_i.

Note that in (132a) the terms $A_i\mu_i + B_iu_i$ show that the μ_{i+1} satisfies the same dynamic equation as the plant equation plus a correction term proportional to $y_{i+1} - H_{i+1}(A_i\mu_i + B_iu_i)$ which may be interpreted as the error in predicting x_{i+1} based on the estimate μ_i of x_i. An alternate expression for the constant multiplying the correction term in (132a) is given by (C20) in Appendix C.

Thus we have seen from (132a) that μ_{i+1} is computable given μ_i, y_{i+1}, and u_i. Using (132b) and the matrix identity in Appendix D Γ_{i+1} is computable from Γ_i. Hence, μ_i and Γ_i are sufficient statistics for x_i and summarizes all available information contained in y^{i-1} on x_i.

There is another way of obtaining the recursion formula for the sufficient statistics. To do this we first obtain the expression for $p(x_{i+1} \mid y^i)$ in terms of $p(x_i \mid y^i)$. The detail is also found in Appendix C.

$$p(x_{i+1} \mid y^i) = \text{const} \exp(-\tfrac{1}{2} \| x_{i+1} - A_i\mu_i - B_iu_i \|^2_{M_i^{-1}}) \qquad (133)$$

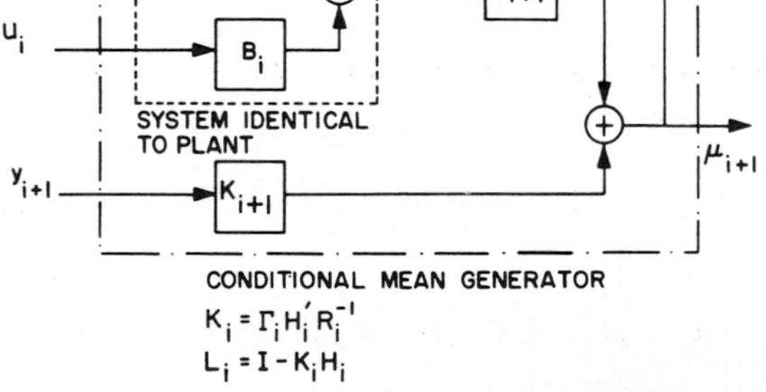

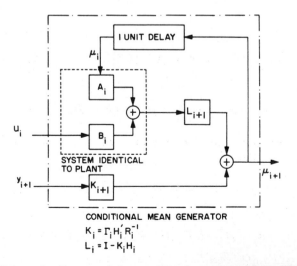

Fig. 2.8. Schematic diagram of the conditional mean generator (Wiener-Kalman filter). This is the optimal estimator in Fig. 2.6.

where

$$M_{i+1}^{-1} = Q_i^{-1} - Q_i^{-1}A_i(\Gamma_i^{-1} + A_i'Q_i^{-1}A_i)^{-1}A_i'Q_i^{-1}$$
$$= (Q_i + A_i\Gamma_iA_i')^{-1} \tag{134}$$

The last expression is obtained using the matrix identity in Appendix D, or more directly knowing that $p(x_{i+1} \mid y^i)$ has a Gaussian distribution.

Since the conditional mean of x_{i+1} is given by

$$\nu_{i+1} \triangleq E(x_{i+1} \mid y^i) = A_i\, E(x_i \mid y^i) + B_iu_i + E(\xi_i \mid y^i)$$
$$= A_i\mu_i + B_iu_i \tag{135}$$

where the independence assumptions of ξ's and η's and (119) are used in putting the last term equal to zero. To obtain the conditional covariance, we compute

$$E[(x_{i+1} - \nu_{i+1})(x_{i+1} - \nu_{i+1})' \mid y^i]$$
$$= E[[A_i(x_i - \mu_i) + \xi_i][A_i(x_i - \mu_i) + \xi_i]' \mid y^i]$$
$$= Q_i + A_i\Gamma_iA_i' \tag{136}$$

since from the independence assumptions of ξ's

$$E[\xi_i(x_i - \mu_i)' \mid y^i] = 0$$

We see, therefore, that M_{i+1} of (134) is given by (136).

From (135) and the recursion relation of μ_i given by (132a), the recursion formula for ν_i is simply given by

$$\nu_{i+1} = A_i\nu_i + Bu_i + A_iK_i[y_i - H_i\nu_i] \tag{137}$$

where

$$K_i = \Gamma_iH_i'R_i^{-1} \tag{138}$$

Note that, since Γ_i's do not depend on particular y's nor on u's, they can be precomputed if necessary.

We see that the derivation of $p(x_{i+1} \mid y^{i+1})$ by first obtaining the conditional mean and the conditional variance of $p(x_{i+1} \mid y^i)$ by (135) and (136) and then by making use of Bayes rule

$$p(x_{i+1} \mid y^{i+1}) = p(y_{i+1} \mid x_{i+1})p(x_{i+1} \mid y^i)\Big/\int [\text{Numerator}]\, dx_{i+1}$$

yields the relations of (132a) and (132b) without too much manipulations of matrices.

Duality Principle

The set of recursion relations to generate μ's and Γ's bears a remarkable resemblance to that given by Eq. (75a-1)–(75a-3) at the end of Section 2,D.

The problem discussed in this section is that of the filtering, i.e., to obtain the conditional mean and conditional variance associated with the Gaussian probability density function where the constant associated with the correction term (called the filter gain), K_i and Γ_i are generated by the following set of equations [see Eqs. (134), (C17), and (C18)]

$$K_i = M_i H_i'(R_i + H_i M_i H_i')^{-1}$$

$$M_{i+1} = Q_i + A_i \Gamma_i A_i'$$

$$\Gamma_i = M_i(I - H_i' K_i')$$

where the system equations are given by (117) and (118) where ξ's and η's are Gaussian random variables with moments given by (119).

The regulator problem discussed in Section 2,D is that of minimizing the quadratic criterion function where the plant equation is given by

$$x_{i+1} = F_i x_i + G_i u_i + \xi_i$$

The result of the minimization is expressed by

$$\min_{u_{i-1},\ldots,u_{N-1}} \sum_{i}^{n} (x_k' V_k x_k + u_{k-1}' P_{k-1} u_{k-1})$$

$$= x_i' I_{N-1} x_i + \rho_i$$

where

$$\begin{aligned} I_{N-i} &\triangleq A_i' J_i A_i \\ L_{N-i} &\triangleq V_i + A_i' J_i A_i \\ J_i &= L_{N-i-1}(I - B_i N_i) \\ N_i &\triangleq (P_i + B_i' L_{N-i-1} B_i)^{+} B_i' L_{N-i-1} \end{aligned}$$

Therefore, by comparing these two sets of equations we can establish the correspondence between these two problems as follows

$$\begin{aligned} K_i &\leftrightarrow N_i' & H_i &\leftrightarrow G_i' \\ M_i &\leftrightarrow L_{N-i-1} & Q_i &\leftrightarrow V_i \\ \Gamma_i &\leftrightarrow J_i & R_i &\leftrightarrow P_i \\ A_i &\leftrightarrow F_i' \end{aligned}$$

This correspondence is sometimes referred to as the duality principle.[89a] Making use of this principle, whatever results we obtain for regulator (filtering) problems can be translated into the corresponding results for filtering (regulator) problems.

D. Proportional Plus Integral Control

Using the sufficient statistics just derived, the optimal control policy for the system of (117) and (118) can now be given explicitly with the criterion function

$$J = \sum_1^N W_i(x_i, u_{i-1}), \qquad W_i = x_i' V_i x_i + u_{i-1}' P_{i-1} u_{i-1}$$

The optimal control policy for this system has already been derived in Section 2 if we take A_k, B_k, and H_k to be deterministic with the additional assumption that ξ_k and η_k are Gaussian random variables with mean 0 and covariances of (119). Then $u_i^* = -\Lambda_i \mu_i$ of (74a) still gives the optimal control policy where μ_i is now given explicitly by (132a). Bars over various matrices can be removed in the expression for Λ_i since A, B, and H are assumed deterministic in this section. Therefore, the optimal controller has the structure shown in Fig. 2.9, where μ-generator has the structure shown in Fig. 2.9. Since ξ and η are now assumed Gaussian, what appeared as an assumption in Section 3—that $(x_i - \mu_i)$ has a conditional covariance matrix independent of x_i and y^i—is now one of the properties of the Gaussian random variables and this constant is Γ_i of (132b). Since μ_0 is proportional to y_0 when $\Sigma_0^{\ 1}$ is a null matrix,

$$\mu_0 = \Gamma_0 H_0' R_0^{-1} y_0$$

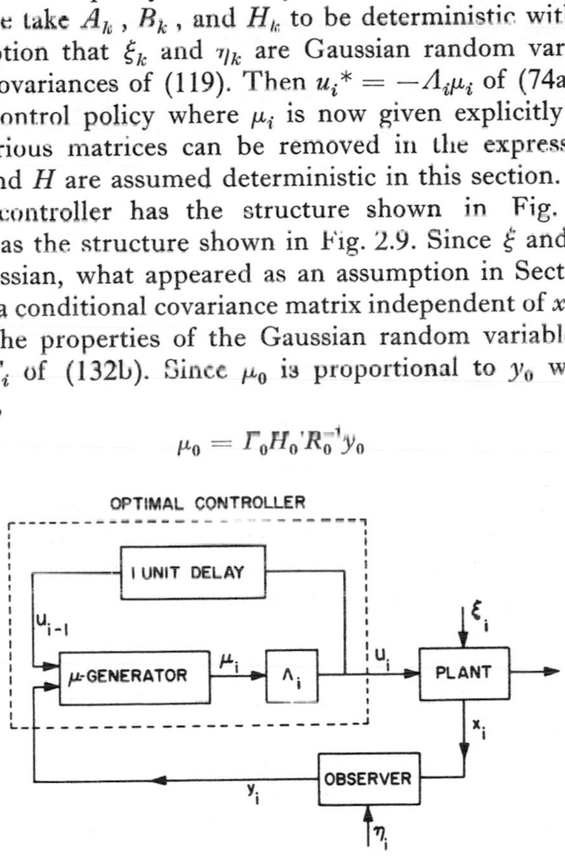

Fig. 2.9. Structure of optimal controller for stochastic system with linear plant and observation equations.

one has

$$A_0\mu_0 + B_0u_0^* = A_0\mu_0 - B_0\Lambda_0\mu_0 = (A_0 - B_0\Lambda_0)\mu_0$$
$$= (A_0 - B_0\Lambda_0)\Gamma_0 H_0' R_0^{-1} y_0$$

Therefore, it is easily seen that μ_i is linear in y^i, $0 \leqslant i \leqslant N-1$. The assumption that Σ_0^{-1} is null implies no a priori knowledge of x_0. Generally, $E(x_i \mid y^i)$ is some (measurable) function of y^i. When Gaussian random variables are involved, we have just seen that $E(x_i \mid y^i)$ turns out to be linear in y^i. This fact may be used to construct an approximation to $E(x_i \mid y^i)$ when the random variables are not Gaussian. From the recursion formula for μ, (132a), with the optimal control u_i^* given by $-\Lambda_i\mu_i$, (132a) can be rewritten as

$$\mu_{i+1} = C_{i+1}\mu_i + K_{i+1}y_{i+1} \tag{139}$$

where

$$C_j = (I - K_jH_j)(A_{j-1} - B_{j-1}\Lambda_{j-1}) \tag{140}$$

and where K_i is given by (138). This can be written as

$$\mu_{i+1} = K_{i+1}y_{i+1} + \sum_{j=0}^{i} C_{i+1} \cdots C_{j+1}K_jy_j$$

Therefore

$$u_i^* = -\Lambda_iK_iy_i - \Lambda_i\left(\sum_{j=0}^{i-1} C_i \cdots C_{j+1}K_jy_j\right), \qquad 1 \leqslant i \leqslant N-1$$

$$u_0^* = -\Lambda_0K_0y_0 \tag{141}$$

which can be interpreted to mean that the optimal control is of the proportional plus integral type,[119] where the first term in (141) gives the control proportional to the measurement of the current state vector and the second term in (141) expresses the control due to the integral on the past state vector measurements. Figure 2.10 gives a block diagram description of the proportional plus integral control generation.

The effects of past observations are therefore weighted according to the weight C. Thus, if $\|(\prod_{k=j+1}^{i-1} C_k)K_j\| \ll \|K_i\|$ for $i \gg j$, then the remote past measurements have negligible effects on the current control variables to be chosen. In the extreme case $C_k = 0$, u_i^* depends only on y_i and past observations y^{i-1} have no effect on u_i^*. If the control problem is such that

$$A_i - B_i\Lambda_i = 0 \tag{142}$$

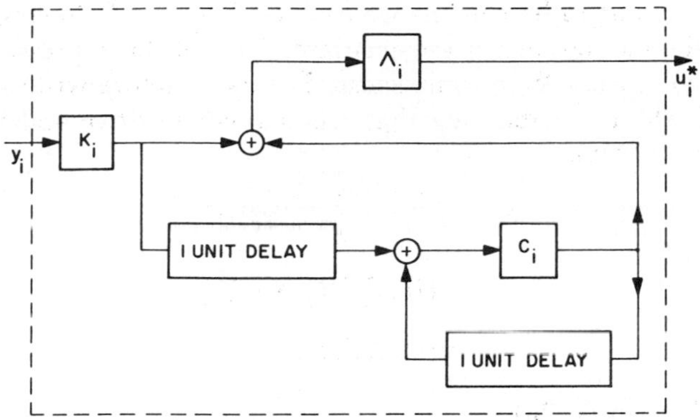

Fig. 2.10. Schematic diagram of proportional-plus-integral controller.

then from (139) and (140) we see that

$$\mu_i = \Gamma_i H_i' R_i^{-1} y_i \qquad \text{for all} \quad i = 0, 1, \ldots, N-1$$

Therefore,

$$u_i^* = -\Lambda_i \Gamma_i H_i' R_i^{-1} y_i\,, \qquad 0 \leqslant i \leqslant N-1$$

is the optimal control policy. Namely, the optimal controller becomes a pure proportional controller. One-dimensional case of (142) has been mentioned at the end of Section 3,A.

One sufficient condition that (142) holds is that $P_i = 0$ and that B_i^{-1} exists for all $i = 0, 1, \ldots, N-1$. Then, $\Lambda_i = B_i^{-1} A_i$ and Condition (142) will be met.

a. *Accurate Measurements*

We see from (139) that the control u_i^* consists of proportional part plus the integral part unless $C_j = 0$ of all $j \leqslant i-1$. We have seen one way that $C_j = 0$ results by having $A_j - B_j \Lambda_j = 0$. Now, suppose $A_j - B_j \Lambda_j \neq 0$. Then, unless $K_j H_j = I$, the proportional part does not disappear.

Intuitively speaking, if the measurements of the state vectors are exact and there are no unknown parameters in the problem statements as we are assuming now, then the control at time i will be a function of x_i alone, indicating $K_j H_j$ will be equal to I under the perfect measurements. For systems with poor measurements of the state vectors it is intuitively reasonable that the controller makes use not only of the current measurements but also of past measurements in synthesizing optimal controls.[119]

This turns out to be true, as we can see from the following.

When the measurements are accurate, this will be expressed by small covariance matrices R_j in some sense. Let us therefore write ϵR_j instead of R_j with the understanding that ϵ is a small positive scalar quantity. Then, from (127a),

$$\Gamma_0 = \left(\Sigma_0^{-1} + \frac{1}{\epsilon} H_0' R_0^{-1} H_0\right)^{-1}$$

$$= \epsilon(H_0' R_0^{-1} H_0 + \epsilon \Sigma_0^{-1})^{-1}$$

$$\approx \epsilon(H_0' R_0^{-1} H_0)^{-1}$$

In general, from (132b),

$$\Gamma_i \approx \epsilon(H_i' R_i^{-1} H_i)^{-1}$$

Therefore

$$K_i H_i = \Gamma_i H_i' R_i^{-1} H_i \approx I$$

Thus

$$-u_i^* = \Lambda_i \mu_i \approx \epsilon \Lambda_i (H_i' R_i^{-1} H_i)^{-1} H_i' R_i^{-1} y_i \tag{143}$$

Equation (143) shows that u_i^* is small compared with y_i and the integral part will be negligible compared with the proportional part.

b. *Inaccurate Measurements*

Now, let us examine the relative magnitudes of the integral and the proportional parts when the accuracy of measurements is poor.

We will now suppose that R_j is large or R_j^{-1} is small in some sense. Writing ϵR_j^{-1} instead of R_j^{-1}, where ϵ is a small positive scalar quantity as before, we now have

$$\Gamma_0 = (\Sigma_0^{-1} + \epsilon H_0' R_0^{-1} H_0)^{-1}$$

$$\approx \Sigma_0$$

$$\mu_0 \approx \epsilon \Sigma_0 H_0' R_0^{-1} y_0$$

In general

$$\Gamma_{i+1} = [\epsilon H_{i+1}' R_{i+1}^{-1} H_{i+1} + (Q_i + A_i \Gamma_i A_i')^{-1}]^{-1} \tag{144}$$

Equation (144) can be solved as

$$\Gamma_{i+1} = L_i$$

where

$$L_j \triangleq Q_j + A_j L_{j-1} A_j'$$
$$L_{-1} \triangleq \Sigma_0$$

Thus

$$K_i = \epsilon L_{i-1} H_i' R_i^{-1}$$
$$I - K_i H_i \approx I$$

Thus

$$\mu_i = \epsilon L_{i-1} H_{i-1}' R_{i-1}^{-1} y_i + \epsilon \sum_{k=1}^{i-2} (A_k - B_k \Lambda_k) \Sigma_0 H_0' R_0^{-1} y_0 \tag{145}$$

It is seen from (145) that the integral part is of the same order as the proportional part unless $\| \prod_{k=1}^{i-2} (A_k - B_k \Lambda_k) \|$ is of the order ϵ or less, for example by satisfying the inequality $\| A_k - B_k \Lambda_k \| \ll 1$ for $1 \leqslant k \leqslant i - 2$.

E. Example 4. Correlated Gaussian Noises

Before closing this chapter, we shall briefly outline the derivations of sufficient statistics when ξ-noises and η-noises are correlated, while retaining the assumption that ξ and η are independent at different times. As discussed in Section 2, this independence assumption can also be dropped by dealing with augmented state vectors. See Refs. 33a and 141 for continuous-time counterparts.

Instead of Eq. (119), it is now assumed that ξ and η are jointly normally distributed with

$$\begin{aligned} E(\xi_i) &= E(\eta_i) = 0 \\ E(\xi_i \xi_j') &= Q_i \delta_{ij} \\ E(\eta_i \eta_j') &= R_i \delta_{ij} \\ E(\xi_i \eta_j') &= S_i \delta_{ij} \end{aligned} \tag{146}$$

where Q_i and R_i are assumed positive definite. The joint probability density function for (ξ_i, η_i) has the form

$$p(\xi_i, \eta_i) = \text{const} \exp\left(-\tfrac{1}{2} (\xi_i', \eta_i') C_i^{-1} \begin{pmatrix} \xi_i \\ \eta_i \end{pmatrix}\right) \tag{147}$$

where

$$C_i \triangleq E\left[\begin{pmatrix} \xi_i \\ \eta_i \end{pmatrix} (\xi_i', \eta_i')\right] = \begin{bmatrix} Q_i & S_i \\ S_i' & R_i \end{bmatrix}$$

It is convenient to work with the expression for $p(x_{i+1} \mid y^i)$ rather than $p(x_i \mid y^i)$ now since ξ_i and η_i are correlated.

To obtain the recursion equation for $p(x_i \mid y^{i-1})$, consider

$$p(x_i, y_i, x_{i+1} \mid y^{i-1}).$$

It can be written by the chain rule:

$$p(x_i, y_i, x_{i+1} \mid y^{i-1}) = p(x_i \mid y^{i-1})\, p(x_{i+1}, y_i \mid x_i, y^{i-1}) \tag{148}$$

Also

$$p(x_i, y_i, x_{i+1} \mid y^{i-1}) = p(y_i \mid y^{i-1})\, p(x_i, x_{i+1} \mid y^i)$$

Therefore,

$$\begin{aligned} p(x_{i+1} \mid y^i) &= \int p(x_i, x_{i+1} \mid y^i)\, dx_i \\ &= \text{const} \int p(x_i \mid y^{i-1})\, p(x_{i+1}, y_i \mid x_i, y^{i-1})\, dx_i \end{aligned} \tag{149}$$

where the constant (a function of y^i) is determined by the relation

$$\int p(x_{i+1} \mid y^i)\, dx_{i+1} = 1$$

In (149), $p(x_{i+1}, y_i \mid x_i, y^{i-1})$ is given by

$$p(x_{i+1}, y_i \mid x_i, y^{i-1}) = \text{const} \exp\left(-\frac{1}{2}\left\|\begin{pmatrix} x_{i+1} - A_i x_i - B_i u_i \\ y_i - H_i x_i \end{pmatrix}\right\|^2_{C_i^{-1}}\right) \tag{150}$$

Thus, we obtain the recursion formula

$$p(x_{i+1} \mid y^i) = \text{const} \int p(x_i \mid y^{i-1}) \exp\left(-\frac{1}{2}\left\|\begin{pmatrix} x_{i+1} - A_i x_i - B_i u_i \\ y_i - H_i x_i \end{pmatrix}\right\|^2_{C_i^{-1}}\right) dx_i \tag{151}$$

The relation to be verified by the mathematical induction is now

$$p(x_i \mid y^{i-1}) = \text{const} \exp(-\tfrac{1}{2} \| x_i - v_i \|^2_{\Gamma_i^{-1}}) \tag{152}$$

where (v_i, Γ_i) is the sufficient statistics.

Substituting (152) into (151) and carrying out Integration (151), recursion formula for v_i and Z_i are obtained in much the same way as before. Only the result is listed here:

$$v_{i+1} = A_i v_i + B_i u_i + K_{i+1}(y_i - H_i v_i) \tag{153}$$

where

$$K_{i+1} \triangleq \Gamma_{i+1}(-D_{12}^i + G_i'\Sigma_i F_i) \tag{154a}$$

$$\Gamma_{i+1}^{-1} \triangleq D_{11}^i + G_i'\Sigma_i G_i \tag{154b}$$

$$\Sigma_i^{-1} \triangleq \Gamma_i^{-1} + A_i'G_{11}^i A_i + H_i'D_{22}^i H_i + A_i'D_{12}^i H_i + H_i'D_{12}^{i\prime} A_i \tag{154c}$$

$$G_i \triangleq A_i'D_{11}^i + H_i'D_{12}^{i\prime} \tag{154d}$$

$$F_i \triangleq H_i'D_{22}^i + A_i'D_{12}^i \tag{154e}$$

$$D_{11}^i = (Q_i - S_i R_i^{-1} S_i')^{-1} \tag{154f}$$

$$D_{12}^i = -(Q_i - S_i R_i^{-1} S_i')^{-1} S_i R_i^{-1} \tag{154g}$$

$$D_{22}^i = R_i^{-1} + R_i^{-1} S_i'(Q_i - S_i R_i^{-1} S_i') S_i R_i^{-1} \tag{154h}$$

Assuming x_0 is independent of ξ_0, η_0 and of $N(a, \Lambda_0)$, the initial values are given as follows:

$$v_1 = A_0 a + B_0 u_0 + K_1(y_0 - H_0 a) \tag{155}$$

with Γ_0 replaced by Λ_0 in the expression for K_1 and Σ_0^{-1}.

4. Discussions

There are several related classes of problems that may be investigated using the techniques developed in this chapter.

We have already mentioned the desirability of investigating the control problems with control policy based on observation data k sampling time or more old

$$u_i = \phi_i(y^{i-k}, u^{i-1}), \qquad i = k+1, \ldots, N-1$$

where $u_0, u_1, \ldots, u_k$ must be chosen from some other considerations. Then, instead of generating $p(x_i \mid y^i)$ and $p(y_{i+1} \mid y^i)$, it is necessary to generate $p(x_i \mid y^{i-k})$ and $p(y_i \mid y^{i-k})$. Using these latter density expressions, the formulation of optimal control is formally identical to the one given in this chapter.

The reader is invited to investigate the optimal control problem for the system of Section 3, when the criterion function includes an additional term, representing the cost of computing, which may be taken to be a decreasing function of k.

Another class of problems that are amenable to analysis with the techniques of this chapter is that of control systems with delay. Then defining new augmented state and control vectors appropriately the difference equation for it can be put into a standard form. The theory can now be applied to the augmented systems.

Closely related to control problems with delays either in the plants or in the observation data available for control synthesis are the problems with intermittent observation data.

Although we develop in this book the optimal control synthesis method assuming that system state vectors are observed each sampling time instant, there is a class of systems, be it chemical or aerospace, where it is neither feasible nor desirable to observe the state vectors at every sampling time instant.

For such systems it is more realistic to derive optimal control policies imposing some constraints on the way observations on the state vectors are performed.

One such possibility is to specify the total number of possible observations for N-stage control process and to optimize EJ with respect to a control policy and the spacing of observations. See Kushner[95] for a preliminary study of such systems.

A more straightforward example of systems with constrained observation schemes is a system where observations are taken every k sampling instants for some fixed k. Such a system can be treated by the techniques of this chapter by rewriting the plant (i.e., the state transition) equation in terms of the time instants at which observations are made.

Another way of imposing constraints on observations is to assume that at any time i there is a positive probability that the state vector will not be observed. Such a probability may be constant throughout the process or may be modified by the control variable with possible penalty incurred for modifying the probability. See Eaton[53] for such analysis for purely stochastic systems.

More direct constraint can be imposed on possible observation schemes by incorporating a cost associated with observation in the system performance indices. Realistically, such cost of observations will be functions of state vectors. See Breakwell[33] for an elementary example where the cost of control is taken to be independent of the state vectors.

Note that the recursive procedure developed in Section 2,C for generating $p(x_i \mid y^i)$ can be modified to generate $p(x_j \mid y^i)$ for $j < i$ recursively. Such conditional probability densities can be used to obtain more accurate estimate of x_j based on the observations $y_0, \ldots, y_j$, $y_{j+1}, \ldots, y_i$, rather than on just $y_0, \ldots, y_j$.

Appendix A. Minimization of a Quadratic Form

Consider the problem of finding u which minimizes

$$(u, Su) + 2(u, Tx) \tag{A1}$$

where $(\cdot, \cdot)$ is an inner product and where it is assumed that S is symmetric and positive definite, hence S^{-1} exists.

By completing the square in (A1),

$$(u, Su) + 2(u, Tx) = (u + S^{-1}Tx, S(u + S^{-1}Tx)) - (x, T'S^{-1}Tx)$$

one sees that u which minimizes (A1) is given by u which minimizes

$$(u + S^{-1}Tx, S(u + S^{-1}Tx)) \tag{A2}$$

Since S is positive definite, (A2) is minimized by

$$u + S^{-1}Tx = 0$$

or

$$u = -S^{-1}Tx \tag{A3}$$

and

$$\min_u [(u, Su) + 2(u, Tx)] = -(x, T'S^{-1}Tx) \tag{A4}$$

Now consider the case where x is a random variable and it is desired to minimize

$$E[(u, Su) + 2(u, Tx) \mid y] \tag{A5}$$

with respect to a deterministic $u(y)$ where y is another random variable. (See Appendix I at the end of this book for a more general discussion on conditional expectations.) Then again, by completing the square in (A5),

$$\begin{aligned} I(y) &\triangleq \min_u E\{(u + S^{-1}Tx, S(u + S^{-1}Tx)) - (x, T'S^{-1}Tx) \mid y\} \\ &= -E[(x, T'S^{-1}Ts) \mid y] + \min_u E[(u + S^{-1}Tx, S(u + S^{-1}Tx)) \mid y] \end{aligned} \tag{A6}$$

Defining another random variable w by

$$w = -S^{-1}Tx \tag{A7}$$

one sees that u which minimizes $I(y)$ is the same u which minimizes

$$\min_u E[((u - w), S(u - w)) \mid y] \tag{A8}$$

Equation (A8) can be rewritten by defining

$$\hat{w} = E(w \mid y) \tag{A9}$$

$$\begin{aligned}\min_u E[(u - \hat{w} + \hat{w} - w, S(u - \hat{w} + \hat{w} - w)) \mid y] \\ = \min_u\{[(u - \hat{w}, S(u - \hat{w})) + E((\hat{w} - w), S(\hat{w} - w)) \mid y]\}\end{aligned} \tag{A10}$$

Thus, one sees that

$$u = \hat{w} \tag{A11}$$

minimizes (A10) and (A5). The minimizing u is given from (A7), (A9), and (A11) by

$$u^* = -\Lambda\hat{x} \tag{A12}$$

where

$$\Lambda = S^{-1}T \quad \text{and} \quad \hat{x} = E(x \mid y) \tag{A13}$$

The minimal value of (A5) is given, then, from (A6), (A7), and (A10),

$$\begin{aligned} I(y) &= -E[(x, T'S^{-1}Tx) \mid y] + E[((\hat{w} - w), S(\hat{w} - w)) \mid y] \\ &= -E[(x, T'S^{-1}Tx) \mid y] + E[((x - \hat{x}), T'S^{-1}T(x - \hat{x})) \mid y] \\ &= -(\hat{x}, T'S^{-1}T\hat{x}) \end{aligned} \tag{A14}$$

Note that u^* given by (A12) is such that it satisfies the equation

$$E\{(u - u^*, S(u^* - w)) \mid y\} = 0$$

for any u.

This fact is sometimes referred to as the orthogonality principle.[85,86,109b] See also Chapter V for other instances where the orthogonality principle is applied.

Appendix B. Use of Pseudoinverse in Minimizing a Quadratic Form

Consider

$$I(u) = (u, Su) + 2(u, Tx) + (x, Rx) \tag{B1}$$

where S is positive and symmetric. We know from Appendix A that when S^{-1} exists I is minimized by choosing u to be

$$u = -S^{-1}Tx \tag{B2}$$

and (B1) becomes

$$I = (x, (R - T'S^{-1}T)x)$$
$$\triangleq \| x \|^2_{R-T'S^{-1}T} \tag{B3}$$

When S^{-1} does not exist, we will see that u^* given by

$$u^* = -S^+Tx \tag{B4}$$

minimizes I, where S^+ is the pseudoinverse of S. Pseudoinverses are discussed in Appendix II at the end of this book. As it is discussed there in detail, when the pseudoinverses are involved, the minimizing u are not usually unique unless one imposes the additional condition such as the condition that $\| u \|$ is also minimal. The u given by (B4) is the one with the minimum norm. One can write

$$u = u_1 + u_2$$

where

$$u_1 \in \mathscr{R}(S) \qquad \text{(range space of } S\text{)}$$

and

$$u_2 \in \mathscr{N}(S) \qquad \text{(null space of } S\text{)}$$

Since S is symmetric, $\mathscr{R}(S)$ and $\mathscr{N}(S)$ are orthogonal and we have

$$\| u \|^2 = \| u_1 \|^2 + \| u_2 \|^2$$

To derive (B4) we will rewrite (B1) such that it includes a term

$$\| u + S^+Tx \|_S^2 \geqslant 0 \tag{B5}$$

and a term independent of u. Then (B5) is never negative and it vanishes when $u = u^*$. Then it will be seen that $I(u)$ is minimized by u^* of (B4). Using the identities[142]

$$S^+SS^+ = S^+ \tag{B6a}$$

$$(S^+)' = (S')^+ = S^+ \tag{B6b}$$

$$I(u) = \| u + S^+Tx \|_S^2 + \| x \|^2_{R-T'S^+T} + 2(Tx, (I - S^+S)u) \tag{B7}$$

In (B7), note that

$$(I - S^+S)u = u_1 + u_2 - S^+S(u_1 + u_2)$$
$$= u_1 + u_2 - u_1$$
$$= u_2 \tag{B8}$$

since S^+S restricted to $\mathscr{R}(S)$ is the identity.[142] Also,

$$\| u + S^+Tx \|_S^2 = \| u_1 + S^+Tx \|_S^2 \tag{B9}$$

Thus,

$$I(u) = \| u_1 + S^+Tx \|_S^2 + 2(Tx, u_2) + \| x \|_{R-T'S^+T}^2 \tag{B10}$$

The first term in (B10) is minimized by choosing

$$u_1 = -S^+Tx$$

From the requirement of the minimal norm of u one has

$$u_2 \equiv 0$$

Thus,

$$u^* = -S^+Tx \tag{B11}$$

Appendix C. Calculation of Sufficient Statistics

In this appendix an integral of the form $\int \exp(-\frac{1}{2} E_i)\, dx_i$ is evaluated where E_i is given by (130). By completing the square, E_i can be rewritten as

$$\begin{aligned} E_i &= (x_i - \mu_i)'\Gamma_i^{-1}(x_i - \mu_i) \\ &\quad + (x_{i+1} - A_i\mu_i - B_iu_i - A_i(x_i - \mu_i))' \\ &\quad \times Q_i^{-1}(x_{i+1} - A_i\mu_i - B_iu_i - A_i(x_i - \mu_i)) \\ &\quad + (y_{i+1} - H_{i+1}x_{i+1})'R_{i+1}^{-1}(y_{i+1} - H_{i+1}x_{i+1}) \\ &= (x_i - \mu_i)'[\Gamma_i^{-1} + A_i'Q_i^{-1}A_i](x_i - \mu_i) \\ &\quad - 2(x_i - \mu_i)'A_i'Q_i^{-1}(x_{i+1} - A_i\mu_i - B_iu_i) \\ &\quad + (x_{i+1} - A_i\mu_i - B_iu_i)'Q_i^{-1}(x_{i+1} - A_i\mu_i - B_iu_i) \\ &\quad + (y_{i+1} - H_{i+1}x_{i+1})'R_{i+1}^{-1}(y_{i+1} - H_{i+1}x_{i+1}) \end{aligned} \tag{C1}$$

Let

$$\Pi_i^{-1} = \Gamma_i^{-1} + A_i'Q_i^{-1}A_i \tag{C2}$$

Then

$$\begin{aligned} E_i = {} & [x_i - \mu_i - \Pi_i A_i' Q_i^{-1}(x_{i+1} - A_i\mu_i - B_iu_i)]'\Pi_i^{-1} \\ & \times [x_i - \mu_i - \Pi_i A_i' Q_i^{-1}(x_{i+1} - A_i\mu_i - B_iu_i)] \\ & + (x_{i+1} - A_i\mu_i - B_iu_i)'(Q_i^{-1} - Q_i^{-1}A_i\Pi_iA_i'Q_i^{-1})(x_{i+1} - A_i\mu_i - B_iu_i) \\ & + (y_{i+1} - H_{i+1}x_{i+1})'R_{i+1}^{-1}(y_{i+1} - H_{i+1}x_{i+1}) \end{aligned} \tag{C3}$$

After integration with respect to x_i,

$$\int \exp\left(-\frac{E_i}{2}\right) dx_i = \text{const} \exp\left(-\frac{E_i'}{2}\right) \tag{C4}$$

where

$$\begin{aligned} E_i' = {} & (x_{i+1} - A_i\mu_i - B_iu_i)'M_{i+1}^{-1}(x_{i+1} - A_i\mu_i - B_iu_i) \\ & + (y_{i+1} - H_{i+1}x_{i+1})'R_{i+1}^{-1}(y_{i+1} - H_{i+1}x_{i+1}) \end{aligned} \tag{C5}$$

and where

$$M_{i+1}^{-1} = Q_i^{-1} - Q_i^{-1}A_i\Pi_iA_i'Q_i^{-1} \tag{C6}$$

By substituting (C2) into (C6) and using the identity of Appendix D, M_{i+1}^{-1} can be shown to be equal to

$$M_{i+1}^{-1} = (Q_i + A_i\Gamma_iA_i')^{-1} \tag{C7}$$

The first term $\| x_{i+1} - A_i\mu_i - B_iu_i\|^2_{M_{i+1}^{-1}}$ in (C5) is the result of evaluating $\int p(x_{i+1} \mid x_i, u_i)\, p(x_i \mid y^i)\, dx_i = p(x_{i+1} \mid y^i)$. Therefore, from (C5) one sees that the conditional distribution of x_{i+1} given y^i is normal with

$$E(x_{i+1} \mid y^i) = A_i\mu_i + B_iu_i \tag{C8}$$

and

$$\operatorname{cov}(x_{i+1} \mid y^i) = M_{i+1} = Q_i + A_i\Gamma_iA_i' \tag{C9}$$

The expression E_i' of (C5) can be rewritten as

$$\begin{aligned} E_i' = {} & (x_{i+1} - A_i\mu_i - B_iu_i)'(M_{i+1}^{-1} + H_{i+1}'R_{i+1}^{-1}H_{i+1})(x_{i+1} - A_i\mu_i - B_iu_i) \\ & - 2(x_{i+1} - A_i\mu_i - B_iu_i)'H_{i+1}'R_{i+1}^{-1}(y_{i+1} - H_{i+1}(A_i\mu_i + B_iu_i)) \\ & + \| y_{i+1} - H_{i+1}(A_i\mu_i + B_iu_i)\|^2_{R_{i+1}^{-1}} \end{aligned}$$

$$= \| x_{i+1} - A_i\mu_i - B_iu_i - \Gamma_{i+1}H'_{i+1}R^{-1}_{i+1}[y_{i+1} - H_{i+1}(A_i\mu_i + B_iu_i)]\|^2_{\Gamma^{-1}_{i+1}}$$

$$+ \| y_{i+1} - H_{i+1}(A_i\mu_i + B_iu_i)\|^2_{R^{-1}_{i+1} - R^{-1}_{i+1}H_{i+1}\Gamma_{i+1}H'_{i+1}R^{-1}_{i+1}} \quad \text{(C10)}$$

where

$$\Gamma^{-1}_{i+1} \triangleq M^{-1}_{i+1} + H'_{i+1}R^{-1}_{i+1}H_{i+1} \quad \text{(C11)}$$

Hence

$$p(x_{i+1} \mid y^{i+1}) = \text{const}\exp(-\tfrac{1}{2}\| x_{i+1} - \mu_{i+1}\|^2_{\Gamma^{-1}_{i+1}}) \quad \text{(C12)}$$

and

$$\mu_{i+1} = A_i\mu_i + B_iu_i + K_{i+1}[y_{i+1} - H_{i+1}(A_i\mu_i + B_iu_i)] \quad \text{(C13)}$$

where

$$K_{i+1} \triangleq \Gamma_{i+1}H'_{i+1}R^{-1}_{i+1} \quad \text{(C14)}$$

is the optimal gain of the filter. There is another expression for μ_{i+1} given by

$$\mu_{i+1} = \Gamma_{i+1}[H'_{i+1}R^{-1}_{i+1}y_{i+1} + M^{-1}_{i+1}(A_i\mu_i + B_iu_i)] \quad \text{(C15)}$$

These two expressions are identical since

$$\Gamma_{i+1}H'_{i+1}R^{-1}_{i+1}[y_{i+1} - H_{i+1}(A_i\mu_i + B_iu_i)]$$
$$+ \Gamma_{i+1}(M^{-1}_{i+1} + H'_{i+1}R^{-1}_{i+1}H_{i+1})(A_i\mu_i + B_iu_i)$$
$$= \Gamma_{i+1}H'_{i+1}R^{-1}_{i+1}(y_{i+1} - H_{i+1}(A_i\mu_i + B_iu_i)) + A_i\mu_i + B_iu$$

since

$$\Gamma_{i+1} = (M^{-1}_{i+1} + H'_{i+1}R^{-1}_{i+1}H_{i+1})^{-1}$$

by definition (C11). An alternate expression for Γ_{i+1} can be obtained directly from its definition $\Gamma_{i+1} = \text{cov}(x_{i+1} \mid y^{i+1})$. We do this by computing $\tilde{\Gamma}_i \triangleq \text{cov}(x_i)$ and noting that $\tilde{\Gamma}_i = \Gamma_i$ for all i. Since $\mu_{i+1} = A_i\mu_i + B_iu_i + K_{i+1}(y_{i+1} - H_{i+1}(A_i\mu_i + B_iu_i))$, where K_{i+1} is the gain of the filter, the estimation error satisfies

$$\tilde{x}_{i+1} \triangleq x_{i+1} - \mu_{i+1}$$
$$= A_i(x_i - \mu_i) + \xi_i - K_{i+1}(y_{i+1} - H_{i+1}(A_i\mu_i + B_iu_i))$$
$$= (I - K_{i+1}H_{i+1})(A_i(x_i - \mu_i) + \xi_i) - K_{i+1}\eta_{i+1}$$

therefore, noting that $E\tilde{x}_i = 0$ for all i,

$$E(\tilde{x}_{i+1}\tilde{x}'_{i+1}) \triangleq \tilde{\Gamma}_{i+1}$$
$$= (I - K_{i+1}H_{i+1})(A_i\tilde{\Gamma}_iA_i' + Q_i)(I - K_{i+1}H_{i+1})'$$
$$+ K_{i+1}R_{i+1}K'_{i+1} \tag{C16}$$

Note that the expression for $\tilde{\Gamma}_{i+1}$ given by (C16) is valid not only for the optimal filter gain $K_{i+1} = \Gamma_{i+1}H'_{i+1}R_{i+1}^{-1}$ but for any arbitrary gain. By completing the square in K_{i+1} in (C16),

$$\tilde{\Gamma}_{i+1} = (K_{i+1} - K^*_{i+1})C_i(K_{i+1} - K^*_{i+1})' + [I - K^*_{i+1}H_{i+1}]M_{i+1}$$
$$\times [I - K^*_{i+1}H_{i+1}]' + K^*_{i+1}R_{i+1}K^{*\prime}_{i+1} \tag{C17}$$

where

$$K^*_{i+1} \triangleq M_{i+1}H'_{i+1}C_i^{-1} \tag{C18a}$$

$$C_i \triangleq H_{i+1}M_{i+1}H'_{i+1} + R_{i+1} \tag{C18b}$$

Thus the norm of $\tilde{\Gamma}_{i+1}$ is minimized by choosing K_{i+1} to be equal to K^*_{i+1} since C_i is positive definite. By the matrix identity in Appendix D and by the mathematical induction we see that

$$\tilde{\Gamma}_i = \Gamma_i \qquad \text{for all} \quad i \tag{C19}$$

The equivalence of (C18a) and (C14) is established by means of the matrix identity of Appendix D. Now

$$M_{i+1}H'_{i+1}C_i^{-1} - \Gamma_{i+1}H'_{i+1}R_{i+1}^{-1}$$
$$= M_{i+1}H'_{i+1}C_i^{-1} - (M_{i+1} - M_{i+1}H'_{i+1}C_i^{-1}H_{i+1}M_{i+1})H'_{i+1}R_{i+1}^{-1}$$
$$= M_{i+1}H'_{i+1}[C_i^{-1} - R_{i+1}^{-1} + C_i^{-1}H_{i+1}M_{i+1}H'_{i+1}R_{i+1}^{-1}]$$
$$= M_{i+1}H'_{i+1}\{C_i^{-1}[R_{i+1} + H_{i+1}M_{i+1}H'_{i+1}]R_{i+1}^{-1} - R_{i+1}^{-1}\}$$
$$= M_{i+1}H'_{i+1}\{C_i^{-1}C_iR_{i+1}^{-1} - R_{i+1}^{-1}\} = 0$$

Appendix D. Matrix Identities

The following matrix identities are often useful in obtaining equivalent, computationally convenient expressions for error-covariance matrices and gain matrices.

$$(A + BCB')^{-1} = A^{-1} - A^{-1}BC(C + CB'A^{-1}BC)^{-1}CB'A^{-1}$$
$$(A + BCB')^{-1} = A^{-1} - A^{-1}B(C^{-1} + B'A^{-1}B)^{-1}B'A^{-1}$$

where the indicated inverses are assumed to exist. These are due to Householder.[74] The proof is by direct substitution.

There are similar identities involving pseudoinverses:

$$A^+ + BCB' = [A - ABC(C + CB'ABC)^{-1}CB'A]^+$$
$$A^+ + BCB' = [A - AB(C^+ + B'AB)^{-1}B'A]^+$$

where the indicated inverses are assumed to exist. These identities are due to Farrison.[54]

Another useful formula is the expression for the inverse of a matrix in terms of submatrices:

$$\begin{pmatrix} Q & S \\ S' & R \end{pmatrix}^{-1} = \begin{pmatrix} C_{11} & C_{12} \\ C_{21} & C_{22} \end{pmatrix}$$

where

$$C_{11} = (Q - SR^{-1}S')^{-1}$$
$$C_{12} = -C_{11}SR^{-1}$$
$$C_{21} = C'_{12}$$
$$C_{22} = R^{-1} + R^{-1}S'C_{11}SR^{-1}$$

Chapter III

Adaptive Control Systems and Optimal Bayesian Control Policies

In the previous chapter, we developed the method of deriving optimal control policies for purely stochastic systems. In this chapter we follow the same line of attack to discuss optimal control problems of certain parameter adaptive systems. Namely, we develop methods for obtaining optimal control policies for a class of dynamic systems where some of the key items of information on the optimal control problems are not known exactly. More specifically, we assume in this chapter that there is at least one unknown parameter in control problem descriptions, i.e., we assume that at least one unknown parameter is contained in the plant equation, the observation equation, various probability densities of the noises, initial conditions and/or in the descriptions of the inputs. The unknown parameter is assumed to be a member of a known parameter space. Therefore, the class of control systems considered in this chapter may be regarded as a class of parameter adaptive stochastic control systems. We will further develop in this chapter the procedure introduced in Section 1,B of Chapter II for obtaining optimal control policies by making use of recursively generated conditional densities.

In the next chapter, we give the most comprehensive formulation of the Bayesian optimal control problems for the class of stochastic and adaptive discrete-time dynamic systems.[15] Actually, we could have given this general formulation first and treated the subjects in Chapters II and III as special cases. It is felt, however, that this approach is less revealing, although it may be formally more elegant.

1. General Problem Statement (Scope of the Discussions)

A control system is now assumed to be described by the plant equation

$$x_{k+1} = F_k(x_k, u_k, \xi_k, \alpha), \qquad k = 0, 1, \ldots, N-1 \tag{1}$$

and is observed by y_k:

$$y_k = G_k(x_k, \eta_k, \beta) \tag{2}$$

where x_k, y_k, u_k, ξ_k, and η_k are the same vectors as in Chapter II, and where α and β are parameter vectors of Eqs. (1) and (2),* where $\alpha \in \Theta_\alpha$ and $\beta \in \Theta_\beta$ and where Θ_α and Θ_β are parameter spaces assumed given. The random vectors ξ and η are assumed to be such that their joint probability density $p(\xi^k, \eta^k \mid \theta_1, \theta_2)$ is given, $\theta_1 \in \Theta_1$ and $\theta_2 \in \Theta_2$, where Θ_1 and Θ_2 are known parameter spaces. When each of these parameter spaces contains a single element, all the parameter values are therefore known and the problem will reduce to a purely stochastic or a deterministic one. Therefore at least one parameter space is assumed to contain more than a single element in this chapter.

It will be seen in the course of development of this chapter that the method of this chapter applies equally well to situations where the probability distribution functions of the plant parameters α and/or β contain unknown parameters θ_α and θ_β, $\theta_\alpha \in \Theta_\alpha$, $\theta_\beta \in \Theta_\beta$, with Θ_α and Θ_β known. Example 7 of Chapter I is an example of such a system where the plant time-constant is taken to be a random variable with unknown mean. For additional examples, see Section 3,B.

Since both types of systems can be treated by the method of this chapter, no careful distinction will be made in deriving their optimal control policies.

A prior probability density functions are assumed to be given for each and all unknown parameters as well as for initial state vector x_0. The distribution function for the initial state vector x_0 may contain an unknown parameter θ_3, $\theta_3 \in \Theta_3$, where Θ_3 is assumed known. Known deterministic inputs and/or disturbance to the systems are assumed to be incorporated in (1) and (2).

Most of the formulas of this chapter are developed for systems of (1) and (2) where various random variables are assumed to be independent at each time instant, unless stated otherwise. The control problems of systems with dependent random variables are discussed in Chapter IV.

Desired inputs to the systems are assumed to be stochastic and the probability density function of such an input is assumed to contain a

* These parameters could be time varying. For the simplicity of exposition, they are assumed to be time invariant in this chapter.

parameter vector which may be unknown, $\mu \in \Theta_\mu$, where Θ_μ is assumed given. The symbol $d_k(\mu)$, $k = 0, 1, \ldots, N$, is used to denote a sequence of such random inputs. The actual inputs to the systems are denoted by z_k and are assumed to be related to d_k by

$$z_k = K_k(d_k, \zeta_k) \tag{3}$$

where ζ_k are random noise with known probability densities. The random variables z_k are assumed to be observed. Therefore, the observation data at any time k consists of z^k, y^k, and u^{k-1}. The criterion function J is taken to be essentially the same as in Chapter II:

$$J = \sum_{k=1}^{N} W_k(x_k, d_k, u_{k-1}) \tag{4}$$

It is desired to find an optimal closed-loop control policy which minimizes EJ. Control variables u to be considered in minimizing EJ depend only on the initially available information plus past and current observations and past controls and do not depend explicitly on unknown parameter values. As in Chapter II, optimal control policies are nonrandomized, i.e., each control u_k is specified to be a definite function of observed data only.

Since the optimal control problem in this general formulation is rather complicated, we will proceed in steps and will treat in the next section a class of problems where $\theta_1 \in \Theta_1$ and $\theta_2 \in \Theta_2$ are the only parameters vectors assumed unknown. Problems with unknown α and/or β are discussed in Section 3 of this chapter. A control problem where the distribution for the initial state vector x_0 contains an unknown parameter can be treated quite analogously. Only an example is discussed in Section 2,D in order to avoid repetitions of general formulations. The formulation for more general situations, where all of θ_1, θ_2, θ_3, θ_α, θ_β, and θ_μ are assumed unknown, is quite analogous and it should become apparent by then how to obtain the general formulation. See also Section 7 for further discussions.

2. Systems with Unknown Noise Characteristics

A. Introduction

In this section, we will derive optimal control policies for systems such that the random noises in the plant equation as well as in the observation equation have unknown probability density functions. Inputs to the systems are assumed to be deterministic and known.

The system to be considered in this section, therefore, is described by

$$x_{k+1} = F_k(x_k, u_k, \xi_k) \tag{5}$$

$$y_k = G_k(x_k, \eta_k), \qquad k = 0, 1, \ldots, N-1 \tag{6}$$

where ξ's are random disturbances in the plant. Their probability density functions are assumed to contain unknown parameter θ_1, $\theta_1 \in \Theta_1$. A similar assumption is made for η's with their densities containing the unknown parameter $\theta_2 \in \Theta_2$. The random variables $\xi_0, \ldots, \xi_{N-1}$, $\eta_0, \ldots, \eta_{N-1}$ are all assumed to be independent for all $\theta_1 \in \Theta_1$ and $\theta_2 \in \Theta_2$.* A joint a priori density $p_0(\theta_1, \theta_2, x_0)$ is assumed given. The assumption that ξ's and η's are independent is made to simplify presentations. This assumption can readily be removed by working with the joint density for ξ's and η's rather than with separate densities for ξ's and η's. Problems with dependent noises are taken up in Chapter IV. Since the parameters α and β are assumed known in this section, they are not exhibited in (5) and (6).

Because inputs are known they are incorporated in (5). Instead of (4), the criterion function is taken to be

$$J = \sum_{k=1}^{N} W_k(x_k, u_{k-1}) \tag{7}$$

---

* Suppose ξ_i, $i = 0, 1, \ldots$, are a sequence of random variables which are independent for each $\theta \in \Theta$. Namely

$$p(\xi^i \mid \theta) = \prod_{j=0}^{i} p(\xi_j \mid \theta) \qquad \text{for each} \quad \theta \in \Theta$$

The a priori density function of θ is assumed given by $p_0(\theta)$. This conditional independence does not imply the independence of ξ_i, $i = 0, 1, \ldots$, when θ is not specified. To see this, compute

$$\begin{aligned} p(\xi_i, \xi_j) &= \int p(\xi_i, \xi_j \mid \theta)\, p_0(\theta)\, d\theta \\ &= \int p(\xi_i \mid \theta)\, p(\xi_j \mid \theta)\, p_0(\theta)\, d\theta \end{aligned}$$

On the other hand,

$$p(\xi_i)\, p(\xi_j) = \int p(\xi_i \mid \theta)\, p_0(\theta)\, p(\xi_j \mid \phi)\, p_0(\phi)\, d(\theta, \phi)$$

Thus, generally,

$$p(\xi_i, \xi_j) \neq p(\xi_i)\, p(\xi_j)$$

unless $p_0(\theta)$ is a delta function which means the density function for ξ's are known completely a priori.

As before, an optimal control policy minimizes the expected value of J:

$$EJ = \sum_{k=1}^{N} R_k$$

where $R_k = EW_k$, $1 \leqslant k \leqslant N$.

B. Optimal Control Policy

It can again be shown that only nonrandomized control policies need be considered in optimization. This is done heuristically as follows:

a. *Last Control Stage*

We use the notations of Chapter II. The arguments are almost identical to those of Section 1,B, Chapter II. Assume that we have somehow determined optimal controls $\rho_0^*, \ldots, \rho_{N-2}^*$ and that ρ_{N-1} is the only control function yet to be determined.

As before, R_N is minimized by

$$\min_{\rho_{N-1}} E(W_N \mid y^{N-1}) \tag{8}*$$

for all y^{N-1} where

$$E(W_N \mid y^{N-1}) = \int W_N(x_N, u_{N-1})\, p(x_N, u_{N-1} \mid y^{N-1})\, d(x_N, u_{N-1}) \tag{9}$$

Using the chain rule, write the probability density in (9) as

$$\begin{aligned} p(x_N, u_{N-1} \mid y^{N-1}) &= p(u_{N-1} \mid y^{N-1})\, p(x_N \mid u_{N-1}, y^{N-1}) \\ &= \rho_{N-1}(u_{N-1})\, p(x_N \mid u_{N-1}, y^{N-1}) \end{aligned} \tag{10}$$

In (10), we can write

$$p(x_N \mid u_{N-1}, y^{N-1}) = \int p(x_N \mid x_{N-1}, u_{N-1}, \theta_1)\, p(x_{N-1}, \theta_1 \mid y^{N-1})\, d(x_{N-1}, \theta_1)$$

where $p(x_{i+1} \mid x_i, u_i, \theta_1)$ is obtainable from (5) and the density functions for ξ's. Note that, unlike in Chapter II, $p(x_{i+1} \mid x_i, u_i)$ is not known since the density function of ξ contains the unknown parameter θ_1. It is only when the value for θ_1 is assumed that the density function of ξ_i is completely specified.

* As in Chapter II, the control variables are understood as parts of the conditioning variables when the observed state variables are shown, and are not exhibited explicitly.

Assume that $p(x_{N-1}, \theta_1 \mid y^{N-1})$ is available. We will derive a recursion equation to generate this density function in Section 2,C using the technique of Section 1,C of Chapter II.

Then substituting (10) into (9),

$$E(W_N \mid y^{N-1}) = \int \lambda_N \, \rho_{N-1}(u_{N-1}) \, du_{N-1} \tag{11}$$

where

$$\lambda_N \triangleq \int W_N(x_N, u_{N-1}) \, p(x_N \mid x_{N-1}, u_{N-1}, \theta_1) \times p(x_{N-1}, \theta_1 \mid y^{N-1}) \, d(x_N, x_{N-1}, \theta_1)$$

From (11), the optimal control policy is now seen to be nonrandomized with the optimal control policy $\rho_{N-1}^* = \delta(u_{N-1} - u_{N-1}^*)$, where u_{N-1}^* is u_{N-1} which minimizes λ_N. The minimization is performed for u_{N-1} in U_{N-1}.

Define

$$\gamma_N^* \triangleq \min_{u_{N-1}} \gamma_N, \qquad \text{where} \quad \gamma_N = \lambda_N \tag{12}$$

then

$$\min_{\rho_{N-1}} E(W_N \mid y^{N-1}) = \gamma_N^* \tag{13}$$

b. *Last Two Control Stages*

Now consider the situation where two more control actions remain to be exerted. The probability density for u_{N-2}, ρ_{N-2} are to be chosen so that, when followed by ρ_{N-1}^*, the sum $R_{N-1} + R_N = E(W_{N-1} + W_N)$ is minimized or, equivalently,

$$E(W_{N-1} + W_N \mid y^{N-2}) \tag{14}$$

is minimized for all y^{N-2}.

Proceeding analogously with the last stage case, we write

$$E(W_{N-1} \mid y^{N-2}) = \int \lambda_{N-1} \, \rho_{N-2}(u_{N-2}) \, du_{N-2} \tag{15}$$

where

$$\lambda_{N-1} \triangleq \int W_{N-1}(x_{N-1}, u_{N-2}) \, p(x_{N-1} \mid x_{N-2}, u_{N-2}, \theta_1) \times p(x_{N-2}, \theta_1 \mid y^{N-2}) \, d(x_{N-2}, x_{N-1}, \theta_1)$$

where $p(x_{N-1} \mid x_{N-2}, u_{N-2}, \theta_1)$ is obtained from (5) and the known density for ξ_{N-2} and the conditional density function $p(x_{N-2}, \theta_1 \mid y^{N-2})$

is assumed to be available. The discussion of its computation is deferred until the next section.

To evaluate $E(W_N \mid y^{N-2})$ in (14) note as we did in Section 1,B of Chapter II that

$$E(W_N \mid y^{N-2}) = E(E(W_N \mid y^{N-1}) \mid y^{N-2}) \tag{16}$$

From (14), (15), and (16),

$$\min_{\rho_{N-2}} E(W_{N-1} + W_N{}^* \mid y^{N-2}) = \min_{\rho_{N-2}} \Big[\int \lambda_{N-1}\, \rho_{N-2}(u_{N-2})\, du_{N-2} + E\Big(\int \lambda_N\, \rho_{N-1}^*(u_{N-1})\, du_{N-1} \mid y^{N-2}\Big)\Big] \tag{17}$$

where the asterisk indicate the use of ρ_{N-1}^*. Since we know that ρ_{N-1}^* is nonrandomized, the last term in (17) becomes, from (11) and (13),

$$E\Big(\int \lambda_N\, \rho_{N-1}^*\, du_{N-1} \mid y^{N-2}\Big) = E(\gamma_N{}^* \mid y^{N-2}) \tag{18}$$

Proceeding analogously to Section 1,B of Chapter II, (18) is evaluated as

$$E(\gamma_N{}^* \mid y^{N-2}) = \int \gamma_N{}^*\, p(y_{N-1} \mid u^{N-2}, y^{N-2})\, \rho_{N-2}(u_{N-2})\, d(u_{N-2}, y_{N-1}) \tag{19}$$

Thus, (17) becomes

$$\min_{\rho_{N-2}} E(W_{N-1} + W_N{}^* \mid y^{N-2}) = \min_{\rho_{N-2}} \int \Big[\lambda_{N-1} + \int \gamma_N{}^*\, p(y_{N-1} \mid u^{N-2}, y^{N-2})\, dy_{N-1}\Big] \rho_{N-2}\, du_{N-2} \tag{20}$$

where it is assumed that $p(y_{N-1} \mid u^{N-2}, y^{N-2})$ is known. This density is also derived in Section 2,C.

Define

$$\gamma_{N-1} \triangleq \lambda_{N-1} + \int \gamma_N{}^*\, p(y_{N-1} \mid u^{N-2}, y^{N-2})\, dy_{N-1} \tag{21}$$

then

$$\rho_{N-2}^* = \delta(u_{N-2} - u_{N-2}^*) \tag{22}$$

minimizes (20) where u_{N-2}^* is u_{N-2} in U_{N-2} which minimizes γ_{N-1}:

$$\min_{u_{N-2}} \gamma_{N-1} = \gamma_{N-1}^* \tag{23}$$

c. *General Case*

Proceeding recursively, it is now easy to see that an optimal control function at time k, ρ_k, is determined by

$$\min_{\rho_k} E(W_{k+1} + W_{k+2}^* + \cdots + W_N{}^* \mid y^k)$$

$$= \min_{\rho_k} \int \left[\lambda_{k+1} + \int \gamma_{k+2}^* p(y_{k+1} \mid u^k, y^k)\, dy_{k+1}\right] \rho_k\, du_k$$

where

$$\gamma_{k+1} \triangleq \lambda_{k+1} + \int \gamma_{k+2}^* p(y_{K+1} \mid u^k, y^k)\, dy_k \tag{24}$$

and where

$$\lambda_{k+1} \triangleq \int W_{k+1}(x_{k+1}, u_k)\, p(x_{k+1} \mid x_k, u_k, \theta_1)\, p(x_k, \theta_1 \mid y^k)\, d(x_k, x_{k+1}, \theta) \tag{25}$$

Therefore optimal ρ_k is given by

$$\rho_k{}^* = \delta(u_k - u_k{}^*)$$

where $u_k{}^*$ is u_k which minimizes γ_{k+1}:

$$\min_{u_k \in U_k} \gamma_{k+1} = \gamma_{k+1}^*, \qquad k = 0,\ldots, N-1 \tag{26}$$

Thus, by computing λ's and γ^*'s recursively, the optimal control policy is obtained. The density functions $p(x_k, \theta_1 \mid y^k)$ and $p(y_{k+1} \mid u^k, y^k)$, needed in computing λ's and γ^*'s, are derived next.

Remarks similar to those made at the end of Section 1,B of Chapter II can be made here about the possible simplifications of the recursion formula and of the control policy implementations when sufficient statistics exist.

C. Derivation of Conditional Probability Densities

We have shown that, if $p(x_k, \theta_1 \mid y^k)$ and $p(y_{k+1} \mid y^k, u^k)$, $k = 0,\ldots, N-1$, are available, then (24), (25), and (26) allow us to derive an optimal control policy as a nonrandomized sequence of control vectors $u_0{}^*,\ldots, u_{N-1}^*$. We now generate these conditional probability density functions recursively.

Since it is easier to obtain $p(x_i, \theta_1, \theta_2 \mid y^i)$ recursively, this conditional density is generated instead of $p(x_i, \theta_1 \mid y^i)$. These two densities are related by

$$p(x_i, \theta_1 \mid y^i) = \int p(x_i, \theta_1, \theta_2 \mid y^i)\, d\theta_2 \tag{27}$$

We will now derive $p(\theta_1, \theta_2, x_{i+1} \mid y^{i+1})$, assuming that $p(\theta_1, \theta_2, x_i \mid y^i)$ is available. For this purpose consider $p(\theta_1, \theta_2, x_i, x_{i+1}, y_{i+1} \mid y^i)$. It can be written by applying the chain rule;

$$\begin{aligned} &p(\theta_1, \theta_2, x_i, x_{i+1}, y_{i+1} \mid y^i) \\ &\quad = p(\theta_1, \theta_2, x_i \mid y^i)\, p(x_{i+1} \mid \theta_1, \theta_2, x_i, y^i)\, p(y_{i+1} \mid \theta_1, \theta_2, x_i, x_{i+1}, y^i) \\ &\quad = p(\theta_1, \theta_2, x_i \mid y^i)\, p(x_{i+1} \mid \theta_1, x_i, u_i)\, p(y_{i+1} \mid \theta_2, x_{i+1}) \end{aligned} \tag{28}$$

where the independence assumptions on ξ's and η's are used to obtain the expression on the last line.

In (28), the first term of the right-hand side is assumed to be given, and the other two terms are computed from (5) and (6) and the assumed density functions for $p(\xi_i \mid \theta_1)$ and $p(\eta_{i+1} \mid \theta_2)$.

Now integrate the left-hand side of (28) with respect to x_i to obtain

$$\begin{aligned} \int p(\theta_1, \theta_2, x_i, x_{i+1}, y_{i+1} \mid y^i)\, dx_i &= p(\theta_1, \theta_2, x_{i+1}, y_{i+1} \mid y^i) \\ &= p(y_{i+1} \mid y^i)\, p(\theta_1, \theta_2, \theta_{i+1} \mid y^{i+1}) \end{aligned} \tag{29}$$

Hence, from (28) and (29), the desired recursion equation is obtained as

$$p(\theta_1, \theta_2, x_{i+1} \mid y^{i+1}) = \int p(\theta_1, \theta_2, x_i \mid y^i)\, p(x_{i+1} \mid \theta_1, x_i, u_i) \times \frac{p(y_{i+1} \mid \theta_2, x_{i+1})\, dx_i}{\int [\text{numerator}]\, d(x_{i+1}, \theta_1, \theta_2)} \tag{30}$$

where the denominator gives $p(y_{i+1} \mid y^i)$. From (27), $p(\theta_1, x_i \mid y^i)$ is obtained by integrating (30) with respect to θ_2. By the repeated applications of (30), $p(\theta_1, \theta_2, x_i \mid y^i)$, $i = 0, 1, \ldots, N-1$, are computed recursively, starting from

$$\begin{aligned} p(\theta_1, \theta_2, x_0 \mid y^0) &= \frac{p(\theta_1, \theta_2, x_0, y_0)}{p(y_0)} \\ &= \frac{p_0(\theta_1, \theta_2, x_0)\, p(y_0 \mid \theta_2, x_0)}{\int p_0(\theta_1, \theta_2, x_0)\, p(y_0 \mid \theta_2, x_0)\, d(\theta_1, \theta_2, x_0)} \end{aligned} \tag{31}$$

where $p_0(\theta_1, \theta_2, x_0)$ is the given a priori joint density of θ_1, θ_2, and x_0.

Note that

$$p(\theta_1, x_i \mid y^i) = p(\theta_1 \mid y^i)\, p(x_i \mid \theta_1, y^i)$$

where $p(\theta_1 \mid y^i)$ is the ith a posteriori probability density of θ_1 given y^i, i.e., given all past and current observations on the systems state vectors $y_0, \ldots, y_i$.

If the state vectors happen to be perfectly observable, i.e., if the observation equation is noise free and can be solved for x uniquely, then instead of $p(\theta_1, x_i \mid y^i)$ we use simply $p(\theta_1 \mid x^i)$ in deriving equations similar to (24)–(31).

We can derive a similar recursive relationship for $p(x_i \mid y^i)$ or $p(\xi_i, x_i \mid y^i)$ or, more generally, for $p(\xi_i, \eta_i, x_i \mid y^i)$, $i = 0,..., N-1$. In some problems, the latter is more convenient in computing EJ. For example, the conditional density $p(x_{i+1} \mid x_i, u_i, \xi_i)$ may be simpler to manipulate than that of $p(x_{i+1} \mid x_i, u_i, \theta_1)$. If this is the case write $E(W_i \mid y^{i-1})$ as

$$\begin{aligned} E(W_i \mid y^{i-1}) &= \int W_i(x_i, u_{i-1})\, p(x_i \mid y^{i-1})\, dx_i \\ &= \int W_i(x_i, u_{i-1})\, p(x_i \mid x_{i-1}, u_{i-1}, \xi_{i-1}) \\ &\qquad \times p(x_{i-1}, \xi_{i-1} \mid y^{i-1})\, d(x_i, x_{i-1}, \xi_{i-1}) \end{aligned} \tag{32}$$

where $i = 1,..., N$ and where u's are taken to be nonrandomized. Now to obtain $p(x_j, \xi_j \mid y^j)$, $0 \leqslant j \leqslant N-1$, recursively, write

$$\begin{aligned} &p(\theta_1, \theta_2, \xi_i, x_i, \xi_{i+1}, x_{i+1}, y_{i+1} \mid y^i) \\ &\quad = p(\theta_1, \theta_2, \xi_i, x_i \mid y^i)\, p(\xi_{i+1} \mid \theta_1, \xi_i, x_i, y^i) \\ &\qquad \times p(x_{i+1} \mid \theta_1, \xi_i, x_i, \xi_{i+1}, y^i) \\ &\qquad \times p(y_{i+1} \mid \theta_2, \xi_i, x_i, \xi_{i+1}, x_{i+1}, y^i) \\ &\quad = p(\theta_1, \theta_2, \xi_i, x_i \mid y^i)\, p(\xi_{i+1} \mid \theta_1)\, p(x_{i+1} \mid \xi_i, x_i, u_i) \\ &\qquad \times p(y_{i+1} \mid x_{i+1}, \theta_2) \end{aligned} \tag{33}$$

where the independence assumption of ξ's and η's for any $\theta_1 \in \Theta_1$ and $\theta_2 \in \Theta_2$ is used. From (5),

$$p(x_{i+1} \mid x_i, \xi_i, u_i) = \delta(x_{i+1} - F_i(x_i, \xi_i, u_i))$$

The left-hand side of (33), after x_i and ξ_i are integrated out, can be written as

$$p(\theta_1, \theta_2, \xi_{i+1}, x_{i+1}, y_{i+1} \mid y^i) = p(y_{i+1} \mid y^i)\, p(\theta_1, \theta_2, \xi_{i+1}, x_{i+1} \mid y^{i+1})$$

Thus

$$\begin{aligned} p(\theta_1, \theta_2, \xi_{i+1}, x_{i+1} \mid y^{i+1}) &= \int p(\theta_1, \theta_2, \xi_i, x_i \mid y^i)\, p(\xi_{i+1} \mid \theta_1)\, \delta(x_{i+1} - F_i) \\ &\qquad \times \frac{p(y_{i+1} \mid x_{i+1}, \theta_2)\, d(x_i, \xi_i)}{\int [\text{numerator}]\, d(\theta_1, \theta_2, \xi_{i+1}, x_{i+1})} \end{aligned} \tag{34}$$

Similarly we can compute $p(\xi_i, \eta_i, x_i \mid y^i)$ recursively to obtain the optimal control policies when θ_1 and θ_2 are unknown. Sometimes this form is more convenient to use in deriving optimal control policies. To obtain the recursion relation for $p(\xi_i, \eta_i, x_i \mid y^i)$, write

$$\begin{aligned} p(\theta_1, \theta_2, x_i, \xi_i, \eta_i, x_{i+1}, \xi_{i+1}, \eta_{i+1}, y_{i+1} \mid y^i) \\ = p(\theta_1, \theta_2, x_i, \xi_i, \eta_i \mid y^i)\, p(x_{i+1} \mid x_i, \xi_i, u_i) \\ \times\, p(\xi_{i+1} \mid \theta_1)\, p(\eta_{i+1} \mid \theta_2)\, p(y_{i+1} \mid x_{i+1}, \eta_{i+1}) \end{aligned} \tag{35}$$

where the conditional independence assumption on ξ's and η's have been used. From (5),

$$p(x_{i+1} \mid x_i, u_i, \xi_i) = \delta(x_{i+1} - F_i)$$

From (6),

$$p(y_{i+1} \mid x_{i+1}, \eta_{i+1}) = \delta(y_{i+1} - G_{i+1})$$

Integrating (35) with respect to x_i, ξ_i, and η_i,

$$\begin{aligned} \int p(\theta_1, \theta_2, x_i, \xi_i, \eta_i, x_{i+1}, \xi_{i+1}, \eta_{i+1}, y_{i+1} \mid y^i)\, d(x_i, \xi_i, \eta_i) \\ = p(\theta_1, \theta_2, x_{i+1}, \xi_{i+1}, \eta_{i+1}, y_{i+1} \mid y^i) \\ = p(\theta_1, \theta_2, x_{i+1}, \xi_{i+1}, \eta_{i+1} \mid y^{i+1})\, p(y_{i+1} \mid y^i) \end{aligned}$$

Hence

$$\begin{aligned} p(\theta_1, \theta_2, x_{i+1}, \xi_{i+1}, \eta_{i+1} \mid y^{i+1}) \\ = \int p(\theta_1, \theta_2, x_i, \xi_i, \eta_i \mid y^i)\, \delta(x_{i+1} - F_i)\, \delta(y_{i+1} - G_{i+1}) \\ \times \frac{p(\xi_{i+1} \mid \theta_1)\, p(\eta_{i+1} \mid \theta_2)\, d(x_i, \xi_i, \eta_i)}{\int [\text{numerator}]\, d(\theta_1, \theta_2, x_{i+1}, \xi_{i+1}, \eta_{i+1})} \end{aligned} \tag{36}$$

Integrating both sides of (36) with respect to θ_1 and θ_2, the desired recursion equation results. Equations (30) and (36) have been obtained assuming that ξ_i, $i = 0, 1, \ldots$, and η_j, $j = 0, 1, \ldots$, are all independent for each θ_1 and θ_2.

If this conditional independence assumption is weakened and if it is assumed that ξ_i, $i = 0, 1, \ldots$, is dependent for each θ_1, that the ξ process and the η process are still independent then, by considering $p(\theta_1, \theta_2, \xi_i, x_i, \xi_{i+1}, y_{i+1} \mid y^i)$, for example, instead of Eq. (33), the recursion equation for $p(\theta_1, \theta_2, \xi_i, x_i \mid y^i)$ is obtained as

$$\begin{aligned} p(\theta_1, \theta_2, \xi_{i+1}, x_{i+1} \mid y^{i+1}) \\ = \int p(\theta_1, \theta_2, \xi_i, x_i \mid y^i)\, p(\xi_{i+1} \mid \theta_1, \xi^i)\, \delta(x_{i+1} - F_{i+1}) \\ \times \frac{p(y_{i+1} \mid x_{i+1}, \theta_2)\, d(x_i, \xi_i)}{\int [\text{numerator}]\, d(\theta_1, \theta_2, \xi_{i+1}, x_{i+1})} \end{aligned} \tag{37}$$

The most convenient form should be used for a problem under consideration.

The indicated integrations in these recursion equations should not be carried out by themselves when they involve delta functions. Perform the integration in evaluating $E(W_j \mid y^{j-1})$. It is not usually necessary to compute the denominators in expressions such as (30), (31), and (34) since they are normalization constants.

By repeated applications of (30) or (34), $p(\theta_1, \theta_2, x_i \mid y^i)$ or $p(\theta_1, \theta_2, \xi_i, x_i \mid y^i)$ can be given directly in terms of $p_0(\theta_1, \theta_2, x_0)$, $p(x_{j+1} \mid x_j, u_j, \theta)$, and $p(y_j \mid x_j)$, $0 \leqslant j \leqslant 1$. Fel'dbaum uses this form of the conditional probability density expressions in his works. As an example, let us rewrite the left-hand side of (30) in this form. See also the brief exposition of Fel'dbaum's method in Section 6 for further details. Since

$$p(\theta_1, \theta_2, x_0 \mid y_0) = \frac{p(\theta_1, \theta_2, x_0) p(y_0 \mid x_0, \theta_2)}{\int p(\theta_1, \theta_2, x_0)\, p(y_0 \mid x_0, \theta_2)\, d(\theta_1, \theta_2, x_0)}$$

$$p(\theta_1, \theta_2, x_1 \mid y^1) = \frac{\int p(\theta_1, \theta_2, x_0 \mid y_0)\, p(x_1 \mid \theta_1, x_0, u_0)\, p(y_1 \mid x_1)\, dx_0}{\int [\text{numerator}]\, d(\theta_1, \theta_2, x_1)}$$

$$= \frac{\int p_0(\theta_1, \theta_2, x_0)\, p(x_1 \mid \theta_1, x_0, u_0)\, p(y_0 \mid x_0, \theta_2)\, p(y_1 \mid x_1, \theta_2)\, dx_0}{\int [\text{numerator}]\, d(\theta_1, \theta_2, x_1)}$$

It is easy to see that the general expression is obtained to be

$$p(\theta_1, \theta_2, x_i \mid y^i) = \int p_0(\theta_1, \theta_2, x_0)\, p(y_0 \mid x_0, \theta_2) \times \frac{\prod_{j=1}^{i} p(x_j \mid \theta_1, x_{j-1}, u_{j-1})}{\int [\text{numerator}]\, d(\theta_1, \theta_2, x_i)}\, p(y_j \mid x_j, \theta_2)\, dx^{i-1} \tag{38}$$

Similarly, we can write $p(\theta_1, \theta_2, \xi_i, x_i \mid y^i)$ as

$$p(\theta_1, \theta_2, \xi_i, x_i \mid y^i) = \int p_0(\theta_1, \theta_2, x_0)\, p(y_0 \mid x_0, \theta_2) \times \frac{\prod_{j=1}^{i} \delta(x_j - F_{j-1}) \prod_{j=0}^{i-1} p(\xi_j \mid \theta_1)}{\int [\text{numerator}]\, d(\theta_1, \theta_2, x_i, \xi_i)}\, p(y_j \mid x_j, \theta_2)\, d(x^{i-1}, \xi^{i-1}) \tag{39}$$

D. Examples

a. *System with Unknown Initial Condition*

In Example 3 of Chapter I, we have obtained the optimal control policy for one-dimensional system

$$x_{i+1} = ax_i + bu_i\,, \qquad u_i \in (-\infty, \infty)$$
$$y_i = x_i + \eta_i\,, \qquad 0 \leqslant i \leqslant N-1$$
$$J = \sum_1^N x_i^2$$

under the assumption that a and b are known, and $x_0, \eta_0, \ldots, \eta_{N-1}$ are all independent Gaussian random variables with known mean and variances.

Now assume that the mean of x_0 is unknown, i.e., assume

$$\mathscr{L}(x_0) = N(\theta, \sigma^2)$$

where $\mathscr{L}(\cdot)$ denotes the distribution function, $N(\cdot, \cdot)$ stands for a normal distribution, and where θ is a random variable, the a priori distribution of which is given by an independent Gaussian distribution

$$\mathscr{L}(\theta) = N(\hat{\theta}, \hat{\sigma}^2)$$

The optimal control policy is still given by

$$u_i^* = -a\mu_i/b \qquad 0 \leqslant i \leqslant N-1$$

where μ_i is as defined by (28) of Chapter I. The recursion equation for μ has been derived in Section 3,B of Chapter II as (114a). The expression for μ_0 is the only difference that results from the assumption of unknown θ. The initial value μ_0 is now given by computing

$$p(x_0 \mid y_0) = \frac{\int p_0(\theta)\, p_0(x_0 \mid \theta)\, p(y_0 \mid x_0)\, d\theta}{\int [\text{numerator}]\, dx_0}$$
$$= \text{const} \exp\left(-\frac{(x_0 - \mu_0)^2}{2\sigma_0^2}\right)$$

where

$$\mu_0 = [y_0/r_0^2 + \hat{\theta}/(\sigma^2 + \hat{\sigma}^2)]/[1/r_0^2 + 1/(\sigma^2 + \hat{\sigma}^2)]$$

and where

$$1/\sigma_0^2 = 1/r_0^2 + 1/(\sigma^2 + \hat{\sigma}^2)$$

Thus, the unknown mean θ of x_0 has the effect of replacing σ^2, the variance of x_0, by $\sigma^2 + \hat{\sigma}^2$. Otherwise, the recursion formula for μ and σ^2 as given by Eqs. (114a) and (114d) of Section 3,B, Chapter II, remains valid.

b. *Perfect Observation System with Unknown Plant Noise*

Consider a one-dimensional linear control system described by the plant equation

$$x_{i+1} = ax_i + bu_i + \xi_i, \qquad u_i \in (-\infty, \infty), \quad 0 \leqslant i \leqslant N-1 \tag{40}$$

and assume to be perfectly measured

$$y_i = x_i, \qquad 0 \leqslant i \leqslant N-1 \tag{41}$$

where a and b are known constant plant parameters and where ξ's are random variables assumed to be independently and identically distributed with the distribution function

$$\mathscr{L}(\xi_i) = N(\theta, \sigma_1^2) \tag{42}$$

for each θ on the real line, where θ is the unknown random parameter of the distribution function for ξ. The variance σ^2 is assumed given.

The a priori distribution function for θ is assumed given by

$$\mathscr{L}_0(\theta) = N(\mu, \sigma_0^2) \tag{43}$$

where μ and σ_0^2 are assumed known.

The initial state x_0 of the plant is assumed to be a random variable independent of θ and assumed to be distributed according to

$$\mathscr{L}(x_0) = N(\alpha, \sigma_0^2) \tag{44}$$

where α and σ_2 are assumed known. The criterion function is taken to be

$$J = \sum_1^N q_i x_i^2, \qquad q_i > 0, \quad 1 \leqslant i \leqslant N$$

We will now derive the optimal control policy for this system. According to the general procedure developed in Section 2, in order to derive u_{N-1}^*, we first compute

$$\begin{aligned}
\lambda_N / q_N &\triangleq E(x_N^2 \mid x^{N-1}) \\
&= \int x_N^2 \, p(x_N \mid x^{N-1}) \, dx_N
\end{aligned}$$

$$= \int x_N^2\, p(x_N \mid x_{N-1}, u_{N-1}, \xi_{N-1})\, p(\xi_{N-1} \mid x^{N-1})\, d(x_N, \xi_{N-1})$$

$$= \int (ax_{N-1} + bu_{N-1} + \xi_{N-1})^2\, p(\xi_{N-1} \mid x^{N-1})\, d\xi_{N-1} \tag{45}$$

Define the conditional mean and variance of ξ_i by

$$E(\xi_i \mid x^i) = \mu_i \tag{46a}$$

and

$$\operatorname{var}(\xi_i \mid x^i) = \Gamma_i^2, \qquad 0 \leqslant 1 \leqslant N-1 \tag{46b}$$

From (45) and (46),

$$\lambda_N / q_N = (ax_{N-1} + bu_{N-1} + \mu_{N-1})^2 + \Gamma_{N-1}^2 \tag{47}$$

From (47), if μ_i and Γ_i do not depend on u_i, the optimal control at the $(N-1)$th stage is found to be

$$u_{N-1}^* = -(ax_{N-1} + \mu_{N-1})/b \tag{48}$$

and

$$\gamma_N{}^* = \Gamma_{N-1}^2 \tag{49}$$

Computations of μ's and Γ's are carried out later and given by (59) and (60). There we show that Γ's are all constants and μ_i is independent of u_i, thus satisfying the assumption made in deriving (48). Equation (49) shows that $\gamma_N{}^*$ is a constant. Generally $\gamma_i{}^*$ becomes constant, hence the dependence of γ_{i+1} on u_i is determined by that of λ_{i+1} only and each control stage can be optimized separately. The optimal control policy for this problem, therefore, consists of N one-stage optimal control policy.

The result is given as

$$u_i{}^* = -(ax_i + \mu_i)/b \tag{50}$$

$$\gamma_i = \sum_{i-1}^{N-1} \Gamma_j{}^2, \qquad 0 \leqslant i \leqslant N-1 \tag{51}$$

We compute μ's and Γ's next.

Since x's are perfectly observed, the knowledge of x^i is equivalent to that of ξ^{i-1} since $\xi_i = x_{i+1} - ax_i - bu_i$. Therefore,

$$p(\xi_i \mid x^i) = p(\xi_i \mid \xi^{i-1}) = \int p(\xi_i \mid \theta)\, p(\theta \mid \xi^{i-1})\, d\theta \tag{52}$$

where the conditional independence of ξ for given θ is used. The first factor of the integrand of (52) is given by (42). The second factor is computed recursively.

By the chain rule we write

$$p(\theta, \xi_{i+1} \mid \xi^i) = p(\theta \mid \xi^i)\, p(\xi_{i+1} \mid \theta, \xi^i)$$

$$= p(\theta \mid \xi^i)\, p(\xi_{i+1} \mid \theta), \qquad 0 \leqslant i \leqslant N-1 \tag{53}$$

Therefore,

$$p(\theta \mid \xi^{i+1}) = \frac{p(\theta \mid \xi^i)\, p(\xi_{i+1} \mid \theta)}{\int p(\theta \mid \xi^i)\, p(\xi_{i+1} \mid \theta)\, d\theta}, \qquad 0 \leqslant i \leqslant N-1 \tag{54}$$

To initiate the recursion (54), we note that, by the independence assumption of θ and x_0,

$$p(\theta, \xi_0, x_0) = p(\theta, x_0)\, p(\xi_0 \mid \theta, x_0)$$

$$= p_0(\theta)\, p_0(x)\, p(\xi_0 \mid \theta)$$

Therefore,

$$p(\xi_0 \mid x_0) = \frac{\int p(\theta_0, \xi_0, x_0)\, d\theta}{p(x_0)} = \int p_0(\theta)\, p(\xi_0 \mid \theta)\, d\theta$$

$$= \text{const} \exp\left(-\frac{(\xi_0 - \mu)^2}{2(\sigma_0^2 + \sigma_1^2)}\right) \tag{55}$$

Namely, we have derived

$$\mu_0 = \mu \tag{56a}$$

$$\Gamma_0^2 = \sigma_0^2 + \sigma_1^2 \tag{56b}$$

Assume

$$p(\theta \mid \xi^i) = \text{const} \exp\left(-\frac{(\theta - \theta_i)^2}{2\Sigma_i^2}\right) \tag{57}$$

This is certainly true for $i = 0$ with

$$\theta_0 = \frac{\mu/\sigma_0^2 + \xi_0/\sigma_1^2}{1/\sigma_0^2 + 1/\sigma_1^2} \tag{58a}$$

$$1/\Sigma_0^2 = 1/\sigma_0^2 + 1/\sigma_1^2 \tag{58b}$$

When the right-hand side of (54) is computed, using the assumed form for $p(\theta \mid \xi^i)$, we obtain

$$p(\theta \mid \xi^{i+1}) = \text{const} \exp\left(-\frac{(\theta - \theta_{i+1})^2}{2\Sigma_{i+1}^2}\right) \tag{59a}$$

with

$$\theta_{i+1} = \frac{\theta_i/\Sigma_i^2 + \xi_{i+1}/\sigma_1^2}{1/\Sigma_i^2 + 1/\sigma_1^2} \tag{59b}$$

$$1/\Sigma_{i+1}^2 = 1/\Sigma_i^2 + 1/\sigma_1^2 \tag{59c}$$

the assumed form for the a posteriori probability density function for θ given ξ^i. Thus, (57) is established for all $i = 0, 1,\ldots$. This shows also that (θ_i, Γ_i) is the sufficient statistics for the unknown parameter θ.

From (52), (57), and (59),

$$\mu_i = \theta_{i-1} \tag{60a}$$

$$\Gamma_i^2 = \sigma_1^2 + \Sigma_{i-1}^2, \qquad 1 \leqslant i \leqslant N-1 \tag{60b}$$

From (60b), Γ's are all seen to be constants as asserted earlier. Thus, γ_N^* and all subsequent γ^*'s become constants and each control stage can be optimized separately with the optimal control policy of (51). From (51) we have

$$\gamma_1^* = \min EJ = \sum_0^{N-1} \Gamma_j^2$$

c. *System with Noisy Observation Having Unknown Bias*

Consider a one-dimensional linear control system described by the plant equation

$$x_{i+1} = ax_i + bu_i + \xi_i, \qquad u_i \in (-\infty, \infty), \quad 0 \leqslant i \leqslant N-1 \tag{61}$$

and observed by

$$y_i = x_i + \eta_i, \qquad 0 \leqslant i \leqslant N-1 \tag{62}$$

where a and b are known constant plant parameters and where ξ's are independently and identically distributed with the distribution function given by

$$\mathscr{L}(\xi_i) = N(0, \sigma_0^2) \tag{63}$$

The random variables η are assumed to be independent of ξ's. The random variables η are also assumed to be independently and identically distributed with

$$\mathscr{L}(\eta_i) = N(\theta, \sigma_1^2) \tag{64}$$

for each $\theta \in (-\infty, \infty)$ where θ is the unknown parameter of the distribution.

Its a priori distribution function is assumed to be given by

$$\mathscr{L}_0(\theta) = N(\mu, \sigma_2^2) \tag{65}$$

The initial state x_0 of the plant is assumed to be a random variable, independent of all other random variables and assumed to be distributed according to

$$\mathscr{L}(x_0) = N(\alpha, \sigma_3^2) \tag{66}$$

where α and σ_3 are known. The criterion function is taken to be

$$J = \sum_1^N q_i x_i^2, \qquad q_i > 0$$

The optimal control policy is now derived for the above system.

In the previous two examples, the recursion equations for conditional probability density functions involved a one-dimensional normal distribution function. In this example, we will see that, because of noisy observations, two-dimensional normal distribution functions must be computed in the recursive generations of the conditional density functions. To obtain u_{N-1}^*, compute first

$$\begin{aligned}
\lambda_N &\triangleq E(q_N x_N^2 \mid y^{N-1}) \\
&= \int q_N x_N^2 \, p(x_N \mid y^{N-1}) \, dx_N \\
&= \int q_N x_N^2 \, p(x_N \mid x_{N-1}, u_{N-1}, \xi_{N-1}) \, p(x_{N-1}, \xi_{N-1} \mid y^{N-1}) \, d(x_N, x_{N-1}, \xi_{N-1}) \\
&= \int q_N (a x_{N-1} + b u_{N-1} + \xi_{N-1})^2 \, p(x_{N-1}, \xi_{N-1} \mid y^{N-1}) \, d(x_{N-1}, \xi_{N-1})
\end{aligned} \tag{67}$$

In Eq. (67),

$$p(x_{N-1}, \xi_{N-1} \mid y^{N-1}) = p(\xi_{N-1}) \, p(x_{N-1} \mid y^{N-1}) \tag{68}$$

since ξ_i is independent of ξ^{i-1} and of η^i by assumption. From Eq. (62),

$$p(x_i \mid y^i) = \int p(x_i \mid \eta_i, y^i)\, p(\eta_i \mid y^i)\, d\eta_i, \qquad 0 \leqslant i \leqslant N-1 \tag{69}$$

Substituting Eqs. (68) and (69) into Eq. (67),

$$\begin{aligned}\lambda_N &= \int q_N[(ax_{N-1} + bu_{N-1})^2 + \sigma_0^2]\, p(x_{N-1} \mid \eta_{N-1}, y^{N-1}) \\ &\quad \times p(\eta_{N-1} \mid y^{N-1})\, d(x_{N-1}, \eta_{N-1}) \\ &= \int q_N\{[a(y_{N-1} - \eta_{N-1}) + bu_{N-1}]^2 + \sigma_0^2\}\, p(\eta_{N-1} \mid y^{N-1})\, d\eta_{N-1}\end{aligned} \tag{70}$$

Defining the conditional mean and variance of η_i by

$$\hat{\eta}_i = E(\eta_i \mid y^i), \qquad 0 \leqslant i \leqslant N-1 \tag{71a}$$

and

$$\Gamma_i^2 = \operatorname{var}(\eta_i \mid y^i) \tag{71b}$$

we have

$$\gamma_N = \lambda_N = q_N\{[a(y_{N-1} - \hat{\eta}_{N-1}) + bu_{N-1}]^2 + \sigma_0^2 + a^2\Gamma_{N-1}^2\} \tag{72}$$

Since $\hat{\eta}_{N-1}$ and Γ_{N-1} are independent of u_{N-1}, by minimizing Eq. (72) with respect to u_{N-1} the optimal control variable at time $(N-1)$ is given as

$$u_{N-1}^* = -a(y_{N-1} - \hat{\eta}_{N-1})/b \tag{73}$$

and

$$\gamma_N^* = q_N(\sigma_0^2 + a^2\Gamma_{N-1}^2) \tag{74}$$

Therefore, if μ_{N-1} and Γ_{N-1} are known, so are u_{N-1}^* and γ_N^*.

We also see from Eq. (74) that, since γ_N^* is independent of y_{N-1}, each control stage can be optimized separately and the optimal control policy consists of a sequence of one stage optimal policy

$$u_i^* = -a(y_i - \hat{\eta}_i)/b, \qquad 0 \leqslant i \leqslant N-1 \tag{75}$$

In order to compute μ's and Γ's, we show first that the conditional probability density of θ and η_i are jointly normally distributed, i.e.,

$$p(\theta, \eta_i \mid y^i) = \text{const} \exp\left[-\tfrac{1}{2}(\theta - \hat{\theta}_i, \eta_i - \hat{\eta}_i)\, M_i^{-1} \begin{pmatrix}\theta - \hat{\theta}_i \\ \eta_i - \hat{\eta}_i\end{pmatrix}\right] \tag{76a}$$

where

$$M_i = \operatorname{cov}(\theta, \eta_i \mid y^i) = \begin{pmatrix} M_{11}^i & M_{12}^i \\ M_{21}^i & M_{22}^i \end{pmatrix} \tag{76b}$$

is a constant covariance matrix and where

$$\begin{aligned} \hat{\theta}_i &= E(\theta \mid y^i) \qquad M_{11}^i = \operatorname{var}(\theta \mid y^i) \\ \hat{\eta}_i &= E(\eta_i \mid y^i) \qquad M_{22}^i = \operatorname{var}(\eta_i \mid y^i) \\ M_{12}^i &= M_{21}^i = E[(\theta - \hat{\theta}_i)(\eta_i - \hat{\eta}_i) \mid y^i] \end{aligned} \tag{76c}$$

Then with the notation defined by (71b),

$$\Gamma_i = M_{22}^i$$

To verify (76) for $i = 0$, consider

$$p(\theta, \eta_0 \mid y^0) = \frac{p(\theta, \eta_0, y_0)}{p(y_0)} = \frac{p_0(\theta)\, p(\eta_0 \mid \theta)\, p(y_0 \mid \theta, \eta_0)}{p(y_0)} \tag{77a}$$

where, from (65),

$$p_0(\theta) = \text{const} \exp\left(-\frac{(\theta - \mu)^2}{2\sigma_2^2}\right) \tag{77b}$$

from (64),

$$p(\eta_0 \mid \theta) = \text{const} \exp\left(-\frac{(\eta_0 - \theta)^2}{2\sigma_1^2}\right) \tag{77c}$$

and from (66),

$$p(y_0 \mid \theta, \eta_0) = \text{const} \exp\left(-\frac{(y_0 - \alpha - \eta_0)^2}{2\sigma_3^2}\right) \tag{77d}$$

From (77), (76a) is seen to hold for $i = 0$ with

$$\hat{\theta}_0 = \frac{\mu/\sigma_2^2 + (y_0 - \alpha)/(\sigma_1^2 + \sigma_3^2)}{1/\sigma_2^2 + 1/(\sigma_1^2 + \sigma_3^2)} \tag{78a}$$

$$\hat{\eta}_0 = \frac{\mu/(\sigma_1^2 + \sigma_2^2) + (y_0 - \alpha)/\sigma_3^2}{1/(\sigma_1^2 + \sigma_2^2) + 1/\sigma_3^2} \tag{78b}$$

$$M_{11}^0 = (\sigma_1^2 + \sigma_3^2)\sigma_2^2/(\sigma_1^2 + \sigma_2^2 + \sigma_3^2) \tag{78c}$$

$$M_{12}^0 = M_{21}^0 = \sigma_2^2\sigma_3^2/(\sigma_1^2 + \sigma_2^2 + \sigma_3^2) \tag{78d}$$

$$M_{22}^0 = (\sigma_1^2 + \sigma_2^2)\sigma_3^2/(\sigma_1^2 + \sigma_2^2 + \sigma_3^2) \tag{78e}$$

Note that M_0 is a constant matrix.

Thus (76a) is verified for $i = 0$. Next, assume that (76a) is true for some $i > 0$. We will show that the equation is true for $i + 1$, thus completing the mathematical induction on (76a). To go from i to $(i + 1)$, consider $p(\theta, \eta_i, \eta_{i+1} \mid y^i)$. By the chain rule, this conditional density can be written as

$$p(\theta, \eta_i, \eta_{i+1}, y_{i+1} \mid y^i) = p(\theta, \eta_i \mid y^i)\, p(\eta_{i+1} \mid \theta, \eta_i, y^i) \times p(y_{i+1} \mid \theta, \eta_i, \eta_{i+1}, y^i) \tag{79}$$

where the second factor reduces to $p(\eta_{i+1} \mid \theta)$ since η_i's are conditionally independent of all other η's and ξ's by assumption. From (61) and (62), y satisfies the difference equation

$$y_{i+1} = ay_i + bu_i + \xi_i - a\eta_i + \eta_{i+1} \tag{80}$$

The third factor of (79) is given, therefore, by

$$p(y_{i+1} \mid \theta, \eta_i, \eta_{i+1}, y^i) = \text{const} \exp\left(\frac{(y_{i+1} - ay_i - bu_i + a\eta_i - \eta_{i+1})^2}{2\sigma_0^2}\right)$$

By integrating both sides of (79) with respect to η_i,

$$\begin{aligned} p(\theta, \eta_{i+1}, y_{i+1} \mid y^i) &= p(y_{i+1} \mid y^i)\, p(\theta, \eta_{i+1} \mid y^{i+1}) \\ &= \int p(\theta, \eta_i \mid y^i)\, p(\eta_{i+1} \mid \theta)\, p(y_{i+1} \mid \theta, \eta_i, \eta_{i+1} y^i)\, d\eta_i \end{aligned}$$

Therefore,

$$p(\theta, \eta_{i+1} \mid y^{i+1}) = \frac{\int p(\theta, \eta_i \mid y^i)\, p(\eta_{i+1} \mid \theta)\, p(y_{i+1} \mid \theta, \eta_i ; \eta_{i+1}, y^i) \qquad d\eta_i}{\int p(\theta, \eta_i \mid y^i)\, p(\eta_{i+1} \mid \theta)\, p(y_{i+1} \mid \theta, \eta_i, \eta_{i+1}, y^i)\, d(\theta, \eta_i, \eta_{i+1})} \tag{81}$$

After carrying out the tedious integration in (81), we establish (76a) for $i + 1$ with

$$\hat{\theta}_{i+1} = \frac{[(C_i + D_i)/\sigma_i^2 + B_i D_i - C_i^2]\hat{\theta}_i + (B_i + C_i)Z_i/\sigma_1^2}{\Delta_i^2}$$

$$\hat{\eta}_{i+1} = \frac{(C_i + D_i)\hat{\theta}_i/\sigma_1^2 + [(B_i + C_i)/\sigma_1^2 + B_i D_i - C_i^2]Z_i}{\Delta_i^2}$$

$$M_{11}^{i+1} = (1/\sigma_1^2 + B_i)/\Delta_i^2$$

$$M_{12}^{i+1} = (1/\sigma_1^2 - C_i)/\Delta_i^2$$

$$M_{22}^{i+1} = (1/\sigma_1^2 + D_i)/\Delta_1^2$$

$$Z_i = y_{i+1} - a(y_i - \hat{\eta}_i) - bu_i$$

where

$$\Delta_i^2 = (1/\sigma_1^2 + B_i)(1/\sigma_1^2 + D_i) - (1/\sigma_1^2 - C_i)^2$$

$$B_i = \frac{\nu_{22}^i/\sigma_0^2}{\nu_{22}^i + a^2/\sigma_0^2}$$

$$C_i = \frac{\nu_{12}^i a/\sigma_0^2}{\nu_{22}^i + a^2/\sigma_0^2}$$

$$D_i = \nu_{11}^i - \frac{(\nu_{12}^i)^2}{\nu_{22}^i + a^2/\sigma_0^2}$$

and where

$$M_i^{-1} = \begin{pmatrix} \nu_{11}^i & \nu_{12}^i \\ \nu_{21}^i & \nu_{22}^i \end{pmatrix}$$

Therefore, M_i in (76a) all turn out to be constants which can be precalculated (i.e., calculated off-line).

The only on-line computation in generating u_i^* is that of updating η_i and θ_i where Z_i depends on y_i, y_{i+1}, and u_i.

d. *System with Unknown Noise Variance*

The technique similar to that used in the previous example can be used to treat control problems with unknown noise variances. As an illustration, we derive an optimal control policy for the system of Section 2,D,c given by (61) and (62) assuming now that the variances of the observation noises are unknown, and the mean is known.

We only give a summary of the steps involved since they are quite similar to those of Section 2,D,c. Another approach to treat unknown noise variances is to use $C\eta_i$ instead of η_i with $\mathscr{L}(\eta_i) = N(0, 1)$ and assume C to be the unknown parameter and apply the method of Section 3 of this chapter. Also see Sections 2 and 3 of Chapter VII. For an entirely different approach see Ref. 91a.

Instead of (64), we assume that

$$\mathscr{L}(\eta_i) = N(0, \Sigma)$$

where Σ is the variance which is assumed to be distributed according to

$$p_0(\Sigma) = z_{0,1}\,\delta(\Sigma - \Sigma_1) + z_{0,2}\,\delta(\Sigma - \Sigma_2)$$

where

$$z_{0,1} + z_{0,2} = 1$$

Namely, the unknown variance of the observation noise is assumed to be either Σ_1 or Σ_2 with the *a priori* probability given by $z_{0,1}$ and $z_{0,2}$ respectively.

Other assumptions on the distribution functions of ξ's and x_0 are the same as before. The probability of Σ is now taken to be independent of x_0. With the criterion function as before, each control stage can be optimized separately. To obtain u_i^*, we compute

$$\begin{aligned} \lambda_{i+1} &= q_{i+1} \int x_{i+1}^2 \, p(x_{i+1} \mid y^i) \, dx_{i+1} \\ &= q_{i+1} \int [(ax_i + bu_i)^2 + \sigma_0^2] \, p(x_i \mid y^i) \, dx_i \end{aligned}$$

Defining

$$E(x_j \mid y^j) = \hat{x}_j \quad \text{and} \quad \text{var}(x_j \mid y^j) = \hat{\Gamma}_j, \qquad 0 \leqslant j \leqslant N-1 \tag{82}$$

λ_{i+1} can be expressed as

$$\lambda_{i+1} = q_{i+1}[(a\hat{x}_i + bu_i)^2 + a^2\hat{\Gamma}_i + \sigma_0^2]$$

Under the assumption, to be verified later, that $\hat{x}_i$ and $\hat{\Gamma}_i$ are independent of u_i we obtain

$$u_i^* = -aq_{i+1}\hat{x}_i/b, \qquad 0 \leqslant i \leqslant -1$$

as the optimal control variable at time i.

In order to compute $\hat{x}_i$, consider the joint probability density function $p(x_i, \Sigma \mid y^i)$.

It is easy to see that it satisfies the recursion equation

$$p(x_{i+1}, \Sigma \mid y^{i+1}) = \frac{\int p(x_i, \Sigma \mid y^i) p(x_{i+1} \mid x_i, u_i) p(y_{i+1} \mid x_{i+1}, \Sigma) \, dx_i}{\int [\text{numerator}] \, d(x_{i+1}, \Sigma)}$$

It is also easy to show inductively that

$$p(x_i, \Sigma \mid y^i) = [z_{i,1}\, \delta(\Sigma - \Sigma_1) + z_{i,2}\, \delta(\Sigma - \Sigma_2)] N[\mu_i(\Sigma), \Gamma_i(\Sigma)] \tag{83}$$

The second factor in (83) is the Gaussian probability density function with mean $\mu_i(\Sigma)$ and variance $\Gamma_i(\Sigma)$, where

$$\begin{aligned} \mu_{i+1}(\Sigma) &= [(a\mu_i(\Sigma) + bu_i)/(a\Gamma_i(\Sigma) + \sigma_0^2) \\ &\qquad + y_{i+1}/\Sigma]/[1/(a^2\Gamma_i(\Sigma) + \sigma_0^2) + 1/\Sigma] \\ \mu_0(\Sigma) &= (a/\sigma_3^2 + y_0/\Sigma)/(1/\sigma_3^2 + 1/\Sigma) \\ 1/\Gamma_{i+1}(\Sigma) &= 1/(a^2\Gamma_i(\Sigma) + \sigma_0^2) + 1/\Sigma \\ 1/\Gamma_0(\Sigma) &= 1/\sigma_3^2 + 1/\Sigma \\ z_{i+1,1} &= z_{i,1}\omega_{i,1}/(z_{i,1}\omega_{i,1} + z_{i,2}\omega_{i,2}) \\ z_{i+1,2} &= z_{i,2}\omega_{i,2}/(z_{i,1}\omega_{i,1} + z_{i,2}\omega_{i,2}) \qquad (0 \leqslant i \leqslant N-1) \end{aligned}$$

and where

$$\omega_{i,j} = \frac{\Gamma_i^{1/2}(\Sigma_j)\sigma_0\Sigma_j^{1/2}}{(\Sigma_j + a^2\Gamma_i(\Sigma_j) + \sigma_0{}^2)^{1/2}} \exp\left(-\frac{(y_{i+1} - a\mu_i(\Sigma_j) - bu_i)^2}{2(\Sigma_j + a^2\Gamma_i(\Sigma_j) + \sigma_0{}^2)}\right) \qquad j = 1, 2$$

Then from (82) and (83)

$$\hat{x}_i = z_{i,1}\mu_i(\Sigma_1) + z_{i,2}\mu_i(\Sigma_2)$$

$$\hat{\Gamma}_i = z_{i,1}\Gamma_i(\Sigma_1) + z_{i,2}\Gamma_i(\Sigma_2) + z_{i,1}z_{i,2}[\mu_i(\Sigma_1) - \mu_i(\Sigma_2)]^2$$

the assumption that $\hat{x}_i$ and $\hat{\Gamma}_i$ are independent of u_i is thus seen to be satisfied.

3. Systems with Unknown Plant Parameters

A. Optimal Control Policy

We had an occasion to mention briefly as Example 7 of Chapter I a control problem where the time constant of a system is random with an unknown mean. We did not derive its optimal control policy however. In this section we will derive optimal control policies for systems having unknown plant and/or observation parameters.

Derivations of optimal control policies for this class of systems are carried out quite analogously as in Section 2. Their plant and observation equations are given by (1) and (2).

The derivations hinge on the availability of conditional densities $p(\alpha, \beta, x_i \mid y^i)$, where α and β are unknown plant and observation parameters of the system.

The class of control policies can again be taken to be nonrandomized by the arguments that parallel exactly those of Section 2.

Optimal control policies are derived from

$$\gamma_{k+1}^* = \min_{u_k} \gamma_{k+1} \tag{84}$$

where

$$\gamma_N \triangleq \lambda_N$$

$$\gamma_{k+1} \triangleq \lambda_{k+1} + E(\gamma_{k+2} \mid y^k), \qquad 0 \leqslant k \leqslant N-2$$

and where

$$\lambda_i \triangleq \int W_i(x_i, u_{i-1})\, p(x_i \mid x_{i-1}, \alpha, u_{i-1})\, p(\alpha, x_{i-1} \mid y^{i-1})\, d(x_{i-1}, x_i, \alpha), \qquad 1 \leqslant i \leqslant N \tag{85}$$

To obtain $p(\alpha, x_i \mid y^i)$, which appears in (85) recursively, consider $p(\alpha, \beta, x_i, x_{i+1}, y_{i+1} \mid y^i)$ and write it by the chain rule as

$$\begin{aligned} &p(\alpha, \beta, x_i, x_{i+1}, y_{i+1} \mid y^i) \\ &\quad = p(\alpha, \beta, x_i \mid y^i)\, p(x_{i+1} \mid \alpha, \beta, x_i, y^i)\, p(y_{i+1} \mid \alpha, \beta, x_{i+1}, x_i, y^i) \\ &\quad = p(\alpha, \beta, x_i \mid y^i)\, p(x_{i+1} \mid \alpha, x_i, u_i)\, p(y_{i+1} \mid \beta, x_{i+1}) \end{aligned}$$

Now since

$$\int p(\alpha, \beta, x_i, x_{i+1}, y_{i+1} \mid y^i)\, dx_i = p(y_{i+1} \mid y^i)\, p(\alpha, \beta, x_{i+1} \mid y^{i+1})$$

the recursion equation for the conditional probability density $p(\alpha, \beta, x_i \mid y^i)$ is obtained as

$$\begin{aligned} p(\alpha, \beta, x_{i+1} \mid y^{i+1}) = \int & p(\alpha, \beta, x_i \mid y^i)\, p(x_{i+1} \mid x_i, u_i, \alpha) \\ & \times \frac{p(y_{i+1} \mid \beta, x_{i+1})\, dx_i}{\int [\text{numerator}]\, d(\alpha, \beta, x_{i+1})} \end{aligned} \tag{86}$$

and

$$p(\alpha, x_{i+1} \mid y^{i+1}) = \int p(\alpha, \beta, x_{i+1} \mid y^{i+1})\, d\beta \tag{87}$$

We next consider several examples.

B. Examples

a. *System with Unknown Random Time Constant*

Consider a one-dimensional control system of Example 7, Chapter I, described by the plant equation

$$x_{i+1} = a_i x_i + u_i, \qquad 0 \leqslant i \leqslant N-1, \quad u_i \in (-\infty, \infty) \tag{88}$$

where a's are independently and identically distributed random variables with

$$\mathscr{L}(a_i) = N(\theta, \sigma^2) \tag{89}$$

for each θ where θ is the unknown parameter of the distribution function. It is assumed to have an a priori distribution function

$$\mathscr{L}(\theta) = N(\theta_0, {\sigma_0}^2) \tag{90}$$

The system is assumed to be perfectly observed:

$$y_i = x_i\,, \qquad 0 \leqslant i \leqslant N-1 \tag{91}$$

When the common mean of the random time constants is known, the problem reduces to that of a purely stochastic system. As such, this problem has already been discussed in Section 2 of Chapter II.

By letting $\sigma_0 \to 0$, the solution of this problem reduces to that for the purely stochastic system as we will see shortly.

The criterion function is taken to be

$$J = x_N{}^2 \tag{92}$$

Now

$$\begin{aligned}\gamma_N &= E(x_N{}^2 \mid x^{N-1})\\ &= \int x_N{}^2\, p(x_N \mid x_{N-1}\,, u_{N-1}\,, a_{N-1})\, p(a_{N-1} \mid x^{N-1})\, d(x_N\,, a_{N-1})\\ &= \int (a_{N-1}x_{N-1} + u_{N-1})^2\, p(a_{N-1} \mid x^{N-1})\, da_{N-1}\end{aligned} \tag{93}$$

Because of the assumption of perfect observation, the knowledge of x^{N-1} is equivalent to that of a^{N-2}, since $a_i = (x_{i+1} - u_i)/x_i$ if $x_i \neq 0$ from (88). If $x_i = 0$ for some i, it is easy to see that $u_j = 0$, $j = i$, $i+1,\ldots, N-1$, is optimal from that point on.

Define

$$\hat{a}_i = E(a_i \mid a^{i-1}), \qquad 1 \leqslant i \leqslant N-1 \tag{94}$$

$$\hat{\sigma}_i{}^2 = \operatorname{var}(a_i \mid a^{i-1}), \qquad 1 \leqslant i \leqslant N-1 \tag{95}$$

From Eq. (93), using symbols just defined by (94) and (95),

$$\lambda_N = (\hat{a}_{N-1}x_{N-1} + u_{N-1})^2 + \hat{\sigma}_{N-1}^2 x_{N-1}^2 \tag{96}$$

From Eq. (96), the optimal control variable at time $N-1$ is given by

$$u_{N-1}^* = -\hat{a}_{N-1}x_{N-1} \tag{97}$$

since $\hat{a}_{N-1}$ and $\hat{\sigma}_{N-1}$ can be seen to be independent of u_{N-1}. The minimal value of γ_N is given as

$$\gamma_N{}^* = \hat{\sigma}_{N-1}^2 x_{N-1}^2 \tag{98}$$

Now $\lambda_i = 0$, $i < N$, because of the criterion function (92), and we have

$$\gamma_{N-1} = \int \gamma_N{}^* \, p(x_{N-1} \mid x^{N-2}) \, dx_{N-1} \tag{99}$$

As we will see later, $\hat{\sigma}_{N-1}$ is independent of u_{N-2}.

Therefore, the problem of finding optimal control policy for the remaining $(N-1)$ control stages essentially remains unchanged.

Hence

$$u_i{}^* = -\hat{a}_i x_i \,, \qquad 0 \leqslant i \leqslant N-1 \tag{100}$$

is the optimal control policy and

$$\min EJ = \gamma_1{}^* = \left(\prod_{i=0}^{N-1} \hat{\sigma}_i{}^2 \right) x_0{}^2 \tag{101}$$

It now remains to compute quantities defined by (94) and (95). Now from the conditional independence assumption on θ,

$$p(a_i \mid a^{i-1}) = \int p(a_i \mid \theta) \, p(\theta \mid a^{i-1}) \, d\theta \tag{102}$$

where, from (89),

$$p(a_i \mid \theta) = \text{const} \exp\left(-\frac{(a_i - \theta)^2}{2\sigma^2} \right) \tag{103}$$

To compute $p(\theta \mid a^{i-1})$, we use the recursion formula

$$p(\theta \mid a^j) = \frac{p(\theta \mid a^{j-1}) \, p(a_j \mid \theta, a^{j-1})}{\int p(\theta \mid a^{j-1}) \, p(a_j \mid \theta, a^{j-1}) \, d\theta} \,, \qquad 1 \leqslant j \leqslant N-1 \tag{104}$$

where its initial conditional probability density function is given by

$$\begin{aligned} p(\theta \mid a_0) &= \frac{p_0(\theta) \, p(a_0 \mid \theta)}{\int p_0(\theta) \, p(a_0 \mid \theta) \, d\theta} \\ &= \text{const} \exp\left(-\frac{(\theta - \mu_0)^2}{2\Sigma_0{}^2} \right) \end{aligned} \tag{105}$$

where

$$\mu_0 = \frac{a_0/\sigma^2 + \theta_0/\sigma_0{}^2}{1/\sigma^2 + 1/\sigma_0{}^2} \tag{106a}$$

$$1/\Sigma_0{}^2 = 1/\sigma^2 + 1/\sigma_0{}^2 \tag{106b}$$

As in previous examples, θ has the sufficient statistics and we can write

$$p(\theta \mid a^j) = \text{const} \exp\left(-\frac{(\theta - \mu_j)^2}{2\Sigma_j^2}\right) \tag{107}$$

where the sufficient statistics (μ_i, Σ_i) are given by

$$\mu_j = \frac{\mu_{j-1}/\Sigma_{j-1}^2 + a_j/\sigma^2}{1/\Sigma_{j-1}^2 + 1/\sigma^2}, \qquad 0 \leqslant j \leqslant N-1 \tag{108a}$$

$$1/\Sigma_j^2 = 1/\Sigma_{j-1}^2 + 1/\sigma^2 \tag{108b}$$

where μ_0 and Σ_0 are given by Eq. (106).

Substituting (103) and (104) into Eq. (102),

$$p(a_i \mid a^{i-1}) = \text{const} \exp\left(-\frac{(a_i - \mu_{i-1})^2}{2(\sigma^2 + \Sigma_{i-1}^2)}\right) \tag{109}$$

Thus we have

$$\begin{aligned} \hat{a}_i &= \mu_{i-1}, \qquad 1 \leqslant i \leqslant N-1 \\ \hat{a}_0 &= \theta_0 \end{aligned} \tag{110}$$

and

$$\hat{\sigma}_i^2 = \sigma^2 + \Sigma_{i+1}^2$$

Or, more explicitly,

$$1/\Sigma_j^2 = 1/\sigma_0^2 + (j+1)/\sigma^2$$

$$\hat{a}_{j+1} = \mu_j = \frac{\theta_0/\sigma_0^2 + \Sigma_0^j a_i/\sigma^2}{1/\sigma_0^2 + (j+1)/\sigma^2}$$

$$= \frac{\theta_0/\sigma_0^2 + \Sigma_0^j \left(\dfrac{x_{i+1} - u_i}{x_i \sigma^2}\right)}{1/\sigma_0^2 + (j+1)/\sigma^2}$$

By letting $\sigma_0 \to 0$, we see that $\hat{a}_i$ all reduces to θ_0 and Σ_i to 0. As expected, the optimal control policy given by (100) reduces to the optimal control policy for the corresponding stochastic case; a special case discussed in Section II,2,C.

b. *System with Unknown Time Constant*

Let us consider a problem related to Example 5 of Chapter I.

The plant equation is assumed given by

$$x_{i+1} = ax_i + bu_i + \xi_i, \qquad x_0 \text{ given}, \quad u_i \in (-\infty, \infty) \tag{111}$$

where it is assumed that b is known, that a is a random variable independent of ξ's with

$$\mathscr{L}(a) = N(\theta, \sigma_1^2) \tag{112}$$

where θ is assumed unknown with its a priori probability density given by

$$\mathscr{L}_0(\theta) = N(\theta_0, \sigma_0^2) \tag{113}$$

and where ξ_i's are independently and identically distributed with

$$\mathscr{L}(\xi_i) = N(0, \sigma_2^2) \tag{114}$$

The observation is assumed perfect:

$$y_i = x_i \tag{115}$$

The system is assumed to be a final-value control system. Let us take its criterion function to be

$$J = x_N^2$$

To obtain an optimal control policy, we compute first

$$\begin{aligned}\gamma_N &= E(x_N^2 \mid x^{N-1}) \\ &= \int x_N^2\, p(x_N \mid x_{N-1}, u_{N-1}, a)\, p(a \mid x^{N-1})\, d(x_N, a) \\ &= \int [(a x_{N-1} + b u_{N-1})^2 + \sigma_2^2]\, p(a \mid x^{N-1})\, da \\ &= (\alpha_{N-1} x_{N-1} + b u_{N-1})^2 + \sigma_2^2 + x_{N-1}^2 \Gamma_{N-1}^2 \end{aligned} \tag{116}$$

where

$$\alpha_{N-1} \triangleq E(a \mid x^{N-1}) \tag{117a}$$

$$\Gamma_{N-1} \triangleq \operatorname{var}(a \mid x^{N-1}) \tag{117b}$$

It is now shown that $p(a \mid x^i)$ has the form

$$p(a \mid x^i) = \text{const} \exp\left(-\frac{(a - \alpha_i)^2}{2\Gamma_i}\right), \qquad i = 0, 1, ..., N-1 \tag{118}$$

This form is seen to hold for $i = 0$, since

$$\begin{aligned} p(a \mid x_0) = p_0(a) &= \int p(a \mid \theta)\, p_0(\theta)\, d\theta \\ &= \text{const} \exp\left(-\frac{(a - \theta_0)^2}{2(\sigma_0^2 + \sigma_1^2)}\right) \end{aligned}$$

Therefore, (118) is true with

$$\alpha_0 = \theta_0$$
$$1/\Gamma_0 = 1/(\sigma_0^2 + \sigma_1^2)$$

Assuming that (118) is true for some i, one obtains

$$p(a \mid x^{i+1}) = \text{const} \exp\left(-\frac{(a - \alpha_{i+1})^2}{2\Gamma_{i+1}}\right)$$

using the recursion relation

$$p(a \mid x^{i+1}) = \frac{p(a \mid x^i)\, p(x_{i+1} \mid x_i, u_i, a)}{\int p(a \mid x^i)\, p(x_{i+1} \mid x_i, u_i, a)\, da}$$

where

$$p(x_{i+1} \mid x_i, u_i, a) = \text{const} \exp\left(-\frac{(x_{i+1} - ax_i - bu_i)^2}{2\sigma_2^2}\right)$$

and where

$$\alpha_{i+1} = \frac{\alpha_i/\Gamma_i + x_i(x_{i+1} - bu_i)/\sigma_2^2}{1/\Gamma_i + x_i^2/\sigma_2^2} \tag{119a}$$
$$\alpha_0 = \theta_0$$
$$1/\Gamma_{i+1} = 1/\Gamma_i + x_i^2/\sigma_2^2 \tag{119b}$$
$$\Gamma_0 = \sigma_0^2 + \sigma_1^2$$

This establishes (118) for all $i = 0, 1, \ldots, N-1$. The optimal last control is obtained by minimizing (116) with respect to u_{N-1}:

$$u_{N-1}^* = -\frac{\alpha_{N-1} x_{N-1}}{b} \tag{120}$$

and

$$\gamma_N^* = \sigma_2^2 + \Gamma_{N-1} x_{N-1}^2 \tag{121}$$

Since J depends only on x_N, $\lambda_i = 0$, $i = 1, \ldots, N-2$. Therefore,

$$\begin{aligned}
\gamma_{N-1}^* &= \int \gamma_N^*\, p(x_{N-1} \mid x^{N-2})\, dx_{N-1} \\
&= \int \gamma_N^*\, p(x_{N-1} \mid x_{N-2}, u_{N-1}, a)\, p(a \mid x^{N-2})\, d(x_{N-1}, a) \\
&= \sigma_2^2 + \Gamma_{N-1} \int [(ax_{N-2} + bu_{N-2})^2 + \sigma_2^2]\, p(a \mid x^{N-2})\, da \\
&= \sigma_2^2(1 + \Gamma_{N-1}) + \Gamma_{N-1}[(\alpha_{N-2}x_{N-2} + bu_{N-2})^2 + x_{N-2}^2 \Gamma_{N-2}]
\end{aligned} \tag{122}$$

By comparing (116) with (122), one immediately gets

$$u^*_{N-2} = -\alpha_{N-2} x_{N-2}/b$$

and generally

$$u_i{}^* = -\frac{a_i x_i}{b} \tag{123}$$

where α_i are computed from (119).

c. *System with Unknown Gain*

Let us now re-examine Example 6 of Chapter I. There, we derived u^*_{N-1} as

$$u^*_{N-1} = -\frac{b_{N-1}}{b^2_{N-1} + \sigma^2_{N-1}} (ax_N{}_1)$$

where

$$b_{N-1} = E(b \mid x^{N-1})$$

and

$$\gamma_N{}^* - \frac{\sigma^2_{N-1}}{b^2_{N-1} + \sigma^2_{N-1}} (ax_{N-1})^2 + \Sigma_0{}^2$$

without computing b_{N-1} and σ_{N-1} explicitly.

Let us now compute them under the assumption that the random variable b is Gaussian, independent of ξ's and of x_0 and has the unknown mean θ,

$$L(b) - N(\theta, \Sigma_1{}^2)$$

and that θ itself is a random variable with a priori density function given by

$$L(\theta) - N(\theta_0, \Sigma_2{}^2)$$

where θ_0, Σ_1, and Σ_2 are assumed known.

We first show that

$$p(b \mid x^i) = \text{const} \exp\left(-\frac{(b - b_i)^2}{2\sigma_i{}^2}\right), \qquad i = 0, 1,\dots \tag{124}$$

Since

$$p(b \mid x_0) = p_0(b) = \int p(b \mid \theta)\, p_0(\theta)\, d\theta$$

$$= \text{const} \exp\left(-\frac{(b - \theta_0)^2}{2(\Sigma_1{}^2 + \Sigma_2{}^2)}\right)$$

(124) is certainly true for $i = 0$ with

$$b_0 = \theta_0 \tag{125a}$$

$$1/\sigma_0^2 = 1/\Sigma_1^2 + 1/\Sigma_2^2 \tag{125b}$$

From the recursion relation

$$p(b \mid x^{i+1}) = \frac{p(b \mid x^i)\, p(x_{i+1} \mid b, x_i, u_i)}{\int p(b \mid x^i)\, p(x_{i+1} \mid x_i, b, u_i)\, db} \tag{126}$$

where

$$p(x_{i+1} \mid x_i, b, u_i) = \text{const} \exp\left(-\frac{(x_{i+1} - ax_i - bu_i)^2}{2\Sigma_0^2}\right) \tag{127}$$

one gets

$$p(b \mid x^{i+1}) = \text{const} \exp\left(-\frac{(b - b_{i+1})^2}{2\sigma_{i+1}^2}\right)$$

where

$$b_{i+1} = \frac{b_i/\sigma_i^2 + u_i(x_{i+1} - ax_i)/\Sigma_0^2}{1/\sigma_i^2 + u_i^2/\Sigma_0^2} \tag{128a}$$

and

$$1/\sigma_{i+1}^2 = 1/\sigma_i^2 + u_i^2/\Sigma_0^2 \tag{128b}$$

where Σ_0^2 is the variance of the plant noise, thus verifying (124) for all $i = 0, 1, \ldots$. The statistics (b_i, σ_i^2) are the sufficient statistics for b.

From (128a), therefore,

$$b_{N-1} = \frac{b_{N-2}/\sigma_{N-2}^2 + u_{N-2}(x_{N-1} - ax_{N-2})/\Sigma_0^2}{1/\sigma_{N-2}^2 + u_{N-2}^2/\Sigma_0^2} \tag{129}$$

where b_{N-2} is a function of x^{N-2}.

Since the criterion function depends only on x_N, $\lambda_i = 0$, $i = 1, \ldots, N-1$, and we have

$$\begin{aligned} \gamma_{N-1}^* &= \int \gamma_N^*\, p(x_{N-1} \mid x^{N-2})\, dx_{N-1} \\ &= \int \gamma_N^*\, p(x_{N-1} \mid x_{N-2}, b, u_{N-2})\, p(b \mid x^{N-2})\, d(x_{N-1}, b) \end{aligned} \tag{130}$$

Notice that x_{N-1}^* appears not only explicitly in γ_N^* but also through b_{N-1} in carrying out the integration with respect to x_{N-1}.

The integration

$$\int \gamma_N^* \, p(x_{N-1} \mid x_{N-2}, b, u_{N-2}) \, dx_{N-2} \tag{131}$$

is of the form

$$I = \int_{-\infty}^{\infty} \frac{x^2}{(ax+b)^2 + c^2} \exp\left(-\frac{(x-\mu)^2}{2}\right) dx \qquad a, b, c \text{ real} \tag{132}$$

after a suitable change of variables or, more generally,

$$\int \frac{Q_1(x)}{Q_2(x)} \exp\left(-\frac{x^2}{2}\right) dx \tag{133}$$

where Q_1 and Q_2 are quadratic polynomials in x.

The integration of Eq. (131) cannot be carried explicitly to give an analytically closed expression.

Therefore, it is impossible to obtain expressions for $u_0^*, \ldots, u_{N-2}^*$ explicitly analytically in a closed form. They must be obtained either numerically or by approximation.

Here is an example of a common type of difficulty we face in obtaining optimal control policies. The system of this example is rather simple, yet the assumption of the unknown mean of the random gain made it impossible to obtain the optimal control policy explicitly.

There are many such examples, even when the systems are linear with quadratic performance indices, that they do not admit analytic solutions for optimal control policies.

We note that the integrand γ_N^* in (131) is bounded from above by

$$\gamma_N^* \leqslant (ax_{N-1})^2 + \Sigma_0^2$$

If this upper bound is used in (131), then we have an approximation of γ_{N-1}^* given by

$$\gamma_{N-1}^* \leqslant \Sigma_0^2 + \int (ax_{N-1})^2 \, p(x_{N-1} \mid x_{N-2}, b, u_{N-2}) \, p(b \mid x^{N-2}) \, d(x_{N-1}, b)$$

This approximation is equivalent to one-stage optimization where each control stage is optimized separately.

This approximation yields a suboptimal control policy where

$$u_i = -\frac{b_i}{b_i^2 + \sigma_i^2}(ax_i), \qquad 0 \leqslant i \leqslant N-1$$

Even though (131) cannot be carried out analytically, some insight can be obtained into the structure of optimal control policies.

From (128a) and (128b) we note that

$$b_{i+1} \to b \quad \text{and} \quad \sigma_{i+1} \to 0 \quad \text{as} \quad |u_i| \to \infty$$

Therefore, the coefficient multiplying x_{N-1}^2 in the expression for $\gamma_N{}^*$ approaches zero:

$$\frac{a^2\sigma_{N-1}^2}{b_{N-1}^2 + \sigma_{N-1}^2} \to 0 \quad \text{as} \quad |u_{N-2}| \to \infty$$

Substituting $ax_{N-2} + bu_{N-2} + \xi_{N-2}$ for x_{N-1} in $\gamma_N{}^*$, we have

$$\gamma_N{}^* \to \Sigma_0{}^2(1 + a^2) \quad \text{as} \quad |u_{N-2}| \to \infty$$

If b is known, then the minimum of the expected control cost for the last two stages using an open-loop control policy is equal to $\Sigma_0{}^2(1 + a^2)$, i.e., the contribution from ξ_{N-1} and $a\xi_{N-2}$ terms.

Let us now examine the effects of $|u_{N-3}| \to \infty$. Then

$$x_{N-1} \to a\xi_{N-3} + \xi_{N-2}$$

$$x_N \to ax_{N-1} + bu_{N-1} + \xi_{N-1}$$

By employing the controls given by

$$u_{N-1} = -ab_{N-1}x_{N-1}/(b_{N-1}^2 + \sigma_{N-1}^2)$$

and

$$u_{N-2} = -ab_{N-2}x_{N-2}/(b_{N-2}^2 + \sigma_{N-2}^2)$$

and noting that $b_{N-2} \to b$ and $\sigma_{N-2} \to 0$, we have

$$x_N \to \xi_{N-1}$$

therefore,

$$E(x_N{}^2 \mid x^{N-3}) \to \Sigma_0{}^2$$

Thus, one optimal policy is to let $|u_{N-3}| \to \infty$.

These considerations indicate that this example is singular, i.e., the control cost does not attain its minimum for control policies using finite control variables. To be more meaningful, the criterion function must be modified to include the cost of control, for example, from $J = x_N{}^2$ to

$$J = x_N{}^2 + \lambda \sum_0^{N-1} u_i{}^2$$

With this modified criterion function, we can easily derive optimal control policy when b is known.

It is given by

$$u_{N-i}^* = -a^{2i-1}x_{N-i}b \Big/ \Big(\lambda^2 + b \sum_{j=1}^{i} a^{2(j-1)}\Big)$$

When b is assumed to be the random variable as originally assumed in this example, we encounter the same difficulties in deriving the optimal control policy.

Assuming $| \sigma_i^2/b_i^2 |$ is small, i.e., assuming the learning process on b is nearly completed, we may expand γ^*'s in Taylor series in (σ_i^2/b_i^2).

This approximation results in the control policy

$$u_{N-i} = -a^{2i-1}x_{N-i}b_{N-i}K_{N-i}/(\lambda^2 + L_{N-i})$$

where K_{N-i} and L_{N-i} are complicated algebraic functions of a, λ, b_{N-i}, and σ_{N-i}.

Computational works on this and other approximation schemes are found in a report by Horowitz.[73a] See also Ref. 135a for discussions of suboptimal control policies of a related but simpler problem where b is assumed to be either b_1 or b_2 where the latters are given.

Let us return now to (132) and consider its approximate evaluation.

Since $\exp[-\frac{1}{2}(x-\mu)^2]$ in (132) is very small for $| x - \mu |$ large, one may approximately evaluate I by expanding

$$\frac{x^2}{(ax+b)^2+c^2}$$

about $x = \mu$ and retaining terms up to quadratic in $(x - \mu)$, say. When this is carried out,

$$I \approx \frac{(2\pi)^{1/2}\mu^2}{(a\mu+b)^2+c^2}\left\{1 + \frac{b^2+c^2}{\mu^2[(a\mu+b)^2+c^2]} - 2a\mu\frac{b(a\mu+b)^2+c^2(2a\mu+b)}{\mu^2[(a\mu+b)^2+c^2]^2}\right\} \tag{134}$$

Similarly,

$$\int_{-\infty}^{\infty} \frac{1}{(ax+b)^2+c^2} \exp\left(-\frac{(x-\mu)^2}{2}\right) dx$$
$$\approx \frac{(2\pi)^{1/2}}{(a\mu+b)^2+c^2}\left\{1 - \frac{5a^2(a\mu+b)^2+a^2c^2}{[(a\mu+b)^2+c^2]^2}\right\} \tag{135}$$

After $E(\gamma_N^* \mid x^{N-2})$ is approximately carried out, it will be, in general, a complicated function of u_{N-2}. To find u_{N-2}^*, the following sequential scheme (an approximation in policy space[20]) may be used. First, γ_{N-1} is approximated by a quadratic function of u_{N-2} about some u_{N-2}^0. This u_{N-2}^0 could be the optimal u_{N-2} for the control system with some definite b value.

Minimization of this quadratic form gives u_{N-2}^1 as the optimal u_{N-2}. Then, γ_{N-1} is approximated again by a quadratic function of u_{N-2} about u_{N-2}^1. The optimal u_{N-2} now is denoted by u_{N-1}^2. Generally, γ_{N-1} is approximated by a quadratic form in u_{N-2} about u_{N-2}^i and u_{N-2}^{i+1} is the minimizing u_{N-2}. Under suitable conditions on γ_{N-1}, $u_{N-2}^i \rightarrow u_{N-2}^*$ as $i \rightarrow \infty$. See Ref. 8 for an exposition of a similar successive approximation method.

This sequential determination of the optimal control, coupled with the approximate evaluation of $E(\gamma_{k+1}^* \mid x^{k-1})$, for example, by the Taylor series expansion, can generate $u_k{}^*$, $0 \leqslant k \leqslant N-1$, approximately.

4. Systems with Unknown Plant Parameters and Noise Characteristics

Lastly we will derive recursive formulas for $p(\alpha, \beta, \theta_1, \theta_2, x_i \mid y^i)$ and $p(\alpha, \beta, \theta_1, \theta_2, x_i, \xi_i, \eta_i \mid y^i)$ needed in computing optimal control policies for systems with both unknown plant parameters and noise statistics; the simpler of these two conditional probability density forms should be used for any given problem to evaluate λ_k and γ_k, $1 \leqslant k \leqslant N$. These conditional densities are used quite analogously to (24) and (25) of Section 2 or to (84) and (85) of Section 3 in deriving optimal control policies.

To obtain $p(\alpha, \beta, \theta_1, \theta_2, x_i \mid y^i)$ recursively, consider

$$p(\alpha, \beta, \theta_1, \theta_2, x_i, x_{i+1}, y_{i+1} \mid y^i)$$

and write it by the chain rule as

$$\begin{aligned} &p(\alpha, \beta, \theta_1, \theta_2, x_i, x_{i+1}, y_{i+1} \mid y^i) \\ &\qquad = p(\alpha, \beta, \theta_1, \theta_2, x_i \mid y^i)\, p(x_{i+1} \mid \alpha, \theta_1, x_i, u_i)\, p(y_{i+1} \mid \beta, \theta_2, x_{i+1}) \end{aligned}$$

Integrate both sides with respect to x_i to obtain

$$\begin{aligned} \int p(\alpha, \beta, \theta_1, \theta_2, x_i, x_{i+1}, y_{i+1} \mid y^i)\, dx_i &= p(\alpha, \beta, \theta_1, \theta_2, x_{i+1}, y_{i+1} \mid y^i) \\ &= p(\alpha, \beta, \theta_1, \theta_2, x_{i+1} \mid y^{i+1})\, p(y_{i+1} \mid y^i) \end{aligned}$$

Hence

$$p(\alpha, \beta, \theta_1, \theta_2, x_{i+1} \mid y^{i+1})$$
$$= \int p(\alpha, \beta, \theta_1, \theta_2, x_i \mid y^i)\, p(x_{i+1} \mid \alpha, \theta_1, x_i, u_i)$$
$$\times \frac{p(y_{i+1} \mid \beta, \theta_2, x_{i+1})\, dx_i}{\int [\text{numerator}]\, d(\alpha, \beta, \theta_1, \theta_2, x_{i+1})} \tag{136}$$

Similarly, $p(\alpha, \beta, \theta_1, \theta_2, x_i, \xi_i, \eta_i \mid y^i)$ is obtained recursively by the relation

$$p(\alpha, \beta, \theta_1, \theta_2, x_i, \xi_i, \eta_i, x_{i+1}, \xi_{i+1}, \eta_{i+1}, y_{i+1} \mid y^i)$$
$$= p(\alpha, \beta, \theta_1, \theta_2, x_i, \xi_i, \eta_i \mid y^i)\, p(x_{i+1} \mid x_i, \xi_i, u_i)$$
$$\times\, p(\xi_{i+1} \mid \theta_1)\, p(y_{i+1} \mid x_{i+1}, \theta_2, \eta_{i+1})\, p(\eta_{i+1} \mid \theta_2) \tag{137}$$

where

$$p(x_{i+1} \mid x_i, \xi_i, u_i) = \delta(x_{i+1} - F_i) \qquad \text{from (1)}$$
$$p(y_{i+1} \mid x_{i+1}, \eta_{i+1}) = \delta(y_{i+1} - G_{i+1}) \qquad \text{from (2)}$$

Therefore,

$$p(\alpha, \beta, \theta_1, \theta_2, x_{i+1}, \xi_{i+1}, \eta_{i+1} \mid y^{i+1})$$
$$= \int p(\alpha, \beta, \theta_1, \theta_2, x_i, \xi_i, \eta_i \mid y^i)\, \delta(x_{i+1} - F_i)\, p(\xi_{i+1} \mid \theta_1)$$
$$\times \frac{p(\eta_{i+1} \mid \theta_2)\, \delta(y_{i+1} - G_{i+1})\, d(x_i, \xi_i, \eta_i)}{\int [\text{numerator}]\, d(\alpha, \beta, \theta_1, \theta_2, x_{i+1}, \xi_{i+1}, \eta_{i+1})} \tag{138}$$

The conditional densities (136) and (138) can also be put in forms similar to those of (38) or (39) of Section 2.

5. Sufficient Statistics

In Chapter II, one example of sufficient statistics is discussed to replace the collection of observations made on x_j, $0 \leqslant j \leqslant i$, by μ_i and Γ_i so that $p(x_i \mid y^i, u^{i-1}) = (p(x_i \mid \mu_i, \Gamma_i)$, $i = 0, 1,..., N-1$. One consequence of this is that the optimal control variable u_i^* becomes a function of Γ_i and μ_i, where μ_i is a function of on-line variables u_{i-1}, μ_{i-1}, and y_i and other quantities that can be generated off-line.

Similar simplifications of functional dependence of γ's of (24) or (84) on y^i and u^{i-1} are possible if sufficient statistics exist for some or all of the variables $\alpha, \beta, \theta_1, \theta_2$, and x_i. See Section 3 of Chapter IV for details.

As an example, consider a simple scalar final-value control problem where the state vector is perfectly observed.[5] The plant equation is

$$y_{k+1} = ay_k + u_k + r_k \tag{139}$$

where

$$u_k \in (-\infty, \infty)$$

and where y's are used instead of x's because of the assumption of perfect observation. The criterion function is taken to be $J = W_N(y_N)$. The plant noise r_k's are assumed to be independently and identically distributed binomial random variables

$$r_k = \begin{cases} +c & \text{with probability } \theta \\ -c & \text{with probability } 1-\theta \end{cases} \tag{140}$$

for each θ, where θ is the unknown parameter with its a priori distribution given. Assume, for example, that

$$\theta = \begin{cases} \theta_1 & \text{with probability } z_0 \\ \theta_2 & \text{with probability } 1-z_0 \end{cases} \qquad (0 \leqslant z_0 \leqslant 1) \tag{141*}$$

An aircraft landing system that lends itself to this model is considered by Grishin.[66]

From (139),

$$r_k = y_{k+1} - ay_k - u_k$$

therefore, at time k, the past realization of the noise sequence $(r_0, r_1, \ldots, r_{k-1})$ is available from the knowledge of y^k. Therefore, the joint probability** of $r_0, \ldots, r_{k-1}$ is given by

$$Pr[r_0, r_1, \ldots, r_{k-1} \mid \theta] = \theta^{k-i}(1-\theta)^i \tag{142}$$

where i is the number of times $+c$ is observed and is known from y^k. In other words, any function of $r_0, \ldots, r_{k-1}$ can be computed given (k, i).

---

* Assumption (141) on the form of the unknown parameter θ is not essential for the development. If θ is a continuous variable, $0 \leqslant \theta \leqslant 1$, then an a priori probability density may be taken, for example, to be of Beta type, i.e.,

$$p_0(\theta) = \frac{\Gamma(c+d+2)}{\Gamma(c+1)\Gamma(d+1)} \theta^c(1-\theta)^d, \qquad c, \alpha > 0$$

** In this example, the random variables are discrete and it is convenient to deal with probabilities rather than probability densities. It is, therefore, necessary to modify prior developments in an obvious way. Such modifications will be made without further comments.

The pair (k, i) is said to be sufficient for θ, or the number of times r's are $+c$ is the sufficient statistic for θ. Denote this number i by s_k.

To obtain an optimal control policy for the system (139) one computes, as usual,

$$
\begin{aligned}
\gamma_N(y^{N-1}) &= E(W_N \mid y^{N-1}) \\
&= \int W_N(y_N)\, p(y_N \mid y^{N-1})\, dy_N \\
&= \int W_N(y_N)\, p(y_N \mid y_{N-1}, r_{N-1}, u_{N-1})\, P(r_{N-1} \mid y^{N-1})\, d(y_N, r_{N-1}) \\
&= \int W_N(ay_{N-1} + r_{N-1} + u_{N-1})\, P(r_{N-1} \mid r^{N-2})\, dr_{N-1} \qquad (143)
\end{aligned}
$$

The conditional probability one needs in evaluating γ_N, therefore, is $P(r_i \mid y^i)$ or $P(r_i \mid r^{i-1})$, $0 \leqslant i \leqslant N-1$. One can write it as

$$
\begin{aligned}
Pr(r_i = c \mid y^i) &= Pr[r_i = c \mid r^{i-1}] \\
&= Pr[r_i = c \mid \theta_1] z_i + Pr[r_i = c \mid \theta_2](1 - z_i)
\end{aligned}
$$

where

$$
z_i \triangleq Pr[\theta_1 \mid r^{i-1}] = Pr[\theta_1 \mid s_i], \quad 0 \leqslant i \leqslant N-1
$$

and where $s_i = \frac{1}{2}(i + (1/c) \sum_{j=0}^{i-1} r_j)$ is the number of times $+c$ is observed. Therefore, in (143) the conditioning variable y^{N-1}, which is an N-dimensional vector, is replaced by a single number s_{N-1}, and we can write (143) as

$$
\begin{aligned}
E(W_N \mid y^{N-1}) &= E(W_N \mid s_{N-1}, y^{N-1}) = \gamma_N(y_{N-1}, z_{N-1}) \\
&= z_{N-1}[\theta_1 W_N(ay_{N-1} + c + u_{N-1}) \\
&\quad + (1 - \theta_1) W_N(ay_{N-1} - c + u_{N-1})] \\
&\quad + (1 - z_{N-1})[\theta_2 W_N(ay_{N-1} + c + u_{N-1}) \\
&\quad + (1 - \theta_2) W_N(ay_{N-1} - c + u_{N-1})] \\
&= W_N(ay_{N-1} + c + u_{N-1}) \hat{\theta}_{N-1} \\
&\quad + W_N(ay_{N-1} - c + u_{N-1})(1 - \hat{\theta}_{N-1}) \qquad (144)
\end{aligned}
$$

where $\hat{\theta}_{N-1}$ is the a posteriori estimate of θ, given y^{N-1},

$$
\hat{\theta}_{N-1} \triangleq \theta_1 z_{N-1} + \theta_2 (1 - z_{N-1})
$$

and where

$$z_{N-1} \triangleq Pr[\theta = \theta_1 \mid y^{N-1}] = \frac{1}{1 + [(1 - z_0)/z_0]\alpha_{N-1}}$$

where

$$\alpha_{N-1} \triangleq \left(\frac{\theta_2}{\theta_1}\right)^{s_{N-1}} \left(\frac{1 - \theta_2}{1 - \theta_1}\right)^{N-1-s_{N-1}}$$

Thus $\gamma_N{}^*$, which is generally a function of y^{N-1} and u^{N-2}, is seen to be a function of y_{N-1} and z_{N-1} (or s_{N-1}) only, a reduction in the number of variables from $2N - 3$ to just two.

The derivation of the optimal control policy for this problem and its relation with optimal control policies of the corresponding stochastic systems, where $\theta = \theta_1$ or θ_2 with probability one, is discussed later in Section 1 of Chapter VII.

6. Method Based on Computing Joint Probability Density

Next, we will describe briefly the procedure along the lines proposed by Fel'dbaum[55] to evaluate optimal control policies for the class of system of (1) and (2).

The method consists in evaluating R_i by first computing

$$p(x^i, y^{i-1}, \xi^{i-1}, \eta^{i-1}, \theta_1, \theta_2, \alpha, \beta)$$

rather than by computing $p(\theta_1, \theta_2, \alpha, \beta, \xi_i, \eta_i, x_i \mid y^i)$.

We evaluate R_k for any non-randomized control policies $\phi^{k-1} = (\phi_0, \ldots, \phi_{k-1})$ where $u_i = \phi_i(u^{i-1}, y^i)$, $i = 0, 1, \ldots, k - 1$, since the proof for non-randomized controls proceeds quite analogously. We will first discuss the case when θ_1 and θ_2 are the only unknowns.

A. Systems with Unknown Noise Characteristics

In this section we will obtain optimal control policies for the same class of systems under the same set of assumptions as in Section 2.

Define

$$\begin{aligned} E_{\phi^{k-1}}(W_k) = \int & W_k(x_k, u_{k-1}) \\ & \times p_{\phi^{k-1}}(x^k, y^{k-1}, \xi^{k-1}, \eta^{k-1}, \theta_1, \theta_2) \\ & \times d(x^k, y^{k-1}, \xi^{k-1}, \eta^{k-1}, \theta_1, \theta_2) \end{aligned} \tag{145}$$

where

$$p_{\phi^{k-1}}(x^k, y^{k-1}, \xi^{k-1}, \eta^{k-1}, \theta_1, \theta_2)$$
$$= p(\theta_1, \theta_2)\, p_{\phi^{k-1}}(x_k \mid x^{k-1}, y^{k-1}, \xi^{k-1}, \eta^{k-1}, \theta_1, \theta_2)$$
$$\times\, p_{\phi^{k-1}}(x^{k-1}, y^{k-1}, \xi^{k-1}, \eta^{k-1} \mid \theta_1, \theta_2) \qquad (146)$$

and where

$$p_{\phi^{k-1}}(x^{k-1}, y^{k-1}, \xi^{k-1}, \eta^{k-1} \mid \theta_1, \theta_2)$$
$$= \prod_{i=0}^{k-1} p_{\phi^{i-1}}(x_i, y_i, \xi_i, \eta_i \mid x^{i-1}, y^{i-1}, \xi^{i-1}, \eta^{i-1}, \theta_1, \theta_2) \qquad (147)$$

By convention, the quantities with negative indices are to be ignored, so that, in (147),

$$p_{\phi^{-1}}(x_0, \xi_0, \eta_0 \mid x^{-1}, y^{-1}, \xi^{-1}, \eta^{-1}, \theta_1, \theta_2)$$
$$= p(x_0, \xi_0, \eta_0 \mid \theta_1, \theta_2) \qquad (148)$$

The second term in (146) is simply equal to

$$p_{\phi^{k-1}}(x_k \mid x_{k-1}, \xi_{k-1}, y^{k-1}) = p(x_k \mid x_{k-1}, u_{k-1}, \xi_{k-1})$$
$$= \delta(x_k - F_{k-1}(x_{k-1}, u_{k-1}, \xi_{k-1})) \qquad (149)$$

An abbreviated notation $\delta(x_k - F_{k-1})$ will be used. $\delta(y_i - G_i)$ will stand for $\delta(y_i - G_i(x_i, \eta_i))$ in what follows. The right-hand side of (147) is

$$p_{\phi^{i-1}}(x_i, y_i, \xi_i, \eta_i \mid x^{i-1}, y^{i-1}, \xi^{i-1}, \eta^{i-1}, \theta_1, \theta_2)$$
$$= p_{\phi_{i-1}}(x_i \mid x^{i-1}, y^{i-1}, \xi^{i-1}, \eta^{i-1}, \theta_1, \theta_2)$$
$$\times\, p(\xi_i \mid x^i, \xi^{i-1}, \eta^{i-1}, y^{i-1}, \theta_1, \theta_2)$$
$$\times\, p(\eta_i \mid x^i, \xi^i, \eta^{i-1}, y^{i-1}, \theta_1, \theta_2)$$
$$\times\, p_{\phi_{i-1}}(y_i \mid x^i, y^{i-1}, \xi^i, \eta^i, \theta_1, \theta_2)$$
$$= \delta(x_i - F_{i-1})\, p(\xi_i \mid \xi^{i-1}, \theta_1)\, p(\eta_i \mid \eta^{i-1}, \theta_2)$$
$$\times\, \delta(y_i - G_i), \qquad 1 \leqslant i \leqslant k-1 \qquad (150)$$

where the independence assumption of ξ's and η's is used. The subscripts on p disappear on the densities for ξ and η since they are independent of the controls.

Thus (146) becomes, from (150),

$$p_{\phi^{k-1}}(x^k, y^{k-1}, \xi^{k-1}, \eta^{k-1}, \theta_1, \theta_2)$$
$$= p(\theta_1, \theta_2)\, \delta(x_k - F_{k-1})\, p_0(x_0, \xi_0, \eta_0 \mid \theta_1, \theta_2)$$
$$\times \prod_{i=1}^{k-1} p(\xi_i \mid \xi^{i-1}, \theta_1) p(\eta_i \mid \eta^{i-1}, \theta_2)\, \delta(x_i - F_{i-1})\, \delta(y_i - G_i) \tag{151}$$

If ξ's and η's are serially independent, then

$$p(\xi_i \mid \xi^{i-1}, \theta_1) = p(\xi_i \mid \theta_1) \tag{152}$$

and

$$p(\eta_i \mid \eta^{i-1}, \theta_2) = p(\eta_i \mid \theta_2) \tag{153}$$

As in Chapter II, when no confusion is likely, the superscript or subscript k on ϕ^k or ϕ_k will be omitted when ϕ^k or ϕ_k appears as a subscript of p such as $p_{\phi^k}(...)$, or it may be dropped altogether. It is always clear which ϕ is meant. For example, in $p_\phi(x_{i+1} \mid x_i, \xi_i, y^i)$, ϕ is really ϕ_i and

$$p_{\phi_i}(x_{i+1} \mid x_i, \xi_i, y^i) = p(x_{i+1} \mid x_i, \xi_i, u_i = \phi_i(y^i))$$

If Eq. (2) is invertible, then instead of Eq. (151) the joint probability density can be rewritten as

$$P_{\phi^{k-1}}(x^k, y^{k-1}, \xi^{k-1}, \eta^{k-1}, \theta_1, \theta_2)$$
$$= p(\theta_1, \theta_2) \prod_{i=1}^{k-1} p(\xi_i \mid \xi^{i-1}, \theta_1)\, p(\eta_i \mid \eta^{i-1}, \theta_2)$$
$$\times p(y_i \mid y_{i-1}, u_{i-1}, \xi_{i-1}, \eta_{i-1}, \eta_i)\, p(x_i \mid y_i, \eta_i)$$
$$\times p(x_k \mid x_{k-1}, u_{k-1}, \xi_{k-1}) \tag{154}$$

This expression is simpler if $p(y_i \mid y_{i-1}, u_{i-1}, \xi_{i-1}, \eta_{i-1}, \eta_i)$ is easily computable.

If the values of parameter vectors θ_1 and θ_2 are known, say $\theta_1{}^*$ and $\theta_2{}^*$, then

$$p(\theta_1, \theta_2) = \delta(\theta_1 - \theta_1{}^*)\, \delta(\theta_2 - \theta_2{}^*) \tag{155}$$

but values of θ_1 and θ_2 are actually unknown and only the a priori density function for θ_1 and θ_2 is assumed given as $p_0(\theta_1, \theta_2)$. We use the a posteriori density function for $p(\theta_1, \theta_2)$. After y^k has been observed, define

$$p_k(\theta_1, \theta_2) = p_\phi(\theta_1, \theta_2 \mid y^k)$$
$$= \frac{p_0(\theta_1, \theta_2)\, p_\phi(y^k \mid \theta_1, \theta_2)}{\int p_0(\theta_1, \theta_2)\, p_\phi(y^k \mid \theta_1, \theta_2)\, d(\theta_1, \theta_2)} \tag{156}$$

Equation (156) is evaluated from (154) or (151) using the simpler expression of the two. Equation (156) is rather complicated in general. If (154) is applicable, then (156) becomes a little simpler with

$$p_{\phi^k}(y^k \mid \theta_1, \theta_2) = \int \prod_{i=0}^{k} p(\xi_i \mid \xi^{i-1}, \theta_1)\, p(\eta_i \mid \eta^{i-1}, \theta_2)$$

$$\times\, p(y_i \mid y_{i-1}, u_{i-1}, \xi_{i-1}, \eta_{i-1}, \eta_i)\, d(\xi^k, \eta^k) \qquad (157)$$

Otherwise, one needs to evaluate

$$p_{\phi^{k-1}}(y^i \mid \theta_1, \theta_2) = \int \prod_{i=0}^{k} p(\xi_i \mid \xi^{i-1}, \theta_1)\, p(\eta_i \mid \eta^{i-1}, \theta_2)$$

$$\times\, p(x_i \mid x_{i-1}, u_{i-1}, \xi_{i-1})\, p(y_i \mid x_i, \eta_i)\, d(x^k, \xi^k, \eta^k) \qquad (158)$$

Note the joint density expressions such as (151) and (154) are essentially the same as (38) or (39) which are obtained by the repeated application of the recursion formula for the conditional probability density functions. The method of the present section requires the generation of the joint probability density functions such as (151) or (154), which are used in obtaining the optimal control policies. In our method developed in Chapter II and in the previous sections of this Chapter, the conditional density expressions appear directly in the equations for optimal control policies, and the conditional densities are generated recursively. For example, $p_k(\theta_1, \theta_2)$ of (156) is generated as follows. Using the chain rule,

$$p_\phi(\theta_1, \theta_2, x_i, x_{i+1}, y_{i+1} \mid y^i) = p_\phi(\theta_1, \theta_2, x_i \mid y^i)$$

$$\times\, p_\phi(x_{i+1} \mid x_i, \theta_1, y^i)\, p(y_{i+1} \mid x_{i+1}, \theta_2)$$

Integrating it with respect to x_i,

$$\int p_\phi(\theta_1, \theta_2, x_i, x_{i+1}, y_{i+1} \mid y^i)\, dx_i = p_\phi(\theta_1, \theta_2, x_{i+1} \mid y^{i+1})\, p_\phi(y_{i+1} \mid y^i)$$

thus,

$$p_\phi(\theta_1, \theta_2, x_{i+1} \mid y^{i+1}) = \int p_\phi(\theta_1, \theta_2, x_i \mid y^i)\, p(x_{i+1} \mid x_i, \theta_1, u_i)$$

$$\times\, \frac{p(y_{i+1} \mid x_{i+1}, \theta_2)\, dx_i}{\int [\text{numerator}]\, d(\theta_1, \theta_2, x_{i+1})}$$

and

$$p_\phi(\theta_1, \theta_2 \mid y^{i+1}) = \int p_\phi(\theta_1, \theta_2, x_{i+1} \mid y^{i+1})\, dx_{i+1}$$

B. Optimal Control Policy

The procedure to obtain the optimal control policy is quite similar to that already discussed in Sections 2–4:

$$\hat{\lambda}_k \triangleq \int W_k(x_k, u_{k-1})\, p(x_0, \xi_0, \eta_0 \mid \theta_1, \theta_2)\, p(x_k \mid x_{k-1}, u_{k-1}, \xi^{k-1}) p_k(\theta_1, \theta_2)$$

$$\times \prod_{i=1}^{k-1} p(\xi_i \mid \xi^{i-1}, \theta_1)\, p(\eta_i \mid \eta^{i-1}, \theta_2)\, p(x_i \mid x_{i-1}, u_{i-1}, \xi_{i-1})$$

$$\times\, p(y_i \mid x_i, \eta_i)\, d(x^k, \xi^{k-1}, \eta^{k-1})$$

$$E_{\phi^{k-1}}(W_k) = \int \hat{\lambda}_k\, dy^{k-1} \tag{159}$$

The optimal control policy is now obtained from

$$\min_{u_{k-1}} \hat{\gamma}_k = \hat{\gamma}_k{}^*$$

$$\hat{\gamma}_N \triangleq \hat{\lambda}_N \tag{160}$$

and

$$\hat{\gamma}_k = \left[\hat{\lambda}_k + \int \hat{\gamma}_{k+1}\, dy_k\right]^*, \qquad k = 1,\ldots, N-1$$

where the asterisk indicates u_{N-1}^*, u_{N-2}^*,..., $u_k{}^*$ are substituted in $\hat{\gamma}_k{}^*$.

C. Systems with Unknown Plant Parameters

From the discussions in Sections 6,A and B, it is clear that similar developments are possible when the plant equation contains unknown parameters α and β or, more generally, α, β, θ_1, and θ_2. Since the procedure to treat such systems are almost identical, only results are given for the system when α is the only unknown plant parameter.

An a priori probability density function for α, $p_0(\alpha)$ is assumed given. Again, optimal control policies turn out to be nonrandomized. Hence the probability density for u_k is omitted.

The probability density function one needs is now

$$p_\phi(x^{k+1}, \alpha \mid y^k) = p_k(\alpha)\, p_\phi(x^{k+1} \mid \alpha, y^k), \qquad k = 0, 1, 2,\ldots, N-1 \tag{161}$$

where

$$p_k(\alpha) \triangleq p_\phi(\alpha \mid y^k) \tag{162}$$

and where

$$p_\phi(x^{k+1} \mid \alpha, y^k) = p(x_0) \prod_0^k p(x_{i+1} \mid x_i, u_i, \alpha) \tag{163}$$

Remember that they depend on u^k. Equation (162) can be computed from

$$p_k(\alpha \mid y^k) = \frac{\int p_0(\alpha)\, p_\phi(x^k \mid u^{k-1}, \alpha)\, dx^k}{\int p_0(\alpha)\, p(x^k \mid u^{k-1}, \alpha)\, d(x^k, \alpha)} \tag{164}$$

Define $\hat{\lambda}_k$ by

$$\hat{\lambda}_k = \int W_k(x_k, u_{k-1})\, p_{k-1}(\alpha)\, p_\phi(x^k, y^{k-1} \mid \alpha)\, d(x^k, \alpha)$$

$$= \int W_k\, p(x_0) \prod_0^{k-1} p(y_i \mid x_i) \prod_0^{k-1} p(x_{i+1} \mid x_i, u_k, \alpha)\, p_{k-1}(\alpha)\, d(x^k, \alpha) \tag{165}$$

$$E_{\phi^{k-1}}(W_k) \triangleq \int \hat{\lambda}_k\, dy^{k-1}, \qquad k = 1, \ldots, N \tag{166}$$

Define

$$\hat{\gamma}_N = \hat{\lambda}_N$$

$$\hat{\gamma}_N{}^*(y^{N-1}, u^{N-2}) = \min_{u_{N-1}} \hat{\lambda}_N(y^{N-1}, u^{N-1})$$

$$- \hat{\lambda}_N(y^{N-1}, u^{N-2}, u^*_{N-1}) \tag{167}$$

where $u^*_{N-1} = \phi(y^{N-1}, u^{N-2})$ minimizes (167) with respect to u_{N-1}. Define

$$\hat{\gamma}^*_{N-1}(y^{N-2}, u^{N-3}) = \min_{u_{N-2}} \left[\hat{\lambda}_{N-1} + \int \hat{\gamma}^*(y^{N-1}, u^{N-2})\, dy_{N-1} \right] \tag{168}$$

Optimal u_{N-2} is obtained from (168) as a function of y^{N-2} and u^{N-3}.

In general, by defining

$$\hat{\gamma}_k{}^*(y^{k-1}, u^{k-2}) = \min_{u_{k-1}} \left[\hat{\lambda}_k + \hat{\gamma}^*_{k+1}(y^k, u^{k-1})\, dy_k \right], \qquad k = 1, \ldots, N-1 \tag{169}$$

we thus obtain a sequential procedure for evaluating Bayes' control policy.

7. Discussions

In this chapter, the main problem has been to compute certain conditional densities of the form $p(v_i \mid y^i)$, where the variable v_i contains the unobservable variables such as x_i, (x_i, θ), (θ, x_i, ξ_i), or$(\alpha, \beta, \theta_1, \theta_2, x_i, \xi_i, \eta_i)$, as the case may be.

The variable v_i is chosen in such a way that $p(v_i \mid y^i)$ can be computed recursively starting from $p(v_0 \mid y_0)$ and such that $E(W_k \mid y^{k-1})$ is simply evaluated in terms of $p(v_{k-1} \mid y^{k-1})$. The conditioning variables contain only observable variables or known functions of the observable variables. In the next chapter, we will expand on this point further and develop a general theory of optimal control for a more general class of systems.

So far, all the discussions are on control systems with known deterministic inputs. When stochastic inputs are considered as indicated in Section 1, and a different criterion function

$$J = \sum_{k=1}^{N} W_k(x_k, d_k, u_{k-1})$$

is taken for the same system (1) and (2), where d_k is the desired stochastic response of the system at time k and where actual input is given by z_k,

$$z_k = K_k(d_k, \zeta_k)$$

then a development similar to Sections 2, 3, 4, and 6 to obtain closed-loop optimal control policy is possible if the desired form for u_k is specified to be

$$u_k = \phi(z^k, y^k, u^{k-1})$$

For example, we may assume that the probability density function for d_k is known except for the parameter $\mu \in \Theta_\mu$, Θ_μ given, and that the probability density function for ζ_k, which is assumed to be independent of ξ's and η's, is completely given.

If z^k, in addition to y^k and u^{k-1}, is assumed to be observed, then, using $\int p(\mu \mid z^k)\, p(d_k \mid \mu)\, d\mu$ as the probability density function for d_k, it is possible to discuss optimal control policies for discrete-time systems where θ's, α, β, and/or other parameters may be additionally assumed unknown.

Unlike a posteriori density functions for θ's, α or β, the $p(\mu \mid z^k)$ does not depend on the employed control policy since the z^k are observed outside the control feedback loop. In such cases information on μ is accumulated passively by merely observing a sequence of random variables whose realizations cannot be influenced by any employed control policies.

The procedure of obtaining the optimal control policies in Section 6 accomplishes the same thing as the procedure based on evaluation of conditional expectation

$$\lambda_k = E(W_k \mid y^{k-1})$$

In the former, the computation of λ_k is complicated whereas in the latter, that of $p(v_i \mid y^i)$ is the major computation where v_i could be x_i, (x_i, α) or $(x_i, \alpha, \beta, \theta_1, \theta_2)$, as the case may be. Once $p(v_i \mid y^i)$ is available the computation of λ_k is relatively easy. Thus the method of this book differs from that of Fel'dbaum primarily in the way the computations of $E(W_k)$ are divided. Our method is superior in that the dependence of λ_k on $p(v_i \mid y^i)$ is explicitly exhibited and hence the introduction of sufficient statistics is easily understood. The dependence of λ's on some statistics is also explicitly shown in our method. The similarity of the main recursion equations of Chapters II and III are also more clearly seen in our formulation.

Also, in Section 6, the a posteriori density function for unknown system and/or noise distribution function parameters are incorporated somewhat arbitrarily and heuristically, whereas in our method it is incorporated naturally when $p(v_i \mid y^i)$ are computed.

It is worthwhile to mention again that the problems of optimal control become more difficult when observations are noisy. We have discussed enough examples to see that the derivations of optimal control policies are much easier when state vectors and realizations of random variables are measurable without error than when only noisy measurements on state vectors are given. The difficulties in deriving optimal controls are compounded many times when the statistics of the measurement noises are only partially known.

Chapter IV

Optimal Bayesian Control of Partially Observed Markovian Systems

1. Introduction

In the previous two chapters we have derived formulations for optimal Bayesian control policies for purely stochastic and adaptive systems. We noted that the main recursion equations for optimal control policies are identical for these two classes of systems. The slight differences are in the auxiliary equations that generate certain conditional probability densities for these two classes. The only quantities that are not immediately available and must be generated recursively are the conditional probability densities which are $p(x_i \mid y^i)$ in the case of purely stochastic systems and are $p(x_i, \theta \mid y^i)$ or $p(x_i, \theta_i, \theta_2, \alpha, \beta \mid y^i)$, etc., in the parameter adaptive systems. The other probability densities needed in computing γ's are immediately available from the plant and observation equations and from the assumed probability distribution functions of noises and/or random system parameters.

In each case, the conditioning variables are the variables observed by the controller or some functions of these observed variables, such as y's, u's, or sufficient statistics. The other variables are the quantities not observed by the controller, such as x's or $(x_i, \theta_1, \theta_2, \alpha, \beta)$, etc.

Developments in the previous two chapters are primarily for systems with independent random disturbances, although possible extensions for systems with dependent noises have been pointed out from time to time. In this chapter we consider more general systems where noises ξ and η may be dependent and where unknown plant and observation parameters α and β may be time-varying. We present a formulation general enough to cover much wider classes of control systems than those considered so far. See also Refs. 2, 14–16, 56, 105a, 130, and 135 for subjects related to this chapter.

The class of systems of this chapter is assumed to be described by a plant equation

$$x_{i+1} = F_i(x_i, u_i, \xi_i, \alpha_i), \qquad i = 0, 1, ..., N-1 \tag{1}$$

and the observation equation

$$y_i = G_i(x_i, \eta_i, \beta_i), \qquad i = 0, 1, ..., N-1 \tag{2}$$

where ξ's and η's are noises and where system parameters α and β are subscripted now to include the possibility of these unknown system parameters being time-varying. When they are not subscripted, they are understood to be constants. The criterion function is the same as before:

$$J = \sum_{1}^{N} W_i(x_i, u_{i-1})$$

Only the class of nonrandomized control policies will be considered. It is fairly clear that one can heuristically argue that optimal control policies for systems of (1) and (2) are nonrandomized in much the same way as before. It is fairly clear also that the approach of Chapters II and III, where certain conditional probability densities have been computed recursively to derive optimal control policies, can be extended to cover the class of control problems of this chapter.

As an illustration, consider a system with the unknown plant parameter α and the unknown observation parameter β. The noises ξ and η are assumed to form mutually independent first-order Markov sequences such that the unknown parameters θ_1 and θ_2 characterize their respective transition probability densities, i.e.,

$$p(\xi_{i+1} \mid \xi^i, \theta_1) = p(\xi_{i+1} \mid \xi_i, \theta_1)$$

and

$$p(\eta_{i+1} \mid \eta^i, \theta_2) = p(\eta_{i+1} \mid \eta_i, \theta_2)$$

We know that, if $p(\alpha, x_j, \xi_j \mid y^j)$ is known for all $0 \leqslant j \leqslant N-1$, then

$$\begin{aligned}\lambda_i &\triangleq E(W_i(x_i, u_{i-1}) \mid y^{i-1}) = \int W_i(x_i, u_{i-1})\, p(x_i \mid y^{i-1})\, dx_i \\ &= \int W_i(x_i, u_{i-1})\, p(x_i \mid x_{i-1}, u_{i-1}, \xi_{i-1}, \alpha) \\ &\quad \times p(\alpha, x_{i-1}, \xi_{i-1} \mid y^{i-1})\, d(x_{i-1}, x_i, \alpha, \xi_{i-1})\end{aligned}$$

is computable for all $1 \leqslant i \leqslant N$ and nonrandomized optimal control policies are derived from them.

The conditional density $p(\alpha, x_i, \xi_i \mid y^i)$ is obtained by computing recursively conditional densities of a certain vector which suitably augments (x_i, y_i), all conditioned on y^i. For example, $p(x_i, \xi_i, \eta_i, \theta_1, \theta_2, \alpha, \beta \mid y^i)$ is computed recursively. The derivation of such a recursion relation is carried out as usual. The chain rule is used to write

$$\begin{aligned} & p(x_i, \xi_i, \eta_i, \theta_1, \theta_2, \alpha, \beta, x_{i+1}, \xi_{i+1}, y_{i+1}, \eta_{i+1} \mid y^i) \\ &\quad = p(x_i, \xi_i, \eta_i, \theta_1, \theta_2, \alpha, \beta \mid y^i)\, p(x_{i+1} \mid x_i, \xi_i, \alpha, u_i) \\ &\quad\quad \times p(\xi_{i+1} \mid \xi_i, \theta_1)\, p(\eta_{i+1} \mid \eta_i, \theta_2)\, p(y_{i+1} \mid x_{i+1}, \beta) \end{aligned}$$

where the assumptions on ξ's and η's are used to simplify some of the conditional density expressions. Integrating both sides with respect to x_i, ξ_i, and η_i,

$$\begin{aligned} & \int p(x_i, \xi_i, \eta_i, \theta_1, \theta_2, \alpha, \beta, x_{i+1}, \xi_{i+1}, \eta_{i+1}, y_{i+1} \mid y^i)\, d(x_i, \xi_i, \eta_i) \\ &\quad = p(y_{i+1} \mid y^i)\, p(x_{i+1}, \xi_{i+1}, \eta_{i+1}, \theta_1, \theta_2, \alpha, \beta \mid y^{i+1}) \end{aligned}$$

Therefore,

$$\begin{aligned} & p(x_{i+1}, \xi_{i+1}, \eta_{i+1}, \theta_1, \theta_2, \alpha, \beta \mid y^{i+1}) \\ &\quad = \int p(x_i, \xi_i, \eta_i, \theta_1, \theta_2, \alpha, \beta \mid y^i)\, \delta(x_{i+1} - F_i)\, p(\xi_{i+1} \mid \xi_i, \theta_1) \\ &\quad\quad \times \frac{p(\eta_{i+1} \mid \eta_i, \theta_2)\, \delta(y_{i+1} - G_{i+1})\, d(x_i, \xi_i, \eta_i)}{\int [\text{numerator}]\, d(x_{i+1}, \xi_{i+1}, \eta_{i+1}, \theta_1, \theta_2, \alpha, \beta)} \end{aligned} \tag{3}$$

and

$$p(\alpha, x_i, \xi_i \mid y^i) = \int p(x_i, \xi_i, \eta_i, \theta_1, \theta_2, \alpha, \beta \mid y^i)\, d(\eta_i, \theta_1, \theta_2, \beta)$$

The recursion (3) is started from a given a priori probability density for $(x_0, \xi_0, \eta_0, \theta_1, \theta_2, \alpha, \beta)$:

$$p(x_0, \xi_0, \eta_0, \theta_1, \theta_2, \alpha, \beta \mid y_0) = \frac{p_0(x_0, \xi_0, \eta_0, \theta_1, \theta_2, \alpha, \beta)\, p(y_0 \mid x_0, \beta)}{\int [\text{numerator}]\, d(x_0, \xi_0, \eta_0, \theta_1, \theta_2, \alpha, \beta)}$$

Conditional probability densities and optimal control policies for systems under different sets of assumptions can be similarly derived by first augmenting (x, y) appropriately so that the conditional densities for the augmented vectors are more easily obtainable.

As another example, if the system parameter α is not a constant but a Markov random variable with known transition probability density $p(\alpha_{i+1} \mid \alpha_i)$, and if ξ's and η's are all independent with known densities, then $p(x_i, \alpha_i \mid y^i)$ can be recursively generated similarly to (3) and used to evaluate

$$\begin{aligned}\lambda_{i+1} &= E(W_{i+1}(x_{i+1}, u_i) \mid y^i) \\ &= \int W_{i+1}(x_{i+1}, u_i)\, p(x_{i+1} \mid x_i, \alpha_i, u_i) \\ &\quad \times p(x_i, \alpha_i \mid y^i)\, d(x_i, x_{i+1}, \alpha_i)\end{aligned}$$

where

$$\begin{aligned}p(x_{i+1}, \alpha_{i+1} \mid y^{i+1}) &= \int p(x_i, \alpha_i \mid y^i)\, p(x_{i+1} \mid x_i, \alpha_i, u_i)\, p(\alpha_{i+1} \mid \alpha_i) \\ &\quad \times \frac{p(y_{i+1} \mid x_{i+1})\, d(x_i, \alpha_i)}{\int [\text{numerator}]\, d(x_{i+1}, \alpha_{i+1})}\end{aligned}$$

Instead of cataloging all such systems which are amenable to this approach, we will develop a general method which subsumes these particular cases. The approach we use in deriving optimal control policies for such systems is to augment the state vector x and the observation vector y with appropriate variables in such a way that the augmented state vector becomes a (first-order) Markov sequence. Then, in very much the same way as in Chapters II and III, the optimal control policy is obtained once we compute certain conditional probability densities of the unobserved portion of the augmented state vector, i.e., the components of the augmented state vector which are not available to the controllers, conditioned on the observed portion, i.e., the components of the state vector which are made available to the controllers.

The knowledge of the controller consists, then, of the past controls, the observation data, i.e., the collection of the observed portions of the augmented state vectors and of the *a posteriori* probability distribution function of the unobserved portion of the augmented state vector. This amount of information is summarized by sufficient statistics if they exist.

The derivation of the optimal control policy and the *a posteriori* probability distribution function, assuming the existence of the probability density function, is discussed in Section 3 and 4, respectively.

In the next section, we pursue the subject of Markov properties of the augmented state vectors which are of basic importance. See also Ref. 51a.

2. Markov Properties

A. Introduction

In some cases $\{(x_i, y_i)\}$ is already a first-order Markov sequence, as will be shown presently in this section. When this is not the case, there is more than one way, depending on the assumptions about noises and parameters in plant and observation equations, of augmenting (x_i, y_i) so that the resulting vector becomes a first-order Markov sequence.

Clearly, if $\{\zeta_i\}$ is Markovian, where ζ_i is some augmented state vector, then we do not destroy the Markov property by adding to ζ_i independent random variables with known distribution functions. Simplicity and ease of computing the conditional densities would dictate particular choice in any problem. The question of the minimum dimension of augmented state vectors ζ_i to make $\{\zeta_i\}$ Markovian is important theoretically but will not be pursued here.

Generally speaking, the a posteriori probability density functions such as $p(x_i \mid y^i)$ and $p(x_i, \xi_i, \eta_i \mid y^i)$ are sufficient in the sense that the corresponding density functions at time $i + 1$ are computable from their known value at time i. We can include the a posteriori probability density function as a part of an augmented state vector to make it Markovian. The dimension of such augmented vectors, generally, are infinite. We are primarily interested in finite dimensional augmented state vectors.

As an example of a system where $\{(x_i, y_i)\}$ is a first-order Markov sequence, consider a purely stochastic dynamic system of Chapter II:

$$\begin{aligned} x_{i+1} &= F_i(x_i, u_i, \xi_i) \\ y_i &= G_i(x_i, \eta_i), \qquad i = 0, 1, \ldots, N-1 \end{aligned} \tag{4}$$

where ξ's and η's are mutually independent and independent in time and have known probability densities and (4) contains no unknown parameters. Consider a vector

$$\zeta_i = (x_i, \xi_i, \eta_i, y_i, u_i) \tag{5}$$

In (5), y_i and u_i are the only components observed by the controller. We will see that under certain assumptions $\{\zeta_i\}$-process is a first-order Markov sequence, where the conditional probability of ζ_{i+1} is such that

$$\Pr[\zeta_{i+1} \in E \mid \zeta_0 = z_0, \ldots, \zeta_i = z_i] = \Pr[\zeta_{i+1} \in E \mid \zeta_i = z_i]$$

for all i, where E is any measurable set in the Euclidean space with the same dimension as ζ. This is the transition probability of $\{\zeta\}$-process.

It is assumed furthermore that the transition probability density $p(\zeta_{i+1} \mid \zeta_i)$ exists so that

$$\Pr[\zeta_{i+1} \in E \mid \zeta_i = z_i] = \int_{\zeta_{i+1} \in E} p(\zeta_{i+1} \mid \zeta_i = z_i)\, d\zeta_{i+1}$$

Let us compute the conditional probability density $p(\zeta_{i+1} \mid \zeta^i)$ of (5) assuming that u_i depends only on y_i, or at most on y_i and u_{i-1}. This assumption will be referred to as Assumption Y. We have seen several examples in previous chapters where Assumption Y holds true. Generally speaking Assumption Y implies that y_i is the sufficient statistics for x_i, i.e., $p(x_i \mid y^i) = p(x_i \mid y_i)$ and $p(y_{i+1} \mid y^i, u_i) = p(y_{i+1} \mid y_i, u_i)$. Then y_{i+1} will be a function of y_i and u_{i-1} rather than y^i and u^i, and u_i^* is obtained as a function of y_i rather than of y^i [see, for example, Eq. (21) of Section II, 2, B]. Detailed discussions on the validity of Assumption Y is presented later in this section.

With Assumption Y, we can write $p(\zeta_{i+1} \mid \zeta^i)$ as

$$\begin{aligned} p_{\phi^i}&(x_{i+1}, \xi_{i+1}, \eta_{i+1}, y_{i+1}, u_{i+1} \mid x^i, \xi^i, \eta^i, y^i, u^i) \\ &= p(x_{i+1} \mid x_i, \xi_i, u_i)\, p(\xi_{i+1})\, p(\eta_{i+1}) \\ &\quad \times p(y_{i+1} \mid x_{i+1}, \eta_{i+1})\, p(u_{i+1} \mid y^{i+1}, u^i) \\ &= \delta(x_{i+1} - F_i)\, p(\xi_{i+1})\, p(\eta_{i+1})\, \delta(y_{i+1} - G_{i+1}) \\ &\quad \times \delta(u_{i+1} - \phi_i(y_{i+1}, u_i)) \end{aligned}$$

where the independence assumption of the random noises is used. Thus, we see that

$$p_{\phi^i}(\zeta_{i+1} \mid \zeta^i) = p_{\phi_i}(\zeta_{i+1} \mid \zeta_i)$$

and $p_\phi(\zeta_{i+1} \mid \zeta_i)$ is computable as a function of ϕ_i, or as a function of $u_i = \phi_i(y_i, u_{i-1})$. The vector sequence, $\{\zeta_i\}$, is therefore a first-order Markov sequence where each component of ζ_i can take a continuum of values on the real line. Actually it is not necessary to carry (ξ_i, η_i, u_i) in ζ's of (5). $\{(x_i, y_i)\}$-process is still Markovian with Assumption Y. If Assumption Y holds, then

$$\begin{aligned} p_{\phi^i}(x_{i+1}, y_{i+1} \mid x^i, y^i) &= p(x_{i+1} \mid x_i, u_i = \phi_i(y_i))\, p(y_{i+1} \mid x_{i+1}) \\ &= p_{\phi_i}(x_{i+1}, y_{i+1} \mid x_i, y_i) \end{aligned} \tag{6}$$

where $p(x_{i+1} \mid x_i, u_i)$ is computed from (4) making use of the known distribution of ξ_i and similarly for $p(y_{i+1} \mid x_{i+1})$. If Assumption Y does not hold, however, then u_i depends on y^i and we must consider

$$\zeta_i = (x_i, \xi_i, \eta_i, y^i) \quad \text{or} \quad \zeta_i = (x_i, y^i) \tag{7}$$

instead. Then

$$\begin{aligned} p_{\phi^i}(x_{i+1}, \xi_{i+1}, \eta_{i+1}, y^{i+1} \mid x^i, \xi^i, \eta^i, y^i) \\ = p(x_{i+1} \mid x_i, \xi_i, u_i = \phi_i(y^i))\, p(\xi_{i+1})\, p(\eta_{i+1}) \\ \times p(y_{i+1} \mid x_{i+1}, \eta_{i+1}) \end{aligned}$$

and

$$p_{\phi^i}(\zeta_{i+1} \mid \zeta^i) = p_{\phi_i}(\zeta_{i+1} \mid \zeta_i) \tag{8}$$

and $\{\zeta_i\}$ becomes a first-order Markov sequence. Since the dimension of ζ_i grows with i, this process is not a conventional Markov sequence. One way to avoid the growing state vectors will be discussed later for problems with sufficient statistics.

As another example of constructing a first-order Markov sequence $\{\zeta_i\}$, consider the system of (4) again, this time assuming that the distribution of noises ξ and η contain unknown parameters θ_1 and θ_2, respectively. The random noises are still assumed all independent. Then, we can no longer compute $p(x_{i+1}, y_{i+1} \mid x_i, y_i)$ since $p(x_{i+1} \mid x_i, u_i)$ is a function of θ_1 and $p(y_{i+1} \mid x_{i+1})$ contains θ_2, which are both assumed unknown, i.e., $\{(x_i, y_i)\}$ is no longer Markovian even with Assumption Y.* Consider instead

$$\zeta_i = (x_i, \xi_i, \eta_i, \theta_{1i}, \theta_{2i}, y_i)$$

where

$$\begin{aligned} \theta_{1i} &= \theta_1 \\ \theta_{2i} &= \theta_2, \qquad i = 0, 1, \ldots, N-1 \end{aligned}$$

Then

$$\begin{aligned} p_{\phi^i}(x_{i+1}, \xi_{i+1}, \eta_{i+1}, \theta_{1,i+1}, \theta_{2,i+1}, y_{i+1} \mid x^i, \xi^i, \theta_1{}^i, \theta_2{}^i, y^i) \\ = p(x_{i+1} \mid x_i, \xi_i, u_i = \phi_i(y_i))\, p(\xi_{i+1} \mid \theta_1) \\ \times p(\eta_{i+1} \mid \theta_2)\, \delta(\theta_{1,i+1} - \theta_1)\, \delta(\theta_{2,i+1} - \theta_2) \\ \times p(y_{i+1} \mid x_{i+1}, \eta_{i+1}) \\ = \delta(x_{i+1} - F_i)\, p(\xi_{i+1} \mid \theta_1)\, p(\eta_{i+1} \mid \theta_2) \\ \times \delta(\theta_{1,i+1} - \theta_1)\, \delta(\theta_{2,i+1} - \theta_2)\, \delta(y_{i+1} - G_{i+1}) \end{aligned}$$

---

* It is conditionally Markovian in the sense that

$$p(x_{i+1}, y_{i+1} \mid x^i, y^i, \theta_1, \theta_2) = p(x_{i+1}, y_{i+1} \mid x_i, y_i, \theta_1, \theta_2).$$

This fact may be used advantageously in some cases.

which is computable again knowing ζ_i with Assumption Y, hence $\{\zeta_i\}$ is Markovian with Assumption Y.

Also, as indicated in connection with (3) in the previous section, if we change the independence assumption on ξ's and η's, then $\{(x_i, y_i)\}$ is no longer Markovian even if the noise distributions are assumed known. For example, assume that ξ's and η's are the first-order Markov sequences, and $\{\xi\}$-process is independent of $\{\eta\}$-process. Assume that $p(\xi_{i+1} \mid \xi_i)$ and $p(\eta_{i+1} \mid \eta_i)$ are known. Then, in (6), $p(x_{i+1} \mid x_i, u_i)$ is not known since ξ_i is not given; $p(y_{i+1} \mid x_{i+1})$ is unknown because η_{i+1} is not known. The augmented state vector ζ_i, where

$$\zeta_i = (x_i, \xi_i, \eta_i, y_i)$$

still forms a Markov sequence, however, with Assumption Y. This is seen by

$$\begin{aligned} p_{\phi^i}(x_{i+1}, \xi_{i+1}, \eta_{i+1}, y_{i+1} \mid x^i, \xi^i, \eta^i, y^i) &= p(x_{i+1} \mid x_i, \xi_i, u_i)\, p(\xi_{i+1} \mid \xi_i) \\ &\quad \times p(\eta_{i+1} \mid \eta_i)\, p(y_{i+1} \mid x_{i+1}, \eta_{i+1}) \end{aligned}$$

B. Problems with Sufficient Statistics

In all the examples discussed so far in this chapter, Assumption Y is used to guarantee that u_i is a function of y_i and not of y^i so that a first-order Markov sequence $\{\zeta_i\}$ can be constructed by augmenting y_i and not y^i. Now we consider the possibility of replacing y^i by some sufficient statistics. We have seen in previous chapters that u_i is generally a function of y^i and not just of y_i. This dependence of u_i on y^i occurs through $p(\cdot \mid y^i)$ in computing λ_{i+1}. Intuitively speaking, if sufficient statistics, s_i, exist so that $p(x_{i+1} \mid y^i) = p(x_{i+1} \mid s_i)$, where s_i is some function of s_{i-1}, y_i, and possibly of u_{i-1}, then the dependence of u_i on past observation is summarized by s_i. By augmenting the observed portion of the state vector with the addition of s_i, say

$$\zeta_i = (x_i, \xi_i, \eta_i, y_i, s_i)$$

$\{\zeta\}$-process may become Markovian even without Assumption Y. In order to make this more precise, consider a situation where the conditional density of x_{i+1}, given x_i, θ, and any control u_i, is known, where θ is a random parameter in a known parameter space Θ. That is, it is assumed that

$$p(x_{i+1} \mid x_i, u_i, \theta), \qquad \theta \in \Theta$$

is given, that the observation noise random variables are independent among themselves and of all other random variables, and that $p(y_i \mid x_i)$ is known completely. θ and x_0 are assumed to be independent. Denote their a priori probability density functions by $p_0(\theta)$ and $p_0(x_0)$, respectively.

Such dependence of the conditional density x_{i+1} on θ may arise either through the unknown system parameter θ in the plant equation or through the plant noises whose probability distribution function contains θ. This dependence on θ can occur, for example, for a system with the plant equation

$$x_{i+1} = a(\theta)\, x_i + b(\theta)\, u_i + \xi_i$$

where a and b are known functions of θ and where the ξ_i are serially independent and have a known probability density, or for a system described by

$$x_{i+1} = ax_i + u_i + \xi_i$$

where a is a known constant and ξ's are independently and identically distributed with a probability density $p(\xi_i \mid \theta)$, $\theta \in \Theta$.

We know from Chapter III that, in order to find an optimal u_i, we need the expression for

$$\begin{aligned}\lambda_i &= E(W_i \mid y^{i-1}) \\ &= \int W_i(x_i\,, u_{i-1})\, p(x_i \mid y^{i-1})\, dx_i \\ &= \int W_i(x_i\,, u_{i-1})\, p(x_i \mid x_{i-1}\,, u_{i-1}\,, \theta)\, p(\theta, x_{i-1} \mid y^{i-1})\, d(x_{i-1}\,, x_i\,, \theta) \qquad (9)\end{aligned}$$

where $p(\theta, x_{i-1} \mid y^{i-1})$ can be generated recursively as such, or we can write

$$p(\theta, x_{i-1} \mid y^{i-1}) = p(\theta \mid y^{i-1})\, p(x_{i-1} \mid \theta, y^{i-1}) \qquad (10)$$

and obtain $p(\theta \mid y^{i-1})$ and $p(x_{i-1} \mid \theta, y^{i-1})$ by two separate recursion equations.

The sequence of observations $y_0\,, \ldots$ is related to the sequence $x_0\,,$ $x_1\,, \ldots$ through the observation equation. Hence it is assumed that the sequence contains information on θ, i.e., the joint probability density function of y^i and θ is assumed to exist and not identically equal to zero for almost all realization y^i.

Given any control policy, the a posteriori probability density function of θ given y^i is computed from $p_0(\theta)$ by Bayes' rule. Define

$$p_i(\theta) \triangleq p(\theta \mid y^i) = \frac{p_0(\theta)\, p(y^i \mid \theta)}{p(y^i)} \tag{11}$$

Suppose now that a set of sufficient statistics $s_i = s(y^i)$ exists for θ such that it satisfies the equation

$$s_{j+1} = \psi_1(s_j, y_{j+1}, u_j) \tag{12}$$

When a sufficient statistic exists it is known[73] that the probability density of y^i given θ for any control policy can be factored as

$$p(y^i \mid \theta) = f(\theta, s_i)\, g(y^i) \tag{13}$$

A large class of sufficient statistics satisfy Condition (12). For example, consider a class of probability density functions known as the Koopman–Pitman class.[73] The density function of this class has the form

$$p(y \mid \theta) = \exp\{r(\theta)\, K(y) + S(y) + q(\theta)\}, \qquad -\infty < y < \infty$$

where $r(\theta)$ is a nontrivial continuous function of θ, $S(y)$ and $K'(y) \not\equiv 0$ are continuous in y, and $q(\theta)$ is some function of θ. The density of a Gaussian random variable, for example, belongs to this class. Then,

$$\begin{aligned} p(y^i \mid \theta) &= \exp\left[r(\theta) \sum_0^n K(y_i) + \sum_0^n S(y_i) + (n+1)\, q(\theta)\right] \\ &= R\left[\sum_0^n K(y_i)\right] \exp\left[r(\theta) \sum_0^n K(y_i) + (n+1)\, q(\theta)\right] \frac{\exp(\sum_0^n S(y_i))}{R[\sum_0^n K(y_i)]} \end{aligned}$$

where R is a function that arises in the one-to-one transformation defined by

$$z_0 = \sum_0^n K(y_i)$$

$$z_i = y_i, \qquad 1 \leqslant i \leqslant n$$

so that $\sum_0^n K(y_i)$ is seen to be sufficient and is in the form of (12). From (11) and (13), the a posteriori probability density of θ is given by

$$p_i(\theta) = \frac{p_0(\theta)\, f(\theta, s_i)}{\int d\theta\, p_0(\theta)\, f(\theta, s_i)} = p(\theta \mid s_i) \tag{14}$$

Equation (14) shows that $p_i(\theta)$, the ith a posteriori probability density of θ, depends on y^i only through $s(y^i)$ when s is the sufficient statistic for θ. Then (10) becomes

$$p(\theta, x_{i-1} \mid y^{i-1}) = p(\theta \mid s_{i-1})\, p(x_{i-1} \mid \theta, y^{i-1})$$

Therefore, instead of deriving the recursive relation for $p(\theta, x_j \mid y^j)$, one can obtain $p(x_j \mid \theta, y^j)$ recursively. This recursion equation will be generally easier to manage since θ is now assumed known and can be generated in the usual manner. First, write

$$p(x_j, x_{j+1}, y_{j+1} \mid y^j, \theta) = p(x_j \mid y^j, \theta)\, p(x_{j+1} \mid x_j, u_j, \theta)\, p(y_{j+1} \mid x_{j+1})$$

Now

$$\int p(x_j, x_{j+1}, y_{j+1} \mid y^j, \theta)\, dx_j = p(y_{j+1} \mid y^j, \theta)\, p(x_{j+1} \mid y^{j+1}, \theta)$$

Therefore,

$$\begin{aligned} p(x_{j+1} \mid y^{j+1}, \theta) = \int & p(x_j \mid y^j, \theta)\, p(x_{j+1} \mid x_j, u_j, \theta) \\ & \times \frac{p(y_{j+1} \mid x_{j+1})\, dx_j}{\int [\text{numerator}]\, dx_{i+1}} \end{aligned} \tag{15}$$

with

$$\begin{aligned} p(x_0 \mid y_0, \theta) &= \frac{p(x_0, y_0 \mid \theta)}{p(y_0 \mid \theta)} \\ &= \frac{p_0(x_0 \mid \theta)\, p(y_0 \mid x_0, \theta)}{\int p_0(x_0 \mid \theta)\, p(y_0 \mid x_0, \theta)\, dx_0} \\ &= \frac{p_0(x_0)\, p(y_0 \mid x_0)}{\int p_0(x_0)\, p(y_0 \mid x_0)\, dx_0} \end{aligned}$$

Suppose that (15) is such that another sufficient statistic t_i exists such that $p(x_j \mid \theta, y^j) = p(x_j \mid \theta, t_j)$, where t_{j+1} is a function of t_j, y_{j+1}, and u_j, and that $t_{j+1} = \psi_2(t_j, y_{j+1}, u_j)$. Then, (9) shows that λ_i will be a function of u_{i-1}, s_{i-1}, and t_{i-1}. To show that γ_i also depends at most on u_{i-1}, s_{i-1}, t_{i-1}, and on y_{i-1}, we must next investigate the functional dependence of $E(\gamma_{i+1}^* \mid y^{i-1})$. We know from the above augument that

$$\gamma_N = \lambda_N(u_{N-1}, s_{N-1}, t_{N-1})$$

and therefore

$$u_{N-1}^* = \phi_{N-1}(s_{N-1}, t_{N-1})$$

Then, $\gamma_N{}^*$ will be a function of s_{N-1} and t_{N-1}. In computing γ_{N-1}, we need

$$E(\gamma_N{}^* \mid y^{N-2}) = \int \gamma_N{}^* p(s_{N-1}, t_{N-1} \mid y^{N-2}) \, dy_{N-1}$$

where

$$s_{N-1} = \psi_1(s_{N-2}, y_{N-1}, u_{N-2})$$

and

$$t_{N-1} = \psi_2(t_{N-2}, y_{N-1}, u_{N-2})$$

by assumption. Now

$$\begin{aligned} p(y_{N-1} \mid y^{N-2}) &= \int p(y_{N-1} \mid x_{N-1}) \, p(x_{N-1} \mid x_{N-2}, u_{N-1}, \theta) \\ &\qquad \times p(\theta, x_{N-2} \mid y^{N-2}) \, d(x_{N-1}, x_{N-2}, \theta) \\ &= \int p(y_{N-1} \mid x_{N-1}) \, p(x_{N-1} \mid x_{N-2}, u_{N-2}, \theta) \\ &\qquad \times p(\theta \mid s_{N-2}) \, p(x_{N-2} \mid \theta, t_{N-2}) \, d(x_{N-1}, x_{N-2}, \theta) \end{aligned}$$

Hence $E(\gamma_N{}^* \mid y^{N-2})$ will depend at most on s_{N-2}, t_{N-2}, and on u_{N-2}. By similar reasonings, $E(\gamma_{i+1}^* \mid y^{i-1})$ is seen to depend at most on s_{i-1}, t_{i-1}, and on u_{i-1}. Thus,

$$u_{i-1}^* = \phi_{i-1}(s_{i-1}, t_{i-1}), \qquad 1 \leqslant i \leqslant n$$

To summarize, s_i is the sufficient statistic for θ and t_i is the sufficient statistic for y^i. s_{i+1} and t_{i+1} are computed as known functions of s_i, t_i, u_i, and y_{i+1}. Now we are ready to show that $\{\zeta_i\}$ is a first-order Markov sequence where

$$\zeta_i = (x_i, y_i, t_i, s_i), \qquad 0 \leqslant i \leqslant N-1 \tag{16}$$

This can be shown by computing

$$\begin{aligned} &p(x_{i+1}, y_{i+1}, t_{i+1}, s_{i+1} \mid x^i, y^i, t^i, s^i) \\ &\quad = p(x_{i+1} \mid x^i, y^i, t^i, s^i) \, p(y_{i+1} \mid x_{i+1}) \\ &\qquad \times p(t_{i+1} \mid t_i, y_{i+1}, u_i) \, p(s_{i+1} \mid s_i, y_{i+1}, u_i) \end{aligned}$$

where the assumptions of the dependence of t_{i+1} and s_{i+1} on t_i, s_i, y_{i+1}, and u_i are used. The first factor can be written as

$$p(x_{i+1} \mid x^i, y^i, t^i, s^i) = \int p(x_{i+1} \mid x_i, u_i, \theta) \, p(\theta \mid s_i) \, d\theta$$

since

$$u_i = \phi_i(t_i, s_i)$$

Thus

$$p(\zeta_{i+1} \mid \zeta^i) = p(\zeta_{i+1} \mid \zeta_i)$$

The observed portion of the vector ζ_i is (y_i, t_i, s_i). It can also be shown that $\{\zeta_i\}$, where $\zeta_i = (x_i, \theta_i, y_i, s_i, t_i)$, $\theta_i = \theta$, is also Markovian.

3. Optimal Control Policies

Suppose that $\{\zeta_i\}$-process, where ζ_i is derived by augmenting (x_i, y_i) appropriately, is a first-order Markov sequence with a known transition probability density function. In the previous section several ways of constructing such ζ's are discussed.

Components of the vector ζ_i can usually be grouped into two classes, one group consisting of components not observed and not available for control signal synthesis, the other group consisting of known (vector) functions of components observed and stored by the controller. Denote them by μ_i and ν_i, respectively,

$$\zeta_i = (\mu_i, \nu_i)$$

Therefore, μ_i contains some function of x_i among others and ν_i contains some function of y^i.* For example, if $\zeta_i = (x_i, \xi_i, \eta_i, y_i)$, then $\mu_i = (x_i, \xi_i, \eta_i)$ and $\nu_i = y_i$. The available data at time i to the controller is ν^i, and u_i is to be determined by choosing ϕ_i where

$$u_i = \phi_i(u^{i-1}, \nu^i)$$

a. *Last Stage*

Let us determine u_{N-1}^*, assuming $u_0^*, \ldots, u_{N-2}^*$ have been already chosen. $E(W_N)$ is minimized by minimizing $E(W_N \mid \nu^{N-1})$ for every possible ν^{N-1}. Now, as a function of u_{N-1},

$$\begin{aligned} E(W_N \mid \nu^{N-1}) &= \int W_N(x_N, u_{N-1})\, p(x_N, u_{N-1} \mid \nu^{N-1})\, d(x_N, u_{N-1}) \\ &= \int W_N(x_N, u_{N-1})\, p(u_{N-1} \mid \nu^{N-1})\, p(x_N \mid u_{N-1}, \nu^{N-1})\, d(x_N, u_{N-1}) \\ &= \int W_N(x_N, u_{N-1})\, p(u_{N-1} \mid \nu^{N-1})\, p(\mu_N \mid \mu_{N-1}, u_{N-1}, \nu_{N-1}) \\ &\quad \times p(\mu_{N-1} \mid u_{N-1}, \nu^{N-1})\, d(\mu_N, \mu_{N-1}, u_{N-1}) \end{aligned}$$

---

* In some cases it may be convenient to take ζ_i such that both μ_i and ν_i are functions of observed quantities by the controller. See Section 5 for examples.

assuming $p(\mu_{N-1} \mid \nu^{N-1}, u_{N-1})$ is available. The density $p(\mu_N \mid \mu_{N-1}, \nu_{N-1}, u_{N-1})$ is computed from the known transition density $p(\mu_N, \nu_N \mid \mu_{N-1}, \nu_{N-1}, u_{N-1})$.

Following the line of reasoning in Chapters II and III, one sees that the nonrandomized control is optimal, and is given by

$$p^*(u_{N-1} \mid \nu^{N-1}) = \delta(u_{N-1} - u_{N-1}^*)$$

where u_{N-1}^* minimizes λ_N,

$$\lambda_N(u_{N-1}, \nu^{N-1}) \triangleq \int W_N(x_N, u_{N-1})\, p(\mu_N \mid \mu_{N-1}, u_{N-1}, \nu_{N-1}) \times p(\mu_{N-1} \mid u_{N-1}, \nu^{N-1})\, d(\mu_N, \mu_{N-1})$$

Define

$$\gamma_N^*(\nu^{N-1}) = \min_{u_{N-1}} \lambda_N$$

b. *Last Two Stages*

Next determine u_{N-2}^* in such a way that when followed by u_{N-1}^* it minimizes $E(W_{N-1} + W_N \mid \nu^{N-2})$ for every ν^{N-2}, assuming $u_0^*, \ldots, u_{N-3}^*$ have been determined. As before,

$$E(W_{N-1} \mid \nu^{N-2}) = \int \lambda_{N-1}(u_{N-2}, \nu^{N-2})\, p(u_{N-2} \mid u_{N-2}, \nu^{N-2})\, du_{N-2}$$

assuming $p(\mu_{N-2} \mid u_{N-2}, \nu^{N-2})$ is known. Since

$$E(W_N \mid \nu^{N-2}) = E[E(W_N \mid \nu^{N-1}) \mid \nu^{N-2}]$$

$$\min_{u_{N-2}} E[(W_{N-1} + W_N \mid \nu^{N-2})]_{u_{N-1}^*} = \int [\lambda_{N-1}(u_{N-2}, \nu^{N-2}) + \int \gamma_N^*(\nu^{N-1})\, p(\nu_{N-1} \mid u_{N-2}, \nu^{N-2}) \times d\nu_{N-1}]\, p(u_{N-2} \mid \nu^{N-2})\, du_{N-2}$$

Defining

$$\gamma_{N-1} = \lambda_{N-1} + \int \gamma_N^*\, p(\nu_{N-1} \mid u_{N-2}, \nu^{N-2})\, d\nu_{N-1}$$

where $p(\nu_{N-1} \mid u_{N-2}, \nu^{N-2})$ is assumed known, the optimal control at time $N - 2$, u_{N-2}^*, is found by

$$\gamma_{N-1}^* \triangleq \min_{u_{N-2}} \gamma_{N-1}$$

and the optimal control is given as

$$p^*(u_{N-2} \mid \nu^{N-2}) = \delta(u_{N-2} - u^*_{N-2})$$

c. *General Case*

Generally u^*_{k-1} is found by minimizing γ_k where

$$\lambda_k \triangleq \int W_k(x_k, u_{k-1})\, p(\mu_k \mid \mu_{k-1}, \nu_{k-1}, u_{k-1})\, p(\mu_{k-1} \mid \nu^{k-1}, u_{k-1})\, d(\mu_k, \mu_{k-1})$$

$$\gamma_k \triangleq \lambda_k + \int \gamma^*_{k+1}\, p(\nu_k \mid u_{k-1}, \nu^{k-1})\, d\nu_k, \qquad k = 1, \ldots, N \tag{17}$$

$$\gamma_k{}^* = \min_{u_{k-1}} \gamma_k$$

where $p(\mu_{k-1} \mid u_{k-1}, \nu^{k-1})$ and $p(\nu_k \mid u_{k-1}, \nu^{k-1})$ are assumed known. We see that the optimal control policies are obtainable if $p(\mu_k \mid u_k, \nu^k)$ and $p(\nu_{k+1} \mid u_k, \nu^k)$, $k = 0, \ldots, N-1$, are known.

Therefore, our attention is next turned to computing these conditional probability density functions. Here, it should be pointed out that this approach may be computationally advantageous even when $\{x_k\}$ and $\{y_k\}$ are Markovian by themselves.

4. Derivation of Conditional Probability Densities

It is not generally true that $\{\nu_k\}$ itself is Markovian even though $\{\zeta_k\}$ is. We want to compute the conditional probability densities of parts of the components of a multidimensional Markov sequence conditioned on components that are observed. We assume that the a priori probability density of ζ_0,

$$p_0(\zeta_0) = p_0(\mu_0, \nu_0) \tag{18}$$

is given. Let us now obtain the recursion equation for $p(\mu_i \mid \nu^i)$ and $p(\nu_{i+1} \mid \nu^i)$. By now, the method of obtaining such a recursion relation should be routine for us. We consider

$$p(\mu_i, \mu_{i+1}, \nu_{i+1} \mid \nu^i)$$

By the chain rule, we can write it as

$$\begin{aligned} p(\mu_i, \mu_{i+1}, \nu_{i+1} \mid \nu^i) &= p(\mu_i \mid \nu^i)\, p(\mu_{i+1}, \nu_{i+1} \mid \mu_i, \nu^i) \\ &= p(\mu_i \mid \nu^i)\, p(\mu_{i+1}, \nu_{i+1} \mid \mu_i, \nu_i) \end{aligned}$$

where the last line is obtained from the Markovian property of $\{\zeta_i\}$.

Integrating both sides with respect to μ_i, we have

$$p(\mu_{i+1}, \nu_{i+1} \mid \nu^i) = p(\nu_{i+1} \mid \nu^i)\, p(\mu_{i+1} \mid \nu^{i+1})$$
$$= \int p(\mu_i \mid \nu^i)\, p(\mu_{i+1}, \nu_{i+1} \mid \mu_i, \nu_i)\, d\mu_i$$

Therefore,

$$p(\mu_{i+1} \mid \nu^{i+1}) = \frac{\int p(\mu_i \mid \nu^i)\, p(\mu_{i+1}, \nu_{i+1} \mid \mu_i, \nu_i)\, d\mu_i}{\int [\text{numerator}]\, d\mu_{i+1}} \tag{19}$$

and the denominator gives $p(\nu_{i+1} \mid \nu^i)$.

5. Examples

A. System with Unknown Random Time Constant

Let us rework Example a of Chapter III, Section 3,B, by another method, using the idea of the augmented state vector.

The system equations are given by (88) and (91) of Chapter III.

We know from our previous investigation of this example that a sufficient statistic exists for θ:

$$p(\theta \mid x^k, u^{k-1}) = p(\theta \mid s_k, \sigma_{\theta,k})$$
$$= \frac{1}{(2\pi)^{1/2}\sigma_{\theta,k}} \exp\left(-\frac{(\theta - s_k)^2}{2\sigma^2_{\theta,k}}\right) \tag{20}$$

From (107) and (108) of Chapter III, we can identify s_k with μ_{k-1} and $\sigma_{\theta,k}$ with Σ_{k-1}. With this identification of the sufficient statistics, they are seen to satisfy the recursion equation:

$$s_{j+1} = \frac{\sigma^2_{\theta,j+1}}{\sigma^2} a_j + \frac{\sigma^2_{\theta,j+1}}{\sigma^2_{\theta,j}} s_j \tag{21}$$

$$\frac{1}{\sigma^2_{\theta,j+1}} = \frac{1}{\sigma^2_{\theta,j}} + \frac{1}{\sigma^2} \tag{22}$$

$$s_0 = \theta_0 \qquad \sigma^2_{\theta,0} = {\sigma_0}^2 \tag{23}$$

or

$$\sigma^2_{\theta,j} \triangleq {\sigma_0}^2\sigma^2/(\sigma^2 + j{\sigma_0}^2)$$

and

$$s_j = \frac{\sigma_0{}^2 \sum_0^{j-1} (x_{i+1} - bu_i/x_i) + \sigma^2 \theta_0}{\sigma^2 + j\sigma_0{}^2}$$

Note that $(x_{i+1} - bu_i)/x_i = a_i$ in (21), showing that the value the random variable takes at time i is exactly computable because of no measurement errors. The same comment found in Example b, Section 4,B of Chapter III, applies when $x_i = 0$ for some i.

Since s_k summarizes all the information contained in x^k about θ, from our discussion in Section 2,B, it is seen that controls u_k depending on s_k and x_k are just as good as controls depending on x^k.

Therefore, we consider the class of nonrandomized control policies such that

$$u_i = \phi_i(x_i, s_i), \qquad 0 \leqslant i \leqslant N-1 \tag{24}$$

Define

$$\zeta_i' = (x_i, s_i) \tag{25}$$

Therefore, the augmented state vector ζ_j obeys the augmented plant equation

$$\zeta_{j+1} = \begin{pmatrix} a_j & 0 \\ 0 & \dfrac{\sigma^2_{\theta,j+1}}{\sigma^2_{\theta,j}} \end{pmatrix} \zeta_j + \begin{pmatrix} bu_j \\ \dfrac{\sigma^2_{\theta,j+1}}{\sigma_2{}^2} \quad a_j \end{pmatrix} \tag{26}$$

Since u_j depends only on x_j and s_j and since a_j is mutually independent, (26) shows that $\{\zeta_j\}$ is a first-order Markov chain. This is rather a special case where $\mu_i = x_i$ and $\nu_i = s_i$, i.e., every component of ζ_i is observed.

Its transition probability density is given by

$$p(x_{j+1}, s_{j+1} \mid x_j, s_j, u_j) = p(x_{j+1} \mid x_j, s_j, u_j)\, p(s_{j+1} \mid x_{j+1}, x_j, s_j, u_j) \tag{27}$$

The right-hand side of (28) is computable since

$$\begin{aligned} p(x_{j+1} \mid x_j, s_j, u_j) &= \int p(x_{j+1} \mid x_j, s_j, u_j, \theta)\, p(\theta \mid x_j, s_j, u_j)\, d\theta \\ &= \int p(x_{j+1} \mid x_j, u_j, \theta)\, p(\theta \mid s_j)\, d\theta \end{aligned} \tag{28}$$

where $p(\theta \mid s_j)$ is given by (20). From (21),

$$p(s_{j+1} \mid x_{j+1}, x_j, s_j, u_j) = \delta\left[s_{j+1} - \left(\frac{\sigma^2_{\theta,j+1}}{\sigma^2_{\theta,j}} s_j + \frac{\sigma^2_{\theta,j+1}}{\sigma^2}\left(\frac{x_{j+1} - bu_j}{x_i}\right)\right)\right] \tag{29}$$

An optimal control policy for the problem is now computed using (17). We first compute λ_N by

$$\begin{aligned}\lambda_N &= E(x_N{}^2 \mid x^{N-1}) \\ &= E(x_N{}^2 \mid x_{N-1}, s_{N-1}) \\ &= \int x_N{}^2 \, p(x_N, s_N \mid x_{N-1}, s_{N-1}, u_{N-1}) \, d(x_N, s_N) \\ &= \int x_N{}^2 \, p(x_N \mid x_{N-1}, u_{N-1}, \theta) \, p(\theta \mid s_{N-1}) \, d(x_N, \theta)\end{aligned} \tag{30}$$

From the plant equation (88) of Chapter III and the probability density function of a_i ((89) of Chapter III), $p(x_N \mid x_{N-1}, u_{N-1}, \theta)$ is Gaussian with mean $\theta x_{N-1} + bu_{N-1}$ and variance $\sigma^2 x_{N-1}^2$. Therefore,

$$\begin{aligned}\lambda_N &= \int [(\theta x_{N-1} + bu_{N-1})^2 + \sigma^2 x_{N-1}^2] \, p(\theta \mid s_{N-1}) \, d\theta \\ &= (s_{N-1} x_{N-1} + bu_{N-1})^2 + x_{N-1}^2(\sigma^2 + \sigma_{\theta,N-1}^2)\end{aligned} \tag{31}$$

Therefore,

$$u_{N-1}^* = -s_{N-1} x_{N-1}/b \tag{32}$$

and

$$\gamma_N{}^* = (\sigma^2 + \sigma_{\theta,N-1}^2) x_{N-1}^2 \tag{33}$$

Since this is a final-value problem,

$$\lambda_i = 0, \qquad i = 1, \ldots, N - 1 \tag{34}$$

and

$$\begin{aligned}\gamma_{N-1} &= \int \gamma_N{}^* \, p(x_{N-1}, s_{N-1} \mid x_{N-2}, s_{N-2}, u_{N-2}) \, d(x_{N-1}, s_{N-1}) \\ &= (\sigma^2 + \sigma_{\theta,N-1}^2) \int x_{N-1}^2 \, p(x_{N-1} \mid x_{N-2}, s_{N-2}, u_{N-2}) \, dx_{N-1}\end{aligned} \tag{35}$$

Comparing (35) with (30), we see immediately that, aside from the multiplicative constant factor, minimization of λ_N with respect to u_{N-1} is identical to that of γ_{N-1} with respect to u_{N-2}. Therefore,

$$u_{N-2}^* = -s_{N-2} x_{N-2}/b$$

or, in general,

$$u_i{}^* = -s_i x_i/b, \qquad i = 0, 1, \ldots, N - 1 \tag{36}$$

where s_i is given by (21). Note that, as $\sigma_0{}^2/\sigma_2{}^2 \to 0$, i.e., as our knowledge of the unknown mean θ becomes more precise,

$$s_i \to \theta_0$$

as expected.

B. System with Markovian Gain

Consider a one-dimensional control system described by

$$x_{i+1} = ax_i + b_i u_i\,, \qquad i = 0, 1, \ldots, N-1 \tag{37}$$

where a and x_0 are assumed known. The gain of the system b_i is assumed to form a first-order Markov chain with two possible states,

$$b_i = \begin{cases} \beta_1 \\ \beta_2 \end{cases} \tag{38}$$

with known stationary transition probabilities

$$\Pr[b_{k+1} = \beta_i \mid b_k = \beta_j] \triangleq p_{ij}\,, \qquad i, j = 1, 2$$
$$k = 0, 1, \ldots, N-1 \tag{39}$$

and $\Pr[b_0]$ given. The observations are assumed perfect,

$$y_i = x_i\,, \qquad i = 0, 1, \ldots, N-1 \tag{40}$$

Hence x's are used throughout, instead of y's. The performance index is taken to be

$$J = \sum_1^N (x_i{}^2 + \lambda u_{i-1}^2) \tag{41}$$

Since

$$b_j = \frac{x_{j+1} - ax_j}{u_j} \qquad \text{if} \quad u_j \neq 0$$

the knowledge of x^i implies that the value of b_{i-1} is known. This fact is used to obtain the probability distribution for b_i which we need in evaluating λ_i.*

---

* If $u_{i-1} = 0$ then b_{i-1} is unknown. In this unlikely case, we must work with

$$P(b_i \mid b_{i-2}) = \sum_1^2 P(b_i \mid b_{i-1} = \beta_k) P(b_{i-1} = \beta_k \mid b_{i-2})$$

The augmented state vector for this example can be taken to be

$$\zeta_i = (b_{i-1}, x_i), \qquad i = 1, 2, \ldots, N$$

This example problem is special in that all components of ζ_i are known at time i.*

The fact that $\{\zeta_i\}$ is a first-order Markov sequence is verified by computing the conditional density $P(\zeta_{i+1} \mid \zeta^i)$

$$\begin{aligned} p(\zeta_{i+1} \mid \zeta^i) &= p(b_i, x_{i+1} \mid b^{i-1}, x^i) \\ &= p(b_i \mid b_{i-1}) p(x_{i+1} \mid x_i, u_i, b_i) \\ &= p(\zeta_{i+1} \mid \zeta_i) \end{aligned} \tag{42}$$

assuming $u_i = \phi_i(x_i, b_{i-1})$. We will see shortly that the optimal control variables have the assumed functional dependence.

To derive the optimal control policy, we consider the last control stage first.

Since it is convenient to indicate the dependence of the conditional expectation $E(W_N \mid \zeta_{N-1})$ on the value of b_{N-2}, let us define

$$\begin{aligned} \lambda_{N,k} &\triangleq E(W_N \mid x_{N-1}, b_{N-2} = \beta_k) \\ &= \int (x_N{}^2 + \lambda u_{N-1}^2) P(x_N, b_{N-1} \mid x_{N-1}, b_{N-2} = \beta_k) \, d(x_N, b_{N-1}) \\ &= \sum_{i=1}^{2} \int (x_N{}^2 + \lambda u_{N-1}^2) P(x_N \mid x_{N-1}, b_{N-1} = \beta_i, u_{N-1}) \, p_{ik} \, dx_N \\ &= \sum_{i=1}^{2} [(a x_{N-1} + \beta_i u_{N-1})^2 + \lambda u_{N-1}^2] p_{ik} \end{aligned} \tag{43}$$

Minimizing (43) with respect to u_{N-1}, we obtain the optimal control at time $N - 1$

$$u_{N-1,k}^* = -\Lambda_{N-1,k} x_{N-1}, \qquad k = 1, 2 \tag{44}$$

where

$$\Lambda_{N-1,k} \triangleq \frac{\sum_{i=1}^{2} \beta_i p_{ik}}{\lambda + \sum_{i=1}^{2} \beta_i{}^2 p_{ik}} \, a \tag{45}$$

In the denominator of (45), note that $\sum_{i=1}^{2} \beta_i p_{ik} = E(b_{N-1} \mid b_{N-2} = \beta_k)$. Thus, from (44) and (45) we see that u_{N-1}^* depends on the value of b_{N-2},

* ζ_0 and $p(\zeta_0)$ require an obvious special handling because of $\Pr[b_0]$.

i.e., $u^*_{N-1} = \phi_{N-1}(x_{N-1}, b_{N-2})$ as assumed in connection with (42). Substituting (45) into (43), we obtain

$$\lambda^*_{N,k} \triangleq \min_{u_{N-1}} \lambda_{N,k} = C_{N-1,k} x^2_{N-1} \tag{46}$$

where

$$C_{N-1,k} = a^2\{1 - [E(b_{N-1} \mid b_{N-2} = \beta_k)]^2/[\lambda + E(b^2_{N-1} \mid b_{N-2} = \beta_k)]\}$$

Equation (46) shows that $\lambda_{N,1}$ and $\lambda_{N,2}$ are both quadratic in x_{N-1}. Now we compute the optimal control variable generally. Assume that

$$\gamma^*_{i+1,k} = \min_{u_i,\ldots,u_{N-1}} E\left(\sum_{j=i+1}^{N} W_j \mid x_i, b_{i-1} = \beta_k\right)$$

$$\triangleq C_{i,k} x_i^2, \qquad k = 1, 2, \quad i = 0, 1, \ldots, N-1 \tag{47}$$

By definition,

$$C_{N,k} = 0, \qquad k = 1, 2$$

Then, from (47),

$$\gamma^*_{i,k} = \min_{u_{i-1},\ldots,u_N} E\left(\sum_{j=i}^{N} W_j \mid x_{i+1}, b_{i-2} = \beta_k\right)$$

$$= C_{i-1,k} x^2_{i-1} \tag{48}$$

On the other hand,

$$\gamma^*_{i,k} = \min_{u_{i-1}} \left[\lambda_{i,k} + \sum_{m=1}^{2} E(\gamma^*_{i+1,m} \mid x_{i-1}, b_{i-2} = \beta_k)\right] \tag{49}$$

where

$$\lambda_{i,k} = E(x_i^2 + \lambda u^2_{i-1} \mid x_{i-1}, b_{i-2} = \beta_k)$$

and where

$$\sum_{m=1}^{2} E[\gamma^*_{i+1,m} \mid x_{i-1}, b_{i-2} = \beta_k]$$

$$= \sum_{m=1}^{2} E(C_{i,m} x_i^2 \mid x_{i-1}, b_{i-2} = \beta_k)$$

$$= C_{i,1}(ax_{i-1} + \beta_1 u_{i-1})^2 p_{1k} + C_{i,2}(ax_{i-1} + \beta_2 u_{i-1})^2 p_{2k} \tag{50}$$

Therefore, making use of (50),

$$\gamma_{i,k} = \lambda u_{i-1}^2 + (C_{i,1}+1)p_{1k}(ax_{i-1}+\beta_1 u_{i-1})^2 + (C_{i,2}+1)p_{2k}(ax_{i-1}+\beta_2 u_{i-1})^2, \qquad k = 1, 2 \tag{51}$$

By minimizing (51) with respect to u_{i-1}, we obtain $u_{i-1,k}^*$ to be

$$u_{i-1,k}^* = -\Lambda_{i-1,k} x_{i-1} \tag{52a}$$

where

$$\Lambda_{i-1,k} \triangleq \frac{p_{1k}\beta_1(C_{i,1}+1) + p_{2k}\beta_2(C_{i,2}+1)}{\lambda + p_{1k}\beta_1^2(C_{i,1}+1) + p_{2k}\beta_2^2(C_{i,2}+1)}\, a \tag{52b}$$

where $k = 1$ or 2, depending on $b_{i-2} = \beta_1$ or β_2, respectively. Substituting (52a) into (51), the recursion equation for $C_{j,k}$ is obtained:

$$C_{i-1,k} = a^2 \left\{ 1 + p_{1k}C_{i,1} + p_{2k}C_{2,k} - \frac{[p_{1k}\beta_1(C_{i,1}+1) + p_{2k}\beta_2(C_{i,2}+1)]^2}{\lambda + p_{1k}\beta_1^2(C_{i,1}+1) + p_{2k}\beta_2^2(C_{i,2}+1)} \right\}, \qquad k = 1, 2 \tag{53}$$

Equation (53) can be simplified somewhat by writing it in a vector form. Define

$$C_{i-1} = \begin{pmatrix} C_{i-1,1} \\ C_{i-1,2} \end{pmatrix} \tag{54}$$

Then

$$C_{i-1} = a^2 \begin{pmatrix} 1 \\ 1 \end{pmatrix} + a^2 \begin{pmatrix} p_{11} & p_{21} \\ p_{12} & p_{22} \end{pmatrix} C_i + D_i, \qquad i = 2, 3, \ldots, N \tag{55a}$$

where

$$D_i = \begin{pmatrix} d_{i1}^2/\Delta_{i1} \\ d_{i2}^2/\Delta_{i1} \end{pmatrix} \tag{55b}$$

and where

$$\begin{pmatrix} d_{i,1} \\ d_{i,2} \end{pmatrix} = a \begin{pmatrix} p_{11}\beta_1 & p_{21}\beta_2 \\ p_{12}\beta_1 & p_{22}\beta_2 \end{pmatrix} \left[C_i + a \begin{pmatrix} 1 \\ 1 \end{pmatrix} \right] \tag{55c}$$

$$\begin{pmatrix} \Delta_{i1} \\ \Delta_{i2} \end{pmatrix} = \begin{pmatrix} p_{11}\beta_1^2 & p_{21}\beta_2^2 \\ p_{12}\beta_1^2 & p_{22}\beta_2^2 \end{pmatrix} \left[C_i + \lambda \begin{pmatrix} 1 \\ 1 \end{pmatrix} \right] \tag{55d}$$

Note that the initial vector C_0 must be computed using the a priori probability $\Pr[b_0 = \beta_i]$, $i = 1, 2$, rather than the transition probabilities. From (52b) and (55),

$$\Lambda_{i-1} \triangleq \begin{pmatrix} \Lambda_{i-1,1} \\ \Lambda_{i-1,2} \end{pmatrix} = -\begin{pmatrix} d_{i1}/\Delta_{i1} \\ d_{i2}/\Delta_{i2} \end{pmatrix} \tag{56}$$

Since C's and Λ's can be precomputed, the only operation that the optimal controller must perform on-line at time i is the determination of b_{i-1} to be either β_1 or β_2 by

$$b_{i-1} = \frac{x_i - x_{i-1}}{u_{i-1}}, \qquad i = 1, 2, \ldots, N-1 \tag{57}$$

i.e., $\Pr[b_{i-1} = \beta_k \mid x^i, u^{i-1}] = 1$, where β_k is given by (57). Once $b_{i-1} = \beta_k$ is determined, then $u_i^* = -\Lambda_{i,k} x_i$.

Comment. Instead of the system of (37)–(40), if the system is governed by

$$\begin{aligned} x_{i+1} &= a_i x_i + b u_i \\ y_i &= x_i \end{aligned} \tag{58}$$

where b is now assumed known, and where a_i is such that

$$a_i = \begin{cases} \alpha_1 \\ \alpha_2 \end{cases} \tag{59}$$

$$\Pr[a_{i+1} = \alpha_j \mid a_i = \alpha_k] \triangleq p_{jk} \qquad \text{for all} \quad i = 0, 1, \ldots \tag{60}$$

then the optimization problem of the above system with respect to the performance index

$$J = \sum_1^N (x_i^2 + \lambda u_i^2)$$

can be similarly carried out.

Next consider the same plant equation (37), the Markov parameter (38), and the performance index (41) with *noisy* observation

$$y_i = x_i + \eta_i$$

The previous development has shown that, if the properties of the noise are such that if the values of b_i can be determined exactly from y^{i+1} and u^i, namely

$$\Pr[b_i = \beta_k \mid y^{i+1}, u^i] = 1 \tag{61}$$

for $k = 1$ or 2, then the previously derived optimal control policy is still optimal for this modified noisy observation problem. When (61) is not true, however, then the above policy will no longer be optimal. The reader is invited to rework this example by suitably defining an augmented state vector.

C. Discrete-State Stochastic System

Consider a three-stage discrete-state, discrete-time, stochastic control process whose state at time i is denoted by x_i and the observation of x_i at time i is given by y_i. It is given that x_i is either a_1 or a_2, and y_i is either b_1 or b_2. The criterion of control is to minimize the expected value of

$$J = | x_1 - a_1 | + | x_2 - a_1 | + u_0^2 + u_1^2$$

where

$$x_{i+1} = F_i(u_i , u_i , \xi_i)$$

$$y_i = G_i(x_i , \eta_i), \qquad i = 0, 1, 2$$

ξ_i and η_i are some noise processes. The control u_i is assumed to take on only two values, 0 and m.

The vector $\zeta_i = (x_i , y_i)$ is assumed to be a Markov chain with known stationary transition probabilities, given u_i. The initial probabilities of ζ_0 are also assumed known.

Since this example deals with discrete-state variables, the developments in the main body of the chapter must be modified in an obvious way to deal with probabilities rather than probability densities. Such modifications will be made without further comments.

Four possible states of ζ_0 are labeled as follows:

$$c_1 = (a_1 , b_1),$$
$$c_2 = (a_2 , b_1)$$
$$c_3 = (a_1 , b_2),$$
$$c_4 = (a_2 , b_2)$$

Given

$$\text{Prob}(\zeta_0 = c_i) = g_i , \qquad 1 \leqslant i \leqslant 4$$

where

$$g_1 = 0.45,$$
$$g_2 = 0.05$$
$$g_3 = 0.1,$$
$$g_4 = 0.4$$

and the stationary transition probabilities

$$g_{ij}(u) = \text{Prob}(\zeta_{k+1} = c_i \mid \zeta_k = c_j , u), \qquad k = 0, 1$$

where

$$p(0) = (g_{ij}(0)) = \begin{pmatrix} 0.4 & 0.05 & 0.5 & 0.05 \\ 0.1 & 0.35 & 0 & 0.55 \\ 0.45 & 0 & 0.45 & 0.1 \\ 0.05 & 0.6 & 0.05 & 0.3 \end{pmatrix}$$

and

$$p(m) = (g_{ij}(m)) = \begin{pmatrix} 0.05 & 0.4 & 0.05 & 0.5 \\ 0.5 & 0 & 0.45 & 0.05 \\ 0.05 & 0.55 & 0 & 0.4 \\ 0.4 & 0.05 & 0.5 & 0.05 \end{pmatrix}$$

it is desired to find the optimal sequence of control (u_0, u_1).

Suppose a particular realization of η_i is such that $y_0 = b_1$ and $y_1 = b_2$ are observed at times 0 and 1. Let us now obtain an optimal u_1. Let

$$\gamma_2{}^*(y^1, u_0) = \min_{u_1} E(|x_2 - a_1| + u_1{}^2 \mid y^1, u_0)$$

Define

$$w_0(a_i) = \text{Prob}(x_0 = a_i \mid y_0)$$

Then, since $y_0 = b_1$,

$$w_0(a_i) = \frac{p(a_i, b_1)}{p(a_1, b_1) + p(a_2, b_1)}$$

or

$$w_0(a_1) = \frac{0.45}{0.45 + 0.05} = 0.9$$

$$w_0(a_2) = \frac{0.05}{0.45 + 0.05} = 0.1$$

Let us define

$$w_1(a_i \mid u) = \text{Prob}(x_1 = a_i \mid y^1, u), \qquad i = 1, 2$$

The transition probabilities for x are given by

$$\text{Prob}(x_1 = a_1 \mid x_0 = a_1, u_0) = \text{Prob}(\zeta_1 = c_3 \mid \zeta_0 = c_1, u_0) = g_{31}(u)$$

etc. Therefore,

$$w_1(a_1 \mid u) = \frac{g_{31}(u)\, w_0(a_1) + g_{32}(u)\, w_0(a_2)}{(g_{31}(u) + g_{41}(u))\, w_0(a_1) + (g_{32}(u) + g_{42}(u))\, w_0(a_2)}$$

and

$$w_1(a_2 \mid u) = \frac{g_{41}(u)\, w_0(a_1) + g_{42}(u)\, w_0(a_2)}{(g_{31}(u) + g_{41}(u))\, w_0(a_1) + (g_{32}(u) + g_{42}(u))\, w_0(a_2)}$$

Thus,

$$\gamma_2{}^*(y^1, u_0 = 0) = \min_u \left\{ \sum_{x_1, \zeta_2} (| x_2 - a_1 | + u^2)\, p(\zeta_2 \mid \zeta_1)\, w_1(x_1 \mid 0) \right\}$$

and

$$\gamma_2{}^*(y^1, u_0 = m) = \min_u \left\{ \sum_{x_1, \zeta_2} (| x_2 - a_1 | + u^2)\, p(\zeta_2 \mid \zeta_1)\, w_1(x_1 \mid m) \right\}$$

where the summation over x_1 and ζ_2 ranges over all possible x_1 and ζ_2 states. Since $\zeta_1 = (x_1 , b_2)$, defining $d = | a_2 - a_1 |$,

$$\gamma_2{}^*(y', u_0 = 0) = \min \left\{ \begin{array}{l} d[(g_{23}(0) + g_{43}(0))\, w_1(a_1 \mid 0) \\ \qquad + (g_{24}(0) + g_{44}(0))\, w_1(a_2 \mid 0)], \\ m^2[(g_{13}(m) + g_{33}(m))\, w_1(a_1 \mid 0) \\ \qquad + (g_{14}(m) + g_{34}(m))\, w_1(a_2 \mid 0)] \\ \qquad + (d + m^2)[(g_{23}(m) + g_{43}(m))\, w_1(a_1 \mid 0) \\ \qquad + (g_{24}(m) + g_{44}(m))\, w_1(a_2 \mid 0)] \end{array} \right\}$$

A similar expression for $\gamma_2{}^*(y^1,\ u_0 = m)$ is obtained by replacing $w_1(a_i \mid 0)$ with $w_1(a_i \mid m)$. In performing numerical calculations, the optimal u_1, when $u_0 = 0$ and (b_1 , b_2) have been observed, is given by

$$u_1(y^1, u_0 = 0) = 0$$

and

$$\begin{aligned} u_1(y_1, u_0 = m) &= 0 \qquad \text{if} \quad d < 3.6\, m^2 \\ &= m \qquad \text{if} \quad d > 3.6\, m^2 \end{aligned}$$

Chapter V

Problem of Estimation

We have discussed in Chapters II–IV optimal Bayesian control policies for discrete-time dynamic systems under a wide variety of assumptions on plant equations, observation equations, system parameters, and on random noises.

In this chapter, we consider the problems of estimation and discuss three principal methods of estimation; the least-squares, maximum-likelihood, and Bayesian estimators are discussed for both linear and nonlinear systems. Their interrelations are also indicated.

Not only are the estimation (or identification) problems of interest on their own merits, but also they are of inherent interest as a part of over-all system optimization problems. We have noted that for a limited class of systems the optimal control problems naturally separate into two subproblems: one is the construction of the optimal estimators of state vectors or unknown parameters, and the other is the synthesis of optimal controllers. For this class of systems, therefore, the over-all optimal control schemes are optimal estimators followed by optimal controllers. For a much larger class of control problems, however, the over-all optimization requirements do not permit such a convenient and simplifying separation of the estimation processes from the control processes. For such a class of problems this separation of problems affords initial approximate solutions to the original control problems which may be improved upon if desired.

Such approximation schemes are important in practice. As we have seen in the previous chapters the sets of equations resulting from the formulations of the over-all control system optimization problems in many cases are often too complex to permit exact analytical solutions in closed forms. We must consider approximate solutions of the optimization equations and approximate implementations of optimal control policies for the theory of optimal control to be useful in many practical problems. There are many such approximations. We have mentioned approximations arising from the separations of estimation problems from the over-all control optimal problems with possibly further approximations being introduced in estimation and/or control subproblems.

In Chapter VII we discuss some of the techniques of approximation in control problems plus a few topics on approximate estimation schemes.

1. Least-Squares Estimation

A. Introduction

The method of least squares will be discussed first. One advantage of the method of least squares is that the method does not make explicit assumptions on various statistical properties of random variables involved. We need not know what the noise covariance matrices are so long as they exist in order to construct the least-squares estimators.

We will show later that when noises are Gaussian and plant and observation equations are linear, the results obtained from the method of least squares with appropriate weights agree with those obtainable from maximum likelihood methods, or Bayesian methods.

The subject of the least-squares estimation is an ancient one and there are many ways of introducing the subject of this section.[71a,101] We will use the techniques of dynamic programming and invariant imbedding of R. Bellman.[20] The developments in this chapter are also based in part on a work of Ho and Lee.[72,100]

B. Static System

There are numerous problems involving both static or dynamic systems which are amenable to the method of least squares. We will examine one static problem in some detail. The examination of this particular problem will lead us naturally to the least-squares estimation procedures for state vectors of dynamic systems.

Suppose that we have an equation connecting an observable variable y to some variable or parameter x of a system or of some physical material, say

$$Hx = y \tag{1}$$

where H is a known $m \times n$ matrix, x is an n vector, and y is an m vector.

It is desired to solve (1) for x in terms of H and y. If the observation is exact and if H is invertible, or if the matrix H has rank n (this implies $m \geqslant n$), then one can determine x exactly from one observation y:

$$x = (H'H)^{-1}H'y$$

When either or both of these assumptions are not valid, say $m < n$ and/or y contains observation noise, then one may decide to make a number of observations $y_0, y_1, \ldots, y_k$ on x and choose x which satisfies (1) with $y_0, \ldots, y_k$ in a sense that the sum of the squares of the errors (residuals) are minimized.* With this as a motivation, let us discuss the way of choosing an optimal x from a set of noisy observation data where

$$y_i = H_i x + (\text{measurement noise}), \qquad i = 0, 1, \ldots \tag{2}$$

in the sense that the chosen x minimizes

$$J_k(x) \triangleq \sum_{i=0}^{k} \| H_i x - y_i \|^2_{V_i} \tag{3}$$

where V_i is an $m \times m$ symmetric positive matrix and acts as a weight for different y_i. This implies that we have some idea of the relative magnitudes of the random noises involved, otherwise V may be taken to be the identity matrix. J_k is the criterion function of the estimation problem. The optimal x will be determined sequentially so that one need not re-solve the least-squares problems from the beginning when new observation becomes available.

From (3), one readily sees that

$$J_{k+1}(x) = J_k(x) + \| H_{k+1}x - y_{k+1} \|^2_{V_{k+1}} \tag{4}$$

Denote by x_k^* the optimal x of (3), that is

$$J_k(x_k^*) \leqslant J_k(x) \tag{5}$$

for any x in the Euclidean n space. From (5) and (3), by considering $x = x_k^* + \Delta x$, we obtain the equation x_k^* satisfies:

$$\Delta x' \sum_{i=0}^{k} H_i' V_i (H_i x_k^* - y_i) = 0 \tag{6}$$

for any Δx in the Euclidean n space.†

* There is a close relation between the concept of pseudoinverse[142] of H, its sequential determination and the method of least squares.

† This condition is called the orthogonality principle.[85,86,109b] Note that Δx is a linear function of y^k.

Let us write

$$x_{k+1}^* = x_k^* + \Delta x_{k+1} \tag{7}$$

i.e., the optimal x for J_{k+1} is written as a sum of x_k^*, the optimal x with the data y^k and a correction term due to the additional observation data, y_{k+1}. The correction term can be determined as follows.

From (4) and (7), making use of (6),

$$\begin{aligned} J_{k+1}(x_{k+1}^*) &= J_k(x_k^*) + \sum_{i=0}^{k} (H_i\, \Delta x_{k+1})'\, V_i(H_i\, \Delta x_{k+1}) \\ &\quad + \|(H_{k+1}x_k^* - y_{k+1} + H_{k+1}\, \Delta x_{k+1})\|_{V_{k+1}}^2 \\ &= J_k(x_k^*) + \|(H_{k+1}x_k^* - y_{k+1})\|_{V_{k+1}}^2 \\ &\quad + 2\Delta x_{k+1}'\, H_{k+1}' V_{k+1}(H_{k+1}x_k^* - y_{k+1}) \\ &\quad + \Delta x_{k+1}' \left(\sum_{i=0}^{k+1} H_i' V_i H_i \right) \Delta x_{k+1} \end{aligned} \tag{8}$$

An optimal correction term, Δx_{k+1}, minimizes (8) with respect to Δx_{k+1}. Since (8) is quadratic in the correction term, Δx_{k+1}^* is given by

$$\Delta x_{k+1}^* = -\left(\sum_{i=0}^{k+1} H_i' V_i H_i \right)^+ H_{k+1}'\, V_{k+1}(H_{k+1}x_k^* - y_{k+1}) \tag{9}$$

If the inverse of $(\sum_{i=0}^{k+1} H_i' V_i H_i)$ exists, then the pseudoinverse is to be replaced by the inverse. See Appendix B of Chapter II for derivation. The pseudoinverses are discussed in Appendix II at the end of this book.

Later, in discussing the maximum likelihood estimators, the weights V_i of (3) are identified with the inverses of the covariance matrices of the observation noise random variables. Thus, in many cases the V_i are positive definite and the inverse in (9) will exist.

Define

$$P_{k+1} = \left(\sum_{0}^{k+1} H_i' V_i H_i \right)^+ \tag{10}$$

This is an $(n \times n)$ matrix. Then, from (7) and (9),

$$x_{k+1}^* = x_k^* + P_{k+1}H_{k+1}'V_{k+1}(y_{k+1} - H_{k+1}x_k^*) \tag{11}$$

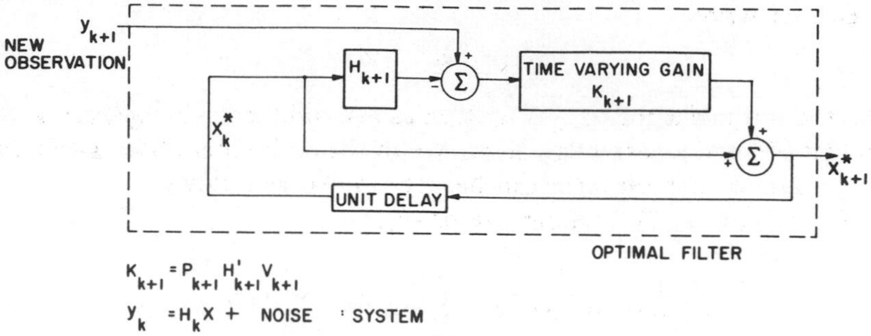

Fig. 5.1. Optimal least-squares estimator for a static system.

where

$$P_{k+1}^{+} = \sum_{0}^{k+1} H_i' V_i H_i = \sum^{k} H_i' V_i H_i + H_{k+1}' V_{k+1} H_{k+1}$$

$$= P_k^{+} + H_{k+1}' V_{k+1} H_{k+1} \tag{12}$$

since $A^{++} = A$ for any matrix A. See Fig. 5.1 for the schematic diagram of the optimal estimator. If there are no measurement errors and if $x_k{}^*$ is exact, then (11) reduces to $x_{k+1}^* = x_k{}^*$ as it should. Equations (11) and (12) are the desired recursive equations for $x_k{}^*$. Using the matrix identity in Appendix D, Chapter II, (11) can also be written as

$$P_{k+1} = P_k - P_k H_{k+1}' (V_{k+1}^{+} + H_{k+1} P_k H_{k+1}')^{-1} H_{k+1} P_k \tag{13}$$

when the indicated inverse exists. From (10), P's are seen to be $(n \times n)$ matrices and $(V_{k+1}^{+} + H_{k+1} P_k H_{k+1}')$ is an $(m \times m)$ matrix. By taking the additional data one by one, i.e., by taking $m = 1$, the inversion of the matrix in (13) is reduced to the trivial operation of inverting a scalar number. Thus, generating P_k by (13) is a much easier task computationally than to invert an $(n \times n)$ matrix of (10) directly.

Note the similarity of the forms of (11) and (12) with those of (132a) and (132b) of Chapter II.

C. Linear Dynamic System

Having solved the least-squares estimation problem of the static system, one can quickly dispose of the least-squares estimation problems for deterministic dynamic systems. The variable x in the previous section is now regarded as the state vector of a system governed by

$$x_{i+1} = A_i x_i\,, \qquad A_i \text{ nonsingular,} \quad i = 0, 1, \ldots \tag{14}$$

where x_i is the n-dimensional state vector of the system at time i. The state vector is assumed to be observed by

$$y_i = H_i x_i + \eta_i , \qquad i = 0, 1,... \tag{15}$$

where H_i is an $(m \times m)$ matrix and where η_i's are measurement noises. It is desired to obtain at time k the best least-squares estimates of x_k as functions of $y_0 ,..., y_k$, i e , obtain x_i^*, $0 \leqslant i \leqslant k$, as a function of y^i such that they minimize the criterion function

$$J_k = \sum_{i=0}^{k} \| H_i x_i - y_i \|_{V_i}^2 \tag{16}$$

where V_i is now taken to be positive definite for simplicity J_k can be regarded as a function of x_k since (14) can be used to express x_i as a function of x_k , $i < k$:

$$x_i = \phi_{k,i}^{-1} x_k$$

where

$$\phi_{k,i} \triangleq \prod_{j=i}^{k-1} A_j , \qquad i = 0, 1, 2,..., k-1 \tag{17}$$

is the transition matrix of the system (14). Thus (16), which is a function of $x_0 ,..., x_k$, can be rewritten as a function of x_k only:

$$J_k(x_k) \triangleq \sum_{i=0}^{k} \| K_i^k x_k - y_i \|_{V_i}^2 \tag{18}$$

where $K_i^k \triangleq H_i \phi_{k,i}^{-1}$, $i = 0, 1, 2,..., k$. The problem is now reduced to minimizing J_k with respect to x_k , or the static problem previously discussed.* From (16), noting that a choice of x_{k+1} implies the choice of $A_k^{-1} x_{k+1}$ as x_k ,

$$J_{k+1}(x_{k+1}) = J_k(A_k^{-1} x_{k+1}) + \|(H_{k+1} x_{k+1} - y_{k+1})\|_{V_{k+1}}^2 \tag{19}$$

Since x_k^*, if exact, produces the exact state variable at time $(k+1)$ by (14), let us write x_{k+1}^* as

$$x_{k+1}^* = A_k x_k^* + \Delta x_{k+1} \tag{20}$$

Then, from (19), quite similarly to (8),

$$J_{k+1}(x_{k+1}^*) = J_k(x_k^*) + (\Delta x_{k+1})' A_k'^{-1} \left(\sum_{i=0}^{k} K_i^{k'} V_i K_i^k \right) A_k^{-1} \Delta x_{k+1}$$

$$+ \| H_{k+1} A x_k^* - y_{k+1} + H_{k+1} \Delta x_{k+1} \|_{V_{k+1}}^2 \tag{21}$$

* A slight, obvious modification of the method works even when A's are singular.

Thus, by minimizing (21) with respect to Δx_{k+1}, we get the sequential scheme of generating the best least-squares estimate for the dynamic system of (14):

$$x_{k+1}^* = A_k x_k^* + P_{k+1} H'_{k+1} V_{k+1}(y_{k+1} - H_{k+1} A_k x_k^*) \tag{22}$$

where P_k is defined analogously to (10). Making use of the relation $K_i^{k+1} = K_i^k A_k^{-1}$,

$$P_{k+1}^{-1} = \sum_{i=0}^{k+1} (K_i^{k+1})' V_i (K_i^{k+1}) = A_k'^{-1} \left(\sum_{i=0}^{k} K_i^{k'} V_i K_i^k \right) A_k^{-1} + H'_{k+1} V_{k+1} H_{k+1}$$

$$= A_k'^{-1} P_k^{-1} A_k^{-1} + H'_{k+1} V_{k+1} H_{k+1} \tag{23}$$

when the indicated inverse exists.

When we compare (16), (22), and (23) with (117), (132a), and (132b) of Chapter II, respectively, we note that they are identical if we equate V_i with R_i^{-1}, P_i with Γ_i, and if we put B_i's and Q_i's identically equal to zero to reduce the system of (117) of Chapter II to that given by (14).

Therefore, if the noises η in (15) are Gaussian random variables with mean 0 and covariance matrices R, then the best least-squares estimate of x_k, x_k^* is the same as μ_k, the conditional mean of x_k given y^k. Thus we see that μ_k minimizes J_k, i.e., the trace of Γ_k. This fact is sometimes stated by saying that μ_k is the minimum variance estimate[39] of x_k.

See Fig. 5.2 for the schematic diagram of the optimal estimator. Figure 5.3 shows the diagram of Fig. 5.2 rearranged in order to show more clearly the way the optimal estimates are constructed. When P does not have the inverse, P^+ should be used in (23) quite analogous to

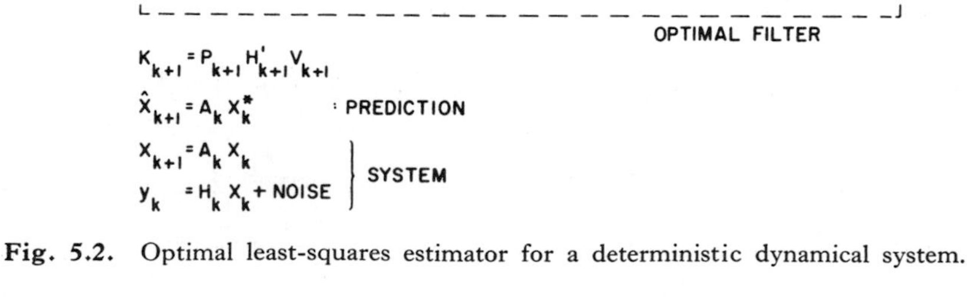

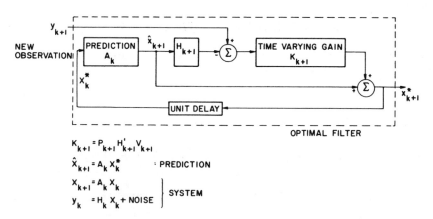

Fig. 5.2. Optimal least-squares estimator for a deterministic dynamical system.

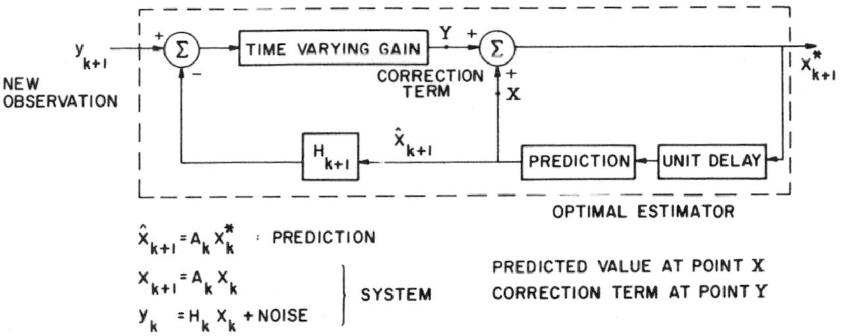

Fig. 5.3. The optimal least-squares estimate at time $k + 1$ consists of the updated optimal estimate at k plus a correction term generated by a new observation at time $k + 1$.

(12) of Section B. If there are no measurement errors and if $x_k{}^*$ is exact, then, of course, (22) reduces to $x_{k+1}^* = A_k x_k{}^*$. When measurement errors are present, $A_k x_k{}^*$ is the best least-squares estimate of x_{k+1}, given $y_0, \ldots, y_k$ but not y_{k+1}.

From (23), $P_{k+1}^{-1} = A_k'^{-1} P_k^{-1} A_k^{-1} + H_{k+1}' V_{k+1} H_{k+1}$. From Appendix II, D, this can be rewritten as

$$P_{k+1} = A_k P_k A_k' - A_k P_k A_k' H_{k+1}' (V_{k+1}^{-1} + H_{k+1} A_k P_k A_k' H_{k+1})^{-1} H_{k+1} A_k P_k A_k' \tag{24}$$

where remarks similar to those of the previous section apply to taking the inverse of $(V_{k+1}^{-1} + H_{k+1} A_k P_k A' H_{k+1}')$.

When (15) is replaced by a more general equation

$$y_i = h(x_i) + \eta_i \tag{25}$$

one can still discuss the problem of obtaining $x_k{}^*$ such that it minimizes

$$J_k = \sum_{i=0}^{k} (h(x_i) - y_i)' V_i (h(x_i) - y_i) \tag{26}$$

J_k is, however, no longer quadratic in x's. The optimal x_{k+1} is still obtained by minimizing $J_{k+1}(Ax_k{}^* + \Delta x_{k+1})$, numerically if necessary, although it is not possible now to give a simple recursion equation for optimal correction term Δx_{k+1}. One may, however, expand $h(x)$ into a Taylor series and treat the linearized problem by means of the technique of this section. Another technique is discussed in Section 1, E of generating sequentially approximate estimates of the state vector when the observation equation is given by (25). See also Section 3 of this chapter for more detail.

D. Noisy Linear Plant

Now consider that not only the observations are noisy but also the system plant is subject to noise:

$$x_{k+1} = A_k x_k + C_k \xi_k \tag{27}$$

$$y_k = H_k x_k + \eta_k \tag{28}$$

where ξ's and η's are random noises. Unlike our previous problems we now have two sources of errors in estimating the state vector. In our previous problems, if x_k is known exactly, so is x_{k+1}. Now, because of ξ's, this is no longer the case. The criterion function may now consist of two kinds of error terms,

$$J_k = \sum_{i=0}^{k} [\| K_i^k x_k - y_i \|_{V_i}^2 + \| x_{i+1} - A_i x_i \|_{T_i}^2] \tag{29}$$

where V_i and T_i are symmetric positive matrices. They express relative weights we attribute to the two error sources. Equation (29) implies that we have a good idea about the relative magnitudes of the various random variables involved. Thus, if we are led to believe that the effects of η are smaller than those of ξ's, then one would tend to believe the observations y more and attach a larger weight to the first term.

Here we can make comments similar to those we made in connection with (22) and (23). That is, by properly identifying the weight matrices V and T with the error covariance matrices R and Q we see that the best least-squares estimate of x_k of the system (27) and (28) is the same as the conditional mean of x_k given y^k. Therefore μ_k is the minimum-variance estimate of x_k.

Detailed discussions on (29) are deferred to Section 3, where the subject of the Bayesian optimal estimates are taken up. There it will become clear that the weight matrix should be taken to be the inverse of the covariance matrix of the noise involved.

E. Nonlinear Systems

a. *Introduction*

We now discuss the least-squares estimation problems of a nonlinear system. Consider the plant and the observation equation given by

$$x_{k+1} = f_k(x_k) \tag{30}$$

$$y_k = h_k(x_k) + \eta_k , \qquad k = 0, 1, \ldots \tag{31}$$

If (30) can be solved for x_k uniquely in terms of x_{k+1} as $x_k = g_k(x_{k+1})$, where g_k is the inverse of f_k, then $x_0, x_1, \ldots, x_{k-1}$ can be expressed in terms of x_k as before and J_k can be regarded as a function of x_k. Defining J_k analogous to (3) or (18),

$$J_{k+1}(x_{k+1}) = J_k(g_k(x_{k+1})) + (h_{k+1}(x_{k+1}) - y_{k+1})' \times V_{k+1}(h_{k+1}(x_{k+1}) - y_{k+1}) \tag{32}$$

The estimate x_{k+1}^*, then, will be expressed as

$$x_{k+1}^* = f_k(x_k^*) + \Delta x_{k+1}$$

The optimal correction term is that Δx_{k+1} which minimizes J_{k+1} with respect to Δx_{k+1}. Equation (32) is, however, no longer quadratic in Δx_{k+1}.

As mentioned in Section 1,C, we may linearize (30) and (31). Then we can apply the technique of Section 1,C.

Instead, we next derive approximately optimal least-squares estimates recursively by the method of invariant imbedding.[20,99]

Sequential estimation problems for general nonlinear dynamic systems are discussed more fully in Section 3.

b. *Approximate Solution*

The method is given for one-dimensional systems in order to present the basic procedure most clearly. It is a discrete-time version of the method proposed by Bellman *et al.*[24]

Consider a plant equation

$$x_{i+1} = x_i + f_i(x_i), \qquad i = 0, 1, \ldots \tag{33}$$

where f_i is assumed differentiable and the observation equation

$$y_i = h_i(x_i) + \eta_i, \qquad i = 0, 1, \ldots \tag{34}$$

where η's are noises in observation, and where h_i is assumed twice differentiable.

Denote by x_i^* the best least-squares estimate of x_i at time i. Namely x_i^* is the best estimate of the current state variable x_i of the system.

We will look for the recursion formula for x_i^* in the form of

$$x_{i+1}^* = x_i^* + g_i(x_i^*) \tag{35}$$

Define the criterion function of estimation by

$$J(x, N) = \sum_0^N v_i[y_i - h_i(x_i)]^2, \qquad v_i \geqslant 0 \tag{36}$$

with the understanding that x is the state vector at time N, i.e., $x_N = x$.

The v_i's are weights of the observations, which implies that some ideas of relative magnitudes of the variances of η_i are available. Otherwise one may take $v_i = 1$, $i = 0, 1, \ldots, N$.

The optimal x_N^*, therefore, satisfies

$$J_x(x_N^*, N) = 0 \tag{37}$$

where J_x is the partial derivative of J with respect to x. Similarly,

$$J_x(x_{N+1}^*, N+1) = 0 \tag{38}$$

From (35), (37), and (38),

$$\begin{aligned} 0 &= J_x(x_{N+1}^*, N+1) \\ &= J_x(x_N^*, N+1) + J_{xx}(x_N^*, N+1)\, g_N(x_N^*) + \cdots \end{aligned} \tag{39}$$

Therefore, we obtain the expression for the best correction term as

$$g_N(x_N^*) \doteqdot -J_x(x_N^*, N+1)/J_{xx}(x_N^*, N+1) \tag{40}$$

To compute J_x and J_{xx} in (40), note from (33) and (36) that

$$\begin{aligned} &J(x, N) + v_{N+1}[y_{N+1} - h_{N+1}(x + f_N(x))]^2 \\ &\quad = J(x + f_N(x), N+1) \\ &\quad = J(x, N+1) + J_x(x, N+1) f_N(x) + \tfrac{1}{2} J_{xx}(x, N+1) f_N^2(x) + \cdots \end{aligned} \tag{41}$$

where the last line is obtained by the Taylor series.

Differentiating (41) with respect to x,

$$\begin{aligned} J_x(x, N) = {} & [1 + f_N'(x)]\{J_x(x, N+1) + J_{xx}(x, N+1) f_N(x) \\ & + 2v_{N+1}[y_{N+1} - h_{N+1}(x + f_N(x))]\, h_{N+1}'(x + f_N(x))\} \\ & + (\text{terms in } J_{xxx} \text{ and higher}) \end{aligned} \tag{42}$$

Substituting x_N^* for x in (42) and noting (37),

$$\begin{aligned} J_x(x_N^*, N+1) \doteqdot {} & - J_{xx}(x_N^*, N+1) f_N(x_N^*) \\ & - 2v_{N+1}[y_{N+1} - h_{N+1}(\hat{x}_{N+1})] h_{N+1}'(\hat{x}_{N+1}) \end{aligned} \tag{43}$$

where

$$\hat{x}_{N+1} \triangleq x_N^* + f_N(x_N^*) \tag{44}$$

is the best estimate of x_{N+1} at time N. Since $J(x, N)$ is nearly quadratic in the neighborhood of x_N^*, terms in J_{xxx} and higher derivatives are neglected in obtaining (43) from (42).

From (40) and (43), therefore,

$$x^*_{N+1} = \hat{x}_{N+1} + K_{N+1}[y_{N+1} - h_{N+1}(\hat{x}_{N+1})] \tag{45}$$

where

$$K_{N-1} = \frac{2v_{N+1}h'_{N+1}(\hat{x}_{N+1})}{J_{xx}(x_N{}^*, N+1)} \tag{46}$$

See Fig. 5.4 for the schematic diagram of the estimator.

Note that (45) has the form identical with the one-dimensional version of the recursion formula of (22) previously obtained for linear dynamic and observation equations. There $\hat{x}_{N+1}$ is $A_N x_N{}^*$ since the plant equation is linear.

One may, therefore, be tempted to interpret the term $2/J_{xx}(x_N{}^*, N+1)$ in K_{N+1} as P_{N+1} of (22) and infer that its inverse satisfies a linear recursion equation similar to (23).

We next show that this is indeed the case when terms in J_{xxx} and of higher derivatives of J are neglected. Define

$$P^{-1}_{N+1} = J_{xx}(x_N{}^*, N+1)/2 \tag{47}$$

Differentiating (42) with respect to x, substituting $x_N{}^*$ for x, and noting that $J_{xx}(x_N{}^*, N) = J_{xx}(x^*_{N-1}, N) +$ (terms in J_{xxx} and higher),

$$\begin{aligned} &J_{xx}(x_N{}^*, N+1)[1 + f_N'(x_N{}^*)]^2 \\ &\quad \doteq J_{xx}(x^*_{N-1}, N) - 2v_{N+1}[y_{N+1} - h_{N+1}(\hat{x}_{N+1})]\, h''_{N+1}(\hat{x}_{N+1}) \\ &\qquad \times [1 + f_N'(x_N{}^*)] + 2v_{N+1}\{h_{N+1}(\hat{x}_{N+1})\,[1 + f_N'(x_N{}^*)]\}^2 \end{aligned} \tag{48}$$

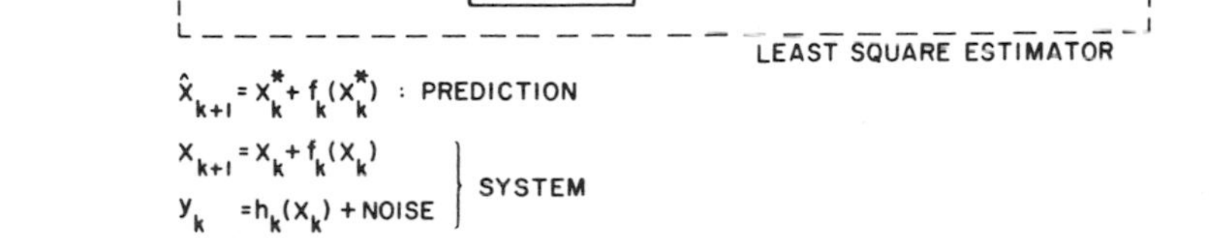

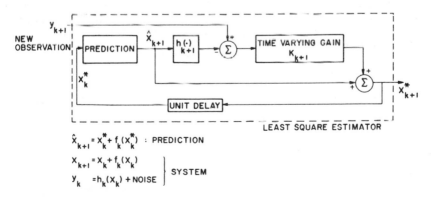

Fig. 5.4. Optimal least-squares estimator for systems with nonlinear plant and observation equations.

Substituting this into (47),

$$P_{N+1}^{-1} = \frac{1}{[1 + f_N'(x_N^*)]^2}\{P_N^{-1} + v_{N+1}(h_{N+1}'(\hat{x}_{N+1})[1 + f_N'(x_N^*)])^2$$

$$- v_{N+1}[y_{N+1} - h_{N+1}(\hat{x}_{N+1})]\, h_{N+1}''(x_{N+1})\,[1 + f_N'(x_N^*)]\} \qquad (49)$$

This is the desired recursion formula for P^{-1}. Note that unless the observation equation is linear, P could become negative. Equation (47) indicates, then, that the estimate will not be optimal, suggesting that the Taylor series expansions and other approximations made in deriving (45) and (46) are no longer valid.

c. *Particular Case*

For a linear system given by

$$x_{i+1} = a_i x_i$$
$$y_i = h_i x_i + \eta_i$$

(45), (46), and (49) reduce to the correct formulas:

$$x_{i+1}^* = a_i x_i^* + K_{i+1}[y_{i+1} - h_i(a_i x_i^*)]$$

where

$$K_{i+1} = v_{i+1} h_{i+1} / P_{i+1}$$

and where

$$P_{i+1}^{-1} = \frac{1}{a_i^2}(P_i^{-1} + v_{i+1} h_{i+1}^2 a_i^2)$$

From (49), it is seen that the computation for P's can be done off-line when the observation equation is linear. When the observation equation is nonlinear both x_{i+1}^* and P_{i+1} must be generated on-line, and the signs of P's must be checked. When negative P's are encountered, the sequential estimation process must be reinitialized since the estimates that have been generated so far have, in all likelihood, drifted away from the true values significantly.

It is a straightforward exercise to repeat the above for the vector case and will not be given here.

F. Linear Control Systems

We consider a system described by

$$x_{i+1} = A_i x_i + B_i u_i \qquad (50)$$

$$y_i = H_i x_i + \eta_i, \qquad i = 0, 1, \ldots \qquad (51)$$

where A_i^{-1} exists. The control vectors u are also assumed to be directly observable. The criterion is taken again to be

$$J_k = \sum_0^k \| H_i x_i - y_i \|_{V_i}^2 \tag{52}$$

In this section, the developments essentially parallel those of Section 1,C. The only difference that the newly introduced control term makes is in the predicted value $\hat{x}_{k+1}$ of x_{k+1} based on the observations $y_0, \ldots, y_k$.

Namely, instead of $Ax_k{}^*$ in (20) of Section 1,C, we will now have

$$x_{k+1}^* = A_k x_k{}^* + B_k u_k + \Delta x_{k+1} \tag{53}$$

Thus x_{k+1}^* can be obtained from Eq. (52) by minimizing it with respect to Δx_{k+1}.

Since the control terms act as known biases in estimating x's it is not actually necessary to derive the expression for optimal Δx_{k+1} all over again.

Define

$$w_i = x_i - \sum_{j=0}^{i-1} \phi_{i,j+1} B_j u_j \tag{54}$$

and

$$z_i = H_i w_i + \eta_i \tag{55}$$

Then, w_i satisfies $w_{i+1} = A_i w_i$. This is the dynamic equation for w's. Then using the optimal estimation formula for w's with the observation

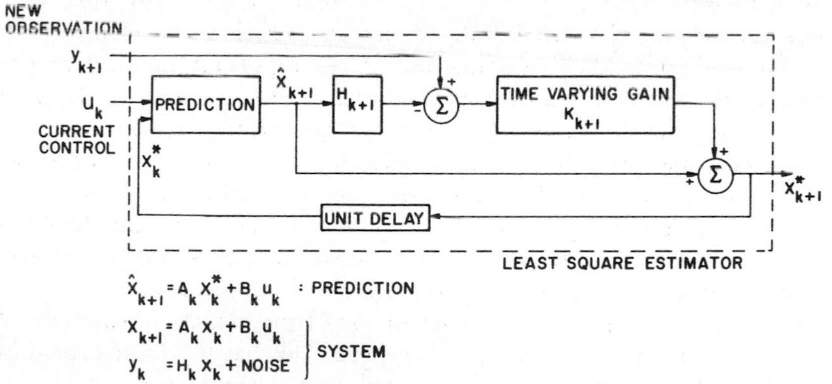

Fig. 5.5. Optimal least-squares estimator for linear control systems.

z's, and noting that $z_{k+1} = y_{k+1} - H_{k+1}(x_{k+1} - w_{k+1})$, we immediately obtain

$$x^*_{k+1} = A_k x_k{}^* + B_k u_k + P_{k+1} H'_{k+1} V_{k+1}[y_{k+1} - H_{k+1}(A_k x_k{}^* + B_k u_k)] \quad (56)$$

where u_0, u_i,..., u_k are the actual controls used up to the present time and P's are as defined by (23). See Fig. 5.5 for the schematic diagram of the optimal estimator.

2. Maximum Likelihood Estimation

A. Introduction

In Section 1, equations for sequentially generating the best least-squares estimates of the state vectors have been derived. One of the most attractive features of the method of least squares is its wide applicability to many practical situations since the method does not assume any statistical properties of the random disturbances beyond the mere existence of finite variances.

We show in this and the next section that, for linear systems with Gaussian random noises, the results obtained by the method of least squares coincide with those obtainable from other well-known estimation methods, such as the maximum likelihood method or Bayesian estimation method upon proper identifications of the weights used in the least-squares estimates. We will first discuss the maximum likelihood estimates.[39,73] For the applications of the maximum likelihood and other similar methods to the estimation of the plant parameters (sometimes called identification problems[72a]) rather than to the estimation of the state vectors, see the detailed discussion in Ref. 91a. See also Ref. 100.

The maximum likelihood method is an important method of point estimation, i.e., method of estimating a value of the unknown parameter or variable, and is used widely in many practical problems.

Roughly speaking, the maximum likelihood method chooses the value of a parameter or a variable to be estimated appearing in the probability distribution functions in such a way as to maximize the likelihood function. A likelihood function is the probability (density) function when regarded as a function of the parameter.

For example, suppose y^k is a set of data from which an estimate of a parameter θ is to be constructed. Suppose also that the joint probability density of y^k, given θ, $p(y^k \mid \theta)$, is available where θ appears as a parameter. When θ is regarded as the variable, then $p(y^k \mid \theta)$ is a likelihood function.

Denoting the maximum likelihood estimate of θ by θ^*, θ^* is given by the relation

$$p(y^k \mid \theta^*) = \max_{\theta} p(y^k \mid \theta)$$

The intuitive reason behind this choice is that the sequence of observations having the maximum density functional value is the most likely one to be realized (observed).

B. Static Systems

Consider first the static system (2) of Section 1

$$y_i = H_i x + \eta_i \tag{57}$$

where η_i's are the m-dimensional Gaussian random vector with

$$E(\eta_i) = 0 \tag{58a}$$

$$E(\eta_i \eta_j') = R_i \delta_{ij} \tag{58b}$$

where R_i is an $m \times m$ positive definite matrix. The probability density function for η_i is then given by

$$p(\eta_i) = \frac{1}{(2\pi)^{m/2} | R_i |^{1/2}} \exp(-\tfrac{1}{2}\, \eta_i' R_i^{-1} \eta_i) \tag{59}$$

where $| R_i |$ is the determinant, and the joint probability density function of $\eta_0, \ldots, \eta_k$ is given by

$$p(\eta_0, \ldots, \eta_k) = (2\pi)^{-\frac{1}{2}m(k+1)} \prod_{i=0}^{k} | R_i |^{-1/2}$$

$$\times \exp\left\{-\tfrac{1}{2} \sum_{i=0}^{k} \eta_i' R_i^{-1} \eta_i\right\} \tag{60}$$

We could write explicitly the density function of the Gaussian random variable η as (59), as soon as we know its mean value and the covariance matrix Eq. (58) because these two quantities are sufficient statistics and serve as the parameters which specify the density function uniquely from a family of distribution functions for Gaussian random variables.* This is a useful fact which is used many times. Gaussian

* Gaussian random variables have many remarkable properties which are in part responsible for their widespread use in theoretical works. We discuss one such property, self-reproducing property of the distribution function forms,[128,129] in Appendix IV on sufficient statistics at the end of the book.

random variables are said to have normal distributions. For a brief discussion on multidimensional Gaussian random variables and their distribution functions, see Appendix III at the end of this book.

By changing variables from η's to y's in (60),

$$p(y_0, y_1, \ldots, y_k \mid x) = (2\pi)^{-\frac{1}{2}m(k+1)} \prod_{i=0}^{k} \mid R_i \mid^{-1/2} \exp(-E_k/2) \tag{61}$$

where

$$E_k = \sum_{i=0}^{k} \eta_i' R_i^{-1} \eta_i = \sum_{0}^{k} \| H_i x - y_i \|_{R_i^{-1}}^2 \tag{62}$$

In (61), the variable to be estimated, x, appears as a parameter of the probability density expression. Namely, by interpreting x as the unknown parameter vector in the joint probability density function, (61) is exactly the likelihood function for the observation $y_0, \ldots, y_k$. The maximum likelihood estimate of x, x_k^*, is that x which maximizes (61) or which minimizes E_k.

By comparing (62) with (3), we see immediately that x_k^* obtained in (11) is the maximum likelihood estimator of x if V_i is identified with R_i^{-1}, $i = 0, 1, 2, \ldots, k$. Furthermore, since x_k^* minimizes E_k,

$$\begin{aligned} x_k^* &= \left(\sum_{i=0}^{k} H_i' R_i^{-1} H_i \right)^{-1} \sum_{i=0}^{k} H_i' R_i^{-1} y_i \\ &= P_k \sum_{i=0}^{k} H_i' R_i^{-1} (H_i x + \eta_i) \\ &= x + P_k \sum_{i=0}^{k} H_i' R_i^{-1} \eta_i \end{aligned} \tag{63}$$

where P_k is as defined in Section 1,B. The schematic diagram of the optimal estimator is identical to Fig. 5.1 when V's are replaced by R^{-1}'s.

Since x is a constant and η's are Gaussian, x_k^* is a Gaussian random variable with

$$E(x_k^* \mid x) = x \tag{64}$$

and

$$\begin{aligned} \operatorname{cov}(x_k^*) &= E[(x_k^* - x)(x_k^* - x)'] \\ &= E\left[P_k \left(\sum_{i=0}^{k} H_i' R_i^{-1} \eta_i \eta_i' R_i^{-1} H_i \right) P_k \right] \\ &= P_k \end{aligned} \tag{65}$$

Thus, under the stated assumptions, $x_k{}^*$ is the unbiased estimator of x, i.e., the mean of the estimator is the variable to be estimated. Define $e_k = x - x_k{}^*$ as the error of estimation. Then P_k in Eq. (65) can be interpreted as the covariance matrix of the error of the estimation.

The conditional error covariance matrices of the state vector estimates have been calculated for systems with linear plant and observation equations in Appendix C of Chapter II when the noises are all Gaussian. We denoted them by Γ_k's. When plants are static with no noises, Γ_k reduces to P_k as it should.

Thus, by identifying R_k^{-1} by V_k of Section 1, we see that, for systems of (57), the maximum likelihood estimate minimizes its error covariance. An estimator is said to be efficient when it has this minimal variance property.[39]

C. Dynamic Systems

We can similarly interpret the least-squares estimates obtained in Section 1,C for the linear dynamic systems as the maximum likelihood estimator by identifying V_i with R_i^{-1}. Namely, given

$$x_{i+1} = A_i x_i \tag{66}$$

$$y_i = H_i x_i + \eta_i \tag{67}$$

where η's are as in Section 2,B,

$$p(\eta^k) = \text{const} \exp(-\tfrac{1}{2} E_k) \tag{68}$$

where

$$\begin{aligned} E_k &= \sum_0^k \eta_i' R_i^{-1} \eta_i \\ &= \sum_0^k \| H_i x_i - y_i \|^2_{R_i^{-1}} \end{aligned} \tag{69}$$

and where $p(\eta^k)$ is to be maximized by choosing x_i to minimize E_k subject to the constraint (66). By comparing (69) with (16) of Section 1,C, one immediately obtains

$$x_{k+1}^* = A_k x_k{}^* + P_{k+1} H_{k+1}' R_{k+1}^{-1} (y_{k+1} - H_{k+1} A_k x_k{}^*) \tag{70}$$

where

$$P_{k+1}^{-1} = (A_k P_k A_k')^{-1} + H_{k+1}' R_{k+1}^{-1} H_{k+1}$$

or

$$P_{k+1} = A_k P_k A_k' - A_k P_k A_k' H_{k+1}' (R_{k+1} + H_{k+1} A_k P_k A_k' H_{k+1}')^{-1} \times H_{k+1} A_k P_k A_k' \tag{71}$$

The schematic diagram of the optimal estimator is identical to Fig. 5.2, where V's are replaced by R's.

Pursuing this line of investigation further, one can discuss the best maximum-likelihood estimator of the state vector for a noisy linear system with noisy observation.

Consider

$$x_{i+1} = A_i x_i \mid C_i \xi_i \tag{72}$$

$$y_i = H_i x_i + \eta_i \tag{73}$$

where A, C, and H are known matrices and ξ_i's and ζ_i's are Gaussian random vectors with*

$$\begin{aligned} E(\xi_i) &= E(\eta_i) = 0 \\ E(\eta_i \eta_j') &= R_i \delta_{ij} \\ E(\xi_i \xi_j') &= Q_i \delta_{ij} \\ E(\xi_i \eta_j') &= 0 \end{aligned} \tag{74}$$

The effect of ξ_i in Eq. (72) is to introduce uncertainty in the value of x_{i+1} given x_i. In other words, we now have the additional probability density function $p(x_{i+1} \mid x_i)$ to deal with in evaluating the error covariance for the estimation error $e_{k+1} = x_{k+1} - x_{k+1}^*$. This adds a term $C_k Q_k C_k'$ to the previously obtained expression for P_{k+1}, i.e., instead of $A_k P_k A_k'$ in (71), one would have

$$A_k P_k A_k' + C_k Q_k C_k' \tag{75}$$

With (75) replacing the expression $A_k P_k A'_k$ in (71), (70) is now a valid expression for the maximum likelihood estimator for the system state vector of (72).

This point will be made much more explicit when the various joint conditional probability densities are evaluated. This is done in the next section where optimal Bayesian estimation of the state vector is discussed.

---

* The reader is invited to consider the case with $E(\xi_i \eta_j') = S_i \delta_{ij}$ as an exercise.

3. Optimal Bayesian Estimation

A. Best Estimators

In Chapters II–IV we have seen that the probability density function $p(x_i \mid y^i)$, or its generalized form $p(\mu_i \mid \nu^i)$, plays an essential role in constructing optimal Bayesian control policies.

We have also seen that, for a certain class of problems with quadratic criterion functions, we can construct optimal control policies if we know only $E(x_i \mid y^i)$ without knowing $p(x_i \mid y^i)$. $E(x_i \mid y^i)$ is far easier to deal with than $p(x_i \mid y^i)$ especially numerically since the latter is a function. It requires, in principle, a table with an infinite number of entries to represent a function numerically. Thus, we may decide to use $E(x_i \mid y^i)$ instead of $p(x_i \mid y^i)$ at least for this class of problems. Therefore, for estimation problems with quadratic criterion functions the conditional expectation $E(x_i \mid y^i)$ is said to be the best (optimal) estimate of x_i given y^i. There are other classes of problems where $E(x_i \mid y^i)$ is not the best estimate. The optimal estimate depends on the types of criterion functions employed. If the criterion function is such that $L(x_i, z) = | x_i - z |$, then the best estimate is given by choosing z to be the median of $p(x_i \mid y^i)$.[22] The maximum likelihood estimate is the best estimate in the sense that it maximizes the $p(x_i \mid y^i)$. For example, Cox investigated the estimation method closely related to the maximum likelihood method.[40,41] He uses the modes of the a posteriori probability distributions as the best estimates. Given $p(x_i \mid y^i)$, one has already three estimates which are best, depending on the criteria used. These estimates are, in general, different. When the density functions, however, are symmetric and unimodal, for example, Gaussian, these three estimates are the same.

In this section we will discuss optimal Bayesian estimates. These are the best estimates in the sense described above (such as the conditional mean or median, etc., depending on the criteria used for problems), where $p(x_i \mid y^i)$ is computed from a priori probability density functions according to the Bayes rule. The conditional means are taken to be the best estimates throughout this section. Namely we use quadratic criterion functions. The procedure to obtain optimal Bayesian estimates should be clear by now since we have been computing $p(x_i \mid y^i)$ all along by the Bayes rule. We have also obtained sufficient statistics for $p(x_i \mid y^i)$ for linear systems with Gaussian random noises in Section 3 of Chapter II. Hence, we will only briefly summarize the steps involved to obtain best Bayesian estimates.

B. Static System

Consider the problem of estimating x, given y, where

$$y = G(x, \eta) \tag{76}$$

and where x is an n-dimensional state vector, y is the observation vector (m-dimensional), and η is the noise vector (q-dimensional).

Let us now compute $p(x \mid y)$.

Assume the probability density function $p(x, \eta)$ is given. This will be the case, for example, if $p(x)$ and $p(\eta)$ are given and x and η are independent. Then, from (76) and $p(x, \eta)$, $p(y)$ and $p(y \mid x)$ are obtained by the Bayes rule,

$$p(x \mid y) = \frac{p(x)\, p(y \mid x)}{p(y)} \tag{77}$$

If (76) is invertible for η,

$$\eta = g^{-1}(x, y)$$

where g^{-1} is the inverse of G, then

$$p(x, y) = p(x, g^{-1}(x, y)) \mid J \mid$$

where J is the Jacobian

$$J = \det \left(\frac{\partial \eta}{\partial y} \right)$$

and

$$p(x \mid y) = \frac{p(x, y)}{p(y)} \tag{78}$$

Thus, the a posteriori density $p(x \mid y)$ is obtained from either (77) or (78) and its mean, median, or mode can be computed.

As an example, consider a linear system given by

$$y = Hx + \eta \tag{79}$$

where x is an n-vector, H is an $m \times n$ matrix, and where η is an m vector. Assume that x and η are independent and that $p(x, \eta) = p_1(x), p_2(\eta)$, where $p_1(x)$ is Gaussian with

$$E(x) = \bar{x}, \qquad \operatorname{cov}(x) = P_0 \tag{80}$$

and where $p_2(\eta)$ is a Gaussian with

$$E(\eta) = 0, \qquad \text{cov}(\eta) = R \tag{81}$$

From (79)–(81), y is seen to be a Gaussian random vector with

$$E(y) = H\bar{x}, \qquad \text{cov}(y) = HP_0H' + R \tag{82}$$

Hence,

$$p_3(y) = [(2\pi)^{m/2}| R + HP_0H' |^{1/2}]^{-1} \exp(-\tfrac{1}{2}(y - H\bar{x})'(R + HP_0H')^{-1}(y - H\bar{x}))$$

Since the Jacobian is 1,

$$\begin{aligned} p(x, y) &= p(x, \eta) = p_1(x)\, p_2(\eta) \\ &= p_1(x)\, p_2(y - Hx) \end{aligned}$$

and

$$\begin{aligned} p(x \mid y) &= \frac{p_1(x)\, p_2(y - Hx)}{p_3(y)} \\ &= C \exp(-\tfrac{1}{2}\{(x - \bar{x})'P_0^{-1}(x - \bar{x}) + (y - Hx)'R^{-1}(y - Hx) \\ &\quad - (y - H\bar{x})'(R + HP_0H')^{-1}(y - H\bar{x})\}) \end{aligned} \tag{83}$$

where

$$C = \frac{1}{(2\pi)^{n/2}} \cdot \frac{| HP_0H' + R |^{1/2}}{| P_0 |^{1/2} | R |^{1/2}}$$

By completing squares in (83) (See Appendix A at the end of this chapter),

$$p(x \mid y) = C \exp(-\tfrac{1}{2}(x - x^*)'P^{-1}(x - x^*)) \tag{84}$$

where

$$x^* = \bar{x} + PH'R^{-1}(y - H\bar{x}) \tag{85}$$

and

$$P^{-1} = P_0^{-1} + H'R^{-1}H \tag{86}$$

or, from the matrix identity in Appendix D at the end of the Chapter II,

$$P = P_0 - P_0H'(R + HP_0H')^{-1}HP^0$$

Since $p(x \mid y)$ is symmetric and unimodal about x^*, all three best estimates, i.e., the conditional mean, mediam, and mode of $p(x \mid y)$, are given by x^*.

Incidentally, we have just rederived in the example the Wiener–Kalman filter for a single-stage estimation problem.

C. Dynamic System

We next discuss estimation problems for general dynamic systems. Consider a dynamic system described by

$$x_{i+1} = F_i(x_i, \xi_i) \tag{87}$$

and observed by

$$y_i = G_i(x_i, \eta_i) \tag{88}$$

where the subscript i refers to the ith time instant and ξ_i is the noise in the dynamics of the system.

Assume that $p(x_0 \mid y_0)$ is computable from the a priori information on (87) and (88) and that we can obtain probability density functions $p(x_{i+1} \mid x_i)$ and $p(y_i \mid x_i)$ from those of ξ_i and η_i and ξ_i and η_i are independent. As in Chapters II–IV, we can generate $p(x_i \mid y^i)$ recursively. By the Bayes rule,

$$p(x_{k+1} \mid y^{k+1}) = \frac{p(x_{k+1}, y_{k+1} \mid y^k)}{p(y_{k+1} \mid y^k)} \tag{89}$$

Also, by applying the chain rule to $p(x_k, x_{k+1}, y_{k+1} \mid y^k)$, we write

$$p(x_k, x_{k+1}, y_{k+1} \mid y^k) = p(x_k \mid y^k)\, p(x_{k+1} \mid x_k)\, p(y_{k+1} \mid x_{k+1})$$

Integrating the above with respect to x_k,

$$p(x_{k+1}, y_{k+1} \mid y^k) = \int p(x_k \mid y^k)\, p(x_{k+1} \mid x_k)\, p(y_{k+1} \mid x_{k+1})\, dx_k \tag{90}$$

From Eqs. (89) and (90),

$$p(x_{k+1} \mid y^{k+1}) = \frac{\int p(x_k \mid y^k)\, p(x_{k+1} \mid x_k)\, p(y_{k+1} \mid x_{k+1})\, dx_k}{\int p(x_k \mid y_k)\, p(x_{k+1} \mid x_k)\, p(y_{k+1} \mid x_{k+1})\, d(x_k, x_{k+1})} \tag{91}$$

is the recursion formula for $p(x_i \mid y^i)$, $i = 0, 1, \ldots$. Using (91), various optimal estimates of x_{k+1} can now be obtained by specifying the estimation criterion functions.

If the assumptions of independence of ξ_i and η_i are removed, then one must deal with $p(x_{k+1} \mid x^k)$ and $p(y_{k+1} \mid x^{k+1})$ instead of $p(x_{k+1} \mid x_k)$ and $p(y_{k+1} \mid x_{k+1})$. Then

$$
\begin{aligned}
p(x^{k+1}, y^{k+1}) &= p(x_{k+1}, x^k, y_{k+1}, y^k) \\
&= p(y^k)\, p(x^k \mid y^k)\, p(x_{k+1} \mid x^k, y^k)\, p(y_{k+1} \mid x^{k+1}, y^k)
\end{aligned}
$$

and

$$
\begin{aligned}
p(x^{k+1} \mid y^{k+1}) &= \frac{p(x^{k+1}, y^{k+1})}{p(y^{k+1})} \\
&= \frac{p(x^k \mid y^k)\, p(x_{k+1} \mid x^k, y^k)\, p(y_{k+1} \mid x^{k+1}, y^k)}{p(y_{k+1} \mid y^k)} \\
&= \frac{p(x^k \mid y^k)\, p(x_{k+1} \mid x^k, y^k)\, p(y_{k+1} \mid x^{k+1}, y^k)}{\int p(x^k \mid y^k)\, p(x_{k+1} \mid x^k, y^k)\, p(y_{k+1} \mid x^{k+1}, y^k)\, dx^{k+1}} \qquad (92)
\end{aligned}
$$

D. Example. Sequential (Kalman) Filter

As an illustration of the previous section, let us rederive the equation for the best estimate x_k^* of x_k when the system is linear and the random noises are Gaussian:

$$
\begin{aligned}
x_{i+1} &= A_i x_i + C_i \xi_i \\
y_i &= H_i x_i + \eta_i, \qquad i = 0, 1, \ldots
\end{aligned}
\qquad (93)
$$

with the assumption that ξ_i and η_i are independent white Gaussian random vectors such that

$$
\begin{aligned}
E(\xi_i) = E(\eta_i) &= 0, && \text{all } i \\
\operatorname{cov}(\xi_i, \xi_j) &= Q_i \delta_{ij} \\
\operatorname{cov}(\eta_i, \eta_j) &= R_i \delta_{ij} \\
\operatorname{cov}(\xi_i, \eta_j) &= 0, && \text{all } i \text{ and } j
\end{aligned}
$$

The details of the derivation are found in Section 3 and Appendix C of Chapter II. The best estimates with correlated noises are also found in Section 3 of Chapter II.

The probability density function $p(x_i \mid y^i)$ has been shown to be Gaussian, hence has the sufficient statistics

$$
E(x_i \mid y^i) \triangleq x_i^*
$$

and

$$\operatorname{cov}(x_i \mid y^i) \triangleq \Gamma_i$$

Now $p(x_{k+1} \mid y^k)$ is Gaussian with

$$E(x_{k+1} \mid y^k) = A_k x_k{}^* \triangleq \hat{x}_{k+1}$$

$$\operatorname{cov}(x_{k+1} \mid y^k) = P_k$$

where

$$P_{k+1} \triangleq \operatorname{cov}(x_{k+1} \mid y^k) = A_k \Gamma_k A_k{}' + C_k Q_k C_k$$

Since $p(y_{k+1} \mid y^k)$ is Gaussian with

$$E(y_{k+1} \mid y^k) = H_k\, E(x_{k+1} \mid y^k) = H_k \hat{x}_{k+1}$$

$$\operatorname{cov}(y_{k+1} \mid y^k) = H_{k+1} P_{k+1} H'_{k+1} + R_{k+1}$$

from (89) and (93),

$$p(x_{k+1} \mid y^{k+1}) = \text{const} \exp[-\tfrac{1}{2}(x_{k+1} - x^*_{k+1})' \Gamma^{-1}_{k+1}(x_{k+1} - x^*_{k+1})] \qquad (94)$$

where

$$x^*_{k+1} = \hat{x}_{k+1} + K_{k+1}(y_{k+1} - H_{k+1}\hat{x}_{k+1}) \qquad (95)$$

$$K_{k+1} = \Gamma_{k+1} H'_{k+1} R^{-1}_{k+1} \qquad (96)$$

$$\Gamma^{-1}_{k+1} = P^{-1}_{k+1} + H'_{k+1} R^{-1}_{k+1} H_{k+1}$$

or

$$\Gamma_{k+1} = P_{k+1} - P_{k+1} H'_{k+1}(H_{k+1} P_{k+1} H'_{k+1} + R_{k+1})^{-1} H_{k+1} P_{k+1} \qquad (97)$$

where

$$P_{k+1} = A_k \Gamma_k A_k{}' + C_k Q_k C_k{}' \qquad (98)$$

$\Gamma_0 = \operatorname{cov}[x_0 \mid y_0]$ is given from the a priori information on the system.

Alternate expressions for Γ's and K's have been obtained in Section 4 of Chapter II as

$$K_i = P_i H_i{}'[H_i P_i H_i{}' + R_i]^{-1} \qquad (96)'$$

$$\Gamma_{i+1} = [I - K_{i+1} H_{i+1}] P_{i+1} [I - K_{i+1} H_{i+1}]' + K_{i+1} R_{i+1} K'_{i+1} \qquad (97)'$$

Symbol M_i was used there instead of P_i with C's replaced by identity matrices.

It is important to realize that even if the random noises are not Gaussian, the best linear estimate of x_i given y^i, i.e., the estimate which is linear in the observations $y_0, y_1, \ldots, y_i$ is given by (95). The estimate x_i^* is the orthogonal projection of x_i on the linear manifold spanned by y^i. The best estimate with a quadratic criterion function, $E(x_i \mid y^i)$, is the best linear estimate when all variables, x's and y's, are Gaussian random variables, adding further importance to this estimate.

E. Control Systems

Let us modify the example discussed in the last section by adding a control term to the plant equation (93):

$$x_{i+1} = A_i x_i + B_i u_i + C_i \xi_i \tag{99}$$

$$y_i = H_i x_i + \eta_i \tag{100}$$

where u_i is the closed-loop control vector, i.e., u_i is some function of y^i. Under the same set of assumptions, we can derive the expression for x_{k+1}^* in terms of x_k^* and u_k. As before, by computing $p(x_{k+1} \mid y^{k+1})$, one can obtain x_{k+1}^* in a straightforward manner. The only difference now is that

$$E(x_{k+1} \mid y^k) = A_k x_k^* + B_k u_k$$

whereas $E(x_{k+1} \mid y^k) = A_k x_k^*$ in the last section.

Thus, we obtain

$$x_{k+1}^* = A_k x_k^* + B_k u_k + \Gamma_{k+1} H_{k+1}' R_{k+1}^{-1} (y_{k+1} - H_{k+1} A_k x_k^* - H_{k+1} B_k u_k)$$

where

$$\Gamma_{k+1}^{-1} = P_{k+1}^{-1} + H_{k+1}' R_{k+1}^{-1} H_{k+1}$$

The schematic diagram of the optimal Bayesian estimation is identical to Fig. 5.5, the expression for the gain being the only difference.

F. Kalman Filter for Linearized Nonlinear Systems

a. *Introduction*

Optimal Bayesian filters for general dynamic systems have been discussed in Section 3,C. The special case is discussed in Section 3,D, where the plant and the observation equations are both linear and when the conditional means are taken to be the best estimates.

In this section, we will construct Kalman filters for nonlinear systems by linearizing the plant and the observation equations.[82]

It should be noted, however, that the procedure of linearizing the plant and the observation equations first and constructing an optimal linear filter for the linearized system does not necessarily yield a better approximation than that of obtaining the exact or approximate conditional probability densities for the nonlinear system, as was done in Section 3,C, and then approximating it further if desired by appropriate linearization for ease of handling and/or implementation. This latter approach will be developed in Section 3,G.

b. *Construction of Filter*

In order to construct an approximate filter for a nonlinear system we linearize a nonlinear plant and observation equations

$$\begin{aligned} x(i+1) &= F(x(i), \xi(i), i) \\ y(i) &= G(x(i), \eta(i), i) \end{aligned} \tag{101}$$

by a Taylor series expansion about a nominal sequence of state vectors $\bar{x}$'s and about $\xi(i) = \eta(i) = 0$, retaining only terms up to the first order. The subscripts are now used to denote components of vectors. The time index is carried as the argument:

$$\begin{aligned} x(i+1) &= F(\bar{x}(i), 0, i) + A(i)\,(x(i) - \bar{x}(i)) + v(i) \\ y(i) &= G(\bar{x}(i), 0, i) + H(i)\,(x(i) - \bar{x}(i)) + w(i) \end{aligned} \tag{102}$$

where $\bar{x}(i)$ is the nominal $x(i)$ and where $A(i)$ is the Jacobian matrix of F with respect to x. Its (i, j)th element is given by

$$A_{jk}(i) \triangleq \left(\frac{\partial F}{\partial x}\right)_{jk}$$

which is the partial derivative of the jth component of F by the kth component of x and the partial derivative is evaluated at $x(i) = \bar{x}(i)$, $\xi(i) = \eta(i) = 0$, and i. Similarly, we compute

$$H(i) \triangleq \left[\left(\frac{\partial G}{\partial x}\right)_{jk}\right]_{(\bar{x}(i),0,i)}$$

$$v_j(i) = \sum_k \frac{\partial F_j(\bar{x}(i), 0, i)}{\partial \xi_k} \xi_k(i)$$

$$w_j(i) = \sum_k \frac{\partial G_j(\bar{x})i), 0, i)}{\partial \eta_k} \eta_k(i)$$

where $v_j(i)$ is the jth component of the vector $v(i)$. Assume

$$E(v(i)) = E(w(i)) = 0$$
$$E(v(i)\, v'(j)) = V(i)\, \delta_{ij}$$
$$E(w(i)\, w'(j)) = W(i)\, \delta_{ij}$$
$$E(v(i)\, w'(j)) = 0$$

Define

$$\begin{aligned} \alpha(i) &= x(i) - \bar{x}(i) \\ \beta(i+1) &= x(i+1) - F(\overline{x(i)}, 0, i) \\ \gamma(i) &= y(i) - G(\overline{x(i)}, 0, i) \end{aligned} \tag{103}$$

Then

$$\begin{aligned} \beta(i+1) &= A(i)\,\alpha(i) + v(i) \\ \gamma(i) &= H(i)\,\alpha(i) + w(i) \end{aligned} \tag{104}$$

are the linearized plant and observation equations. Using symbols defined as

$$\alpha^*(i) = E(\alpha(i) \mid \gamma(0),..., \gamma(i))$$
$$\hat{\beta}(i+1) = E(\beta(i+1) \mid \gamma(0),..., \gamma(i))$$
$$\beta^*(i+1) = E(\beta(i+1) \mid \gamma(0),..., \gamma(i+1))$$
$$\hat{\beta}(i+1) = A(i)\,\alpha^*(i)$$

the Kalman filter for the system of (104) is governed by

$$\beta^*(i+1) = \hat{\beta}(i+1) + K(i+1)\,[\gamma(i+1) - H(i+1)\,\hat{\beta}(i+1)] \tag{105}$$

Then from (103) the approximately optimal estimate is given by

$$x^*(i+1) = F(\overline{x(i)}, 0, i) + \beta^*(i+1) \tag{106}$$

and

$$\alpha^*(i) = x^*(i) - \bar{x}(i)$$

The expressions for error-covariance matrices can be similarly obtained.

If the nominal $\bar{x}$'s are chosen to satisfy the nonlinear plant equation with no noise, then $\alpha(i)$ and $\beta(i)$ coincide. If F and G are linearized about $x^*(i)$, instead of about the nominal $\bar{x}$, then

$$\alpha^*(i) = 0$$

since

$$\alpha(i) = x(i) - x^*(i)$$

Hence

$$\hat{\beta}(i+1) = 0$$

and

$$\beta^*(i+1) = K(i+1)\,\gamma(i+1) \tag{107}$$

Define

$$\hat{x}(i+1) = F(x^*(i), 0, i) \tag{108}$$

Then

$$x^*(i+1) = \hat{x}(i+1) + K(i+1)\,[y(i+1) - G(\hat{x}(i+1), 0, i)] \tag{109}$$

is the Kalman filter for the linearized system, where the gain is computed recursively from

$$\begin{aligned}\Gamma(i+1) = {} & [I - K(i+1)\,H(i+1)]\,M(i+1)\,[I - K(i+1)\,H(i+1)]' \\ & + K(i+1)\,R(i+1)\,K'(i+1)\end{aligned} \tag{110}$$

where

$$M(i+1) = A(i)\,\Gamma(i)\,A'(i) + V(i)$$

$$K(i+1) = M(i+1)\,H'(i+1)\,[H(i+1)\,M(i+1)\,H'(i+1) + W(i+1)]^{-1}$$

c. *Numerical Example*

A numerical example is now presented. The example is computed by R. E. Orr[109a] and is included here with his consent. In this example the arguments refer to the time instants. The subscripts refer to the components of vectors. Consider a point mass accelerated in a vacuum by the reaction force of expelled mass. Then the acceleration, $a(t)$, is given by

$$a(t) = \frac{F(t)}{m(t)} = \frac{C\dot{m}}{m_0 - \dot{m}t} \tag{111}$$

assuming a constant velocity, C, and flow rate, $\dot{m}$, of expelled mass; m_0 is the mass at an arbitrary time $t_0 = 0$. For simplicity, assume the acceleration to be directly away from a point at which range x and/or range rate $\dot{x}$ are being observed. Variations in the direction of acceleration, as well as motion of the observation point, can be taken into account, but will not be considered here since they do not fundamentally affect the problem.

It is desired to estimate x, $\dot{x}$, and $\ddot{x} = a(t)$ from observations of x and/or $\dot{x}$ contaminated by white noise. Because $a(t)$ is nonlinear, a linear approximation method of the previous section is used and the optimal Kalman filter is obtained for the linearized problem.

Letting C, $\dot{m}$, and m_0 vary by small amounts,

$$\delta a = \frac{(C + \delta C)(\dot{m} + \delta\dot{m})}{m_0 + \delta m_0 - (\dot{m} + \delta\dot{m})t} - a(t)$$

$$= \frac{[\dot{m}(m_0 - \dot{m}t)]\,\delta C + [Cm_0]\,\delta\dot{m} - [C\dot{m}]\,\delta m_0 + [m_0 - \dot{m}t]\,\delta C\,\delta\dot{m}}{[m_0 - \dot{m}t]^2 + [m_0 - \dot{m}t]\,\delta m_0 - [(m_0 - \dot{m}t)t]\,\delta\dot{m}}$$

This expression may be approximated by a linear equation

$$\delta a = \left[\frac{\dot{m}}{m(t)}\right]\delta C + \left[\frac{Cm_0}{[m(t)]^2}\right]\delta\dot{m} - \left[\frac{C\dot{m}}{[m(t)]^2}\right]\delta m_0 \tag{112}$$

if the perturbations are small with respect to the parameters C, $\dot{m}$, and m_0.

The resulting linearized system may be represented diagrammatically as in Fig. 5.6. The uncertainties in C and $\dot{m}$ are assumed to be represented by white noise passed through a first-order filter, while δm_0 is a bias. The "nominal" value of a is independently determined as a known function of time. The state vector $\mathbf{x}$ is taken to be

$$\mathbf{x} = \begin{bmatrix} x \\ \dot{x} \\ \delta C \\ \delta\dot{m} \\ \delta m_0 \end{bmatrix} \tag{113}$$

The observation equation is given by

$$\mathbf{y} = H\mathbf{x} + \boldsymbol{\eta} \tag{114}$$

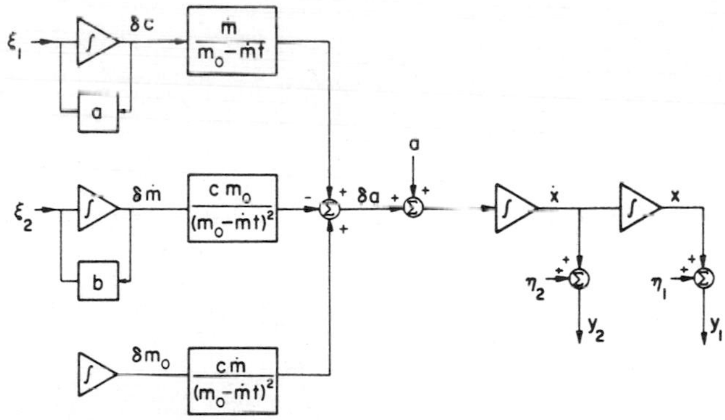

Fig. 5.6. Schematic diagram of a linearized system for the nonlinear estimation problem (112).

or, in its component form,

$$\begin{bmatrix} y_1 \\ y_2 \\ 0 \\ 0 \\ 0 \end{bmatrix} = \begin{bmatrix} 1 & 0 & 0 & 0 & 0 \\ 0 & 1 & 0 & 0 & 0 \\ 0 & 0 & 0 & 0 & 0 \\ 0 & 0 & 0 & 0 & 0 \\ 0 & 0 & 0 & 0 & 0 \end{bmatrix} \begin{bmatrix} x \\ \dot{x} \\ \delta C \\ \delta \dot{m} \\ \delta m_0 \end{bmatrix} + \begin{bmatrix} \eta_1 \\ \eta_2 \\ 0 \\ 0 \\ 0 \end{bmatrix} \tag{114$'$}$$

when x and $\dot{x}$ are observed. If either quantity were to cease being observed, the corresponding element of the H matrix must be put to zero. The plant equation for $\mathbf{x}$ of (113) is given by

$$\mathbf{x}(k+1) = \phi(k)\,\mathbf{x}(k) + \boldsymbol{\xi}(k) \tag{115}$$

where

$$\phi(k) = \begin{bmatrix} 1 & 1 & AC_1(k) & BC_2(k) & \frac{1}{2}C_3(k) \\ 0 & 1 & A'C_1(k) & B'C_2(k) & C_3(k) \\ 0 & 0 & e^{-a} & 0 & 0 \\ 0 & 0 & 0 & e^{-b} & 0 \\ 0 & 0 & 0 & 0 & 1 \end{bmatrix}$$

and where

$$A = \frac{e^{-a} + a + 1}{a^2}$$

$$B = \frac{e^{-b} + b + 1}{b^2}$$

$$A' = \frac{1 - e^{-a}}{a}$$

$$B' = \frac{1 - e^{-b}}{b}$$

and

$$\boldsymbol{\xi}(k) = \begin{bmatrix} 0 \\ 0 \\ \xi_1 \\ \xi_2 \\ 0 \end{bmatrix}$$

The time-varying gains are considered constant during the sampling intervals, i.e.,

$$C_1(k) = \frac{\dot{m}}{m_0 - \dot{m}k}$$

$$C_2(k) = \frac{Cm_0}{(m_0 - \dot{m}k)^2}$$

$$C_3(k) = \frac{-C\dot{m}}{(m_0 - \dot{m}k)^2}$$

If the change in δa is sufficiently small during a sampling interval, a sample-and-hold can be introduced at δa to further simplify the ϕ matrix:

$$\phi(k) = \begin{bmatrix} 1 & 1 & \frac{1}{2}C_1(k) & \frac{1}{2}C_2(k) & \frac{1}{2}C_3(k) \\ 0 & 0 & C_1(k) & C_2(k) & C_3(k) \\ 0 & 0 & e^{-a} & 0 & 0 \\ 0 & 0 & 0 & e^{-b} & 0 \\ 0 & 0 & 0 & 0 & 1 \end{bmatrix} \tag{116}$$

Noise covariance matrices are given by

$$R(k) = \begin{bmatrix} \sigma_1^2 & 0 & 0 & 0 & 0 \\ 0 & \sigma_2^2 & 0 & 0 & 0 \\ 0 & 0 & 0 & 0 & 0 \\ 0 & 0 & 0 & 0 & 0 \\ 0 & 0 & 0 & 0 & 0 \end{bmatrix} \tag{117}$$

$$Q(k) = \begin{bmatrix} 0 & 0 & 0 & 0 & 0 \\ 0 & 0 & 0 & 0 & 0 \\ 0 & 0 & \sigma_3^2 & 0 & 0 \\ 0 & 0 & 0 & \sigma_4^2 & 0 \\ 0 & 0 & 0 & 0 & 0 \end{bmatrix} \tag{118}$$

The initial value of the Γ matrix is given by

$$\Gamma(0) = \begin{bmatrix} \sigma_{x_0}^2 & 0 & 0 & 0 & 0 \\ 0 & \sigma_{\dot{x}_0}^2 & 0 & 0 & 0 \\ 0 & 0 & \sigma_{\delta C_0}^2 & 0 & 0 \\ 0 & 0 & 0 & \sigma_{\delta \dot{m}_0}^2 & 0 \\ 0 & 0 & 0 & 0 & \sigma_{\delta m_0}^2 \end{bmatrix} \tag{119}$$

Letting

$$\phi(k)\, \mathbf{x}^*(k) = \hat{\mathbf{x}}(k+1)$$

or, in terms of its components,

$$\begin{aligned} \hat{x}(k+1) &= x^*(k) + \dot{x}^*(k) + \tfrac{1}{2}C_1(k)\,\delta C^*(k) + \tfrac{1}{2}C_2(k)\,\delta\dot{m}^*(k) \\ &\quad + \tfrac{1}{2}C_3(k)\,\delta m_0^*(k) \\ \hat{\dot{x}}(k+1) &= x^*(k) + C_1(k)\,\delta C^*(k) + C_2(k)\,\delta\dot{m}^*(k) + C_3(k)\,\delta m_0^*(k) \\ \delta\hat{C}(k+1) &= e^{-a}\,\delta C^*(k) \\ \delta\hat{\dot{m}}(k+1) &= e^{-b}\,\delta\dot{m}^*(k) \\ \delta\hat{m}_0(k+1) &= \delta m_0^*(k) \end{aligned}$$

The sequential estimation equations are given by

$$
\begin{aligned}
x^*(k+1) &= \hat{x}(k+1) + K_{11}(y_1 - \hat{x}(k+1)) + K_{12}(y_2 - \hat{\dot{x}}(k+1)) \\
\dot{x}^*(k+1) &= \hat{\dot{x}}(k+1) + K_{21}(y_1 - \hat{x}(k+1)) + K_{22}(y_2 - \hat{\dot{x}}(k+1)) \\
\delta C^*(k+1) &= \delta\hat{C}(k+1) + K_{31}(y_1 - \hat{x}(k+1)) + K_{32}(y_2 - \hat{\dot{x}}(k+1)) \\
\delta\dot{m}^*(k+1) &= \delta\hat{\dot{m}}(k+1) + K_{41}(y_1 - \hat{x}(k+1)) + K_{42}(y_2 - \hat{\dot{x}}(k+1)) \\
\delta m_0^*(k+1) &= \delta\hat{m}_0(k+1) + K_{51}(y_1 - \hat{x}(k+1)) + K_{52}(y_2 - \hat{\dot{x}}(k+1))
\end{aligned} \tag{120}
$$

The error covariance of a is not computed by Γ's because a is not contained in $\mathbf{x}$. Since this covariance is of interest, it is computed as follows.

From (112),

$$E\{\delta a^2\} = E\{(C_1\,\delta C + C_2\,\delta\dot{m} - C_3\,\delta m_0)^2\}$$

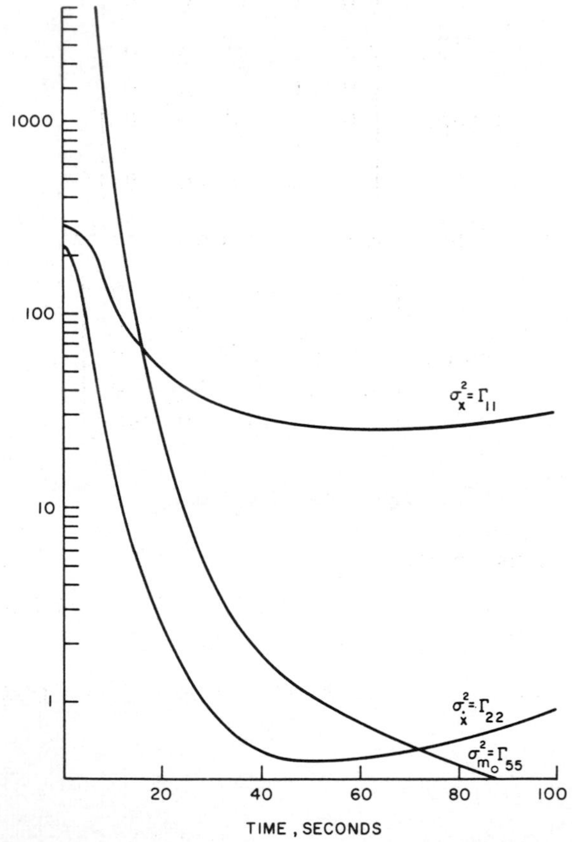

Fig. 5.7. Variances of the estimates of the linearized system versus time.

or

$$\sigma_a^2 = C_1^2\Gamma_{33} + 2C_1C_2\Gamma_{34} - 2C_1C_3\Gamma_{35} + C_2^2\Gamma_{44} - 2C_2C_3\Gamma_{45} + C_3^2\Gamma_{55}$$

Figures 5.7 and 5.8 show the error covariances Γ_{ij} and σ_a^2 versus time when only x is observed ($H_{22} = 0$, $R_{11} = 100$) for the parameter values given in the accompanying tabulation.

Parameter	σ	Time constant of filter t
$C = 10^4$ ft/sec	$\sigma_C = 10.$	10.0 sec
$\dot{m} = 10$ slugs/sec	$\sigma_{\dot{m}} = 0.01$	1.0 sec
$m_0 = 2000$ slugs	$\sigma_{m_0} = 200.$	∞ (bias)

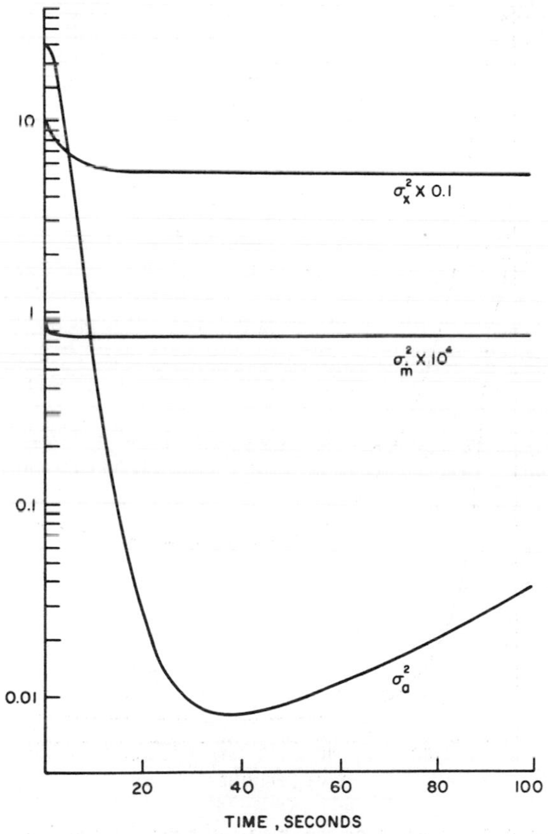

Fig. 5.8. Variances of the estimates of the linearized system versus time.

where t's are the time constants of the filters used to represent errors in C, $\dot{m}$, and m_0.

Note the initial rapid decrease in the error covariances as the first measurements improve the estimates. Since m_0 is a constant, the error covariance of its estimate decreases monotonically as long as measurements are made. C and $\dot{m}$ are constants with additive stochastic variations, so the estimation errors reach constant values; $\dot{x}$ and x, as well as a, are time-varying quantities with additive time-varying stochastic components proportional to $1/m(t)$ and $1/m(t)^2$. After an initial decrease, the error covariances of these quantities begin to increase as the mass becomes smaller. If the process is allowed to continue indefinitely, these error covariances will go to infinity as $m(t) \rightarrow 0$.

The filter gains K_{i1} are shown in Figs. 5.9 and 5.10. Similar reasoning

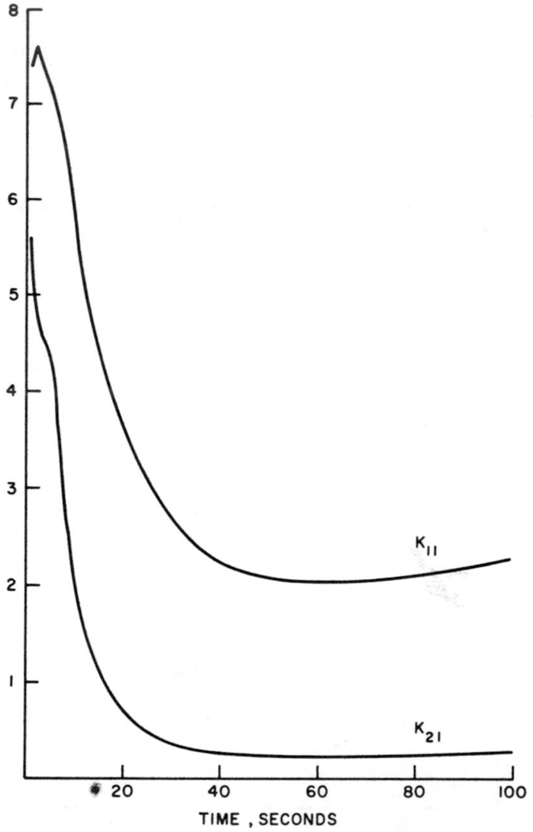

Fig. 5.9. Time-varying gains of the Kalman filter for the linearized system.

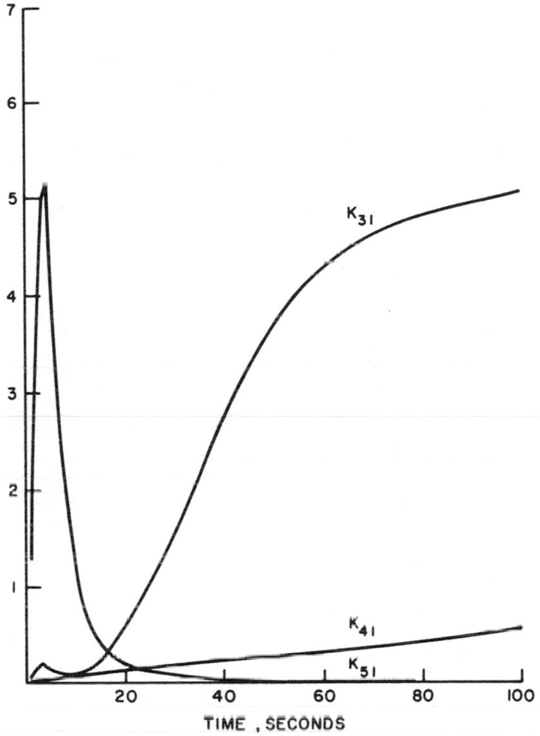

Fig. 5.10. Time-varying gains of the Kalman filter for the linearized system.

to the above applies. The components of the error covariances Γ_{1i}, $2 \leqslant i \leqslant 5$, are shown in Figs. 5.11 and 5.12.

G. Approximate Bayesian Estimation of Nonlinear Systems

a. *Estimation Based on the First Two Moments*

In this section another approximate method of obtaining the conditional means of a posteriori probability densities is carried out for a scalar nonlinear system given by

$$\begin{aligned} x_{i+1} &= f(x_i) + \xi_i \\ y_i &= h(x_i) + \eta_i \end{aligned} \tag{121}$$

under the assumptions that x_0 is Gaussian with mean a and variance

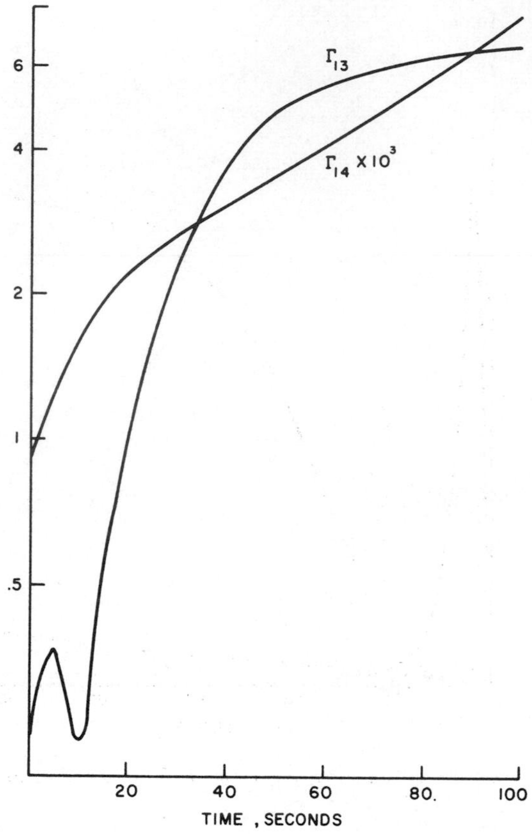

Fig. 5.11. The off-diagonal elements of the error-covariance matrices versus time.

σ^2, that f and h are twice differentiable, and that ξ_i and η_i are Gaussian random variables independent of x_0 with

$$E(\xi_i) = E(\eta_i) = 0$$
$$E(\xi_i\xi_j) = q_i^2\delta_{ij}$$
$$E(\eta_i\eta_j) = r_i^2\delta_{ij}$$
$$E(\xi_i\eta_j) = 0$$

The method similar to Section 3,E of Chapter II can be used when ξ and η are correlated. The following development is given for the uncorrelated ξ and η noises. Unlike Section F, we do not linearize (121) at the beginning.

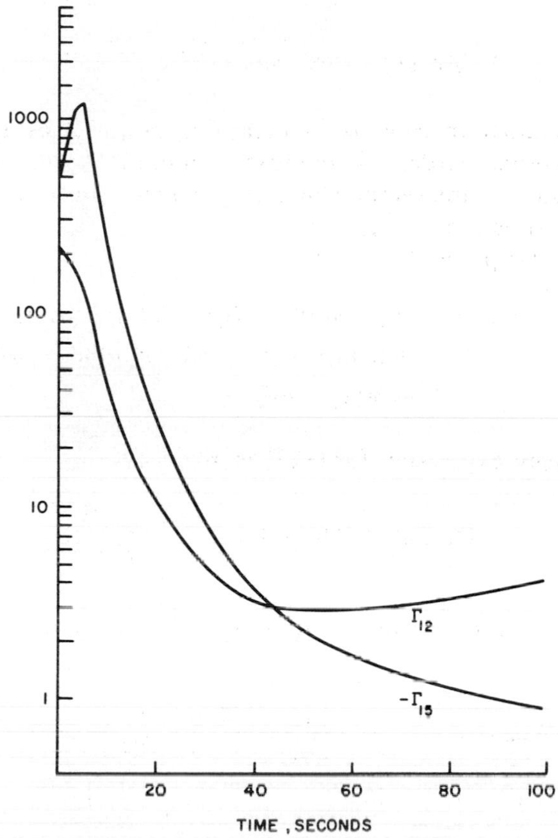

Fig. 5.12. The off-diagonal elements of the error-covariance matrices versus time.

The recursion equation for the conditional probability density $p(x_i \mid y^i)$ is given by

$$p(x_{i+1} \mid y^{i+1}) = \frac{\int p(x_i \mid y^i)\, p(x_{i+1} \mid x_i)\, p(y_{i+1} \mid x_{i+1})\, dx_i}{\int [\text{numerator}]\, dx_{i+1}} \tag{122}$$

The initial conditional density $p(x_0 \mid y_0)$ is given by

$$p(x_0 \mid y_0) = \frac{p(y_0 \mid x_0)\, p_0(x_0)}{\int p(y_0 \mid x_0)\, p_0(x_0)\, dx_0} \tag{123}$$

where

$$p(y_0 \mid x_0) = \text{const} \exp\left(-\frac{(y_0 - h(x_0))^2}{2r_0^{\,2}}\right)$$

and

$$p_0(x_0) = \text{const}\exp\left(-\frac{(x_0 - a)^2}{2\sigma^2}\right)$$

The approximation consists in regarding $p(x_i \mid y^i)$ as approximately Gaussian. In other words, only the first term in the asymptotic expansion of $p(x_i \mid y^i)$, such as the Gram–Charlier or Edgeworth series,[33] is retained in the approximation.

Expanding $h(x_0)$ about $x_0 = a$,

$$\begin{aligned}(y_0 - h(x_0))^2 = (y_0 - h(a))^2 &- 2(y_0 - h(a))\,h'(a)\,(x_0 - a) \\ &+ [h'(a)^2 - (y_0 - h(a))\,h''(a)](x_0 - a)^2 \\ &+ o((x_0 - a)^2)\end{aligned}$$

An approximate expression for (123) is given by

$$p(x_0 \mid y_0) \doteqdot \text{const}\exp\left(-\frac{(x_0 - \mu_0)^2}{2\sigma_0^2}\right) \tag{124}$$

provided

$$1/\sigma^2 + [h'(a)^2 - (y_0 - h(a))\,h''(a)]/r_0^2 > 0$$

where

$$\mu_0 = a + \frac{(y_0 - h(a))\,h'(a)/r_0^2}{1/\sigma^2 + [h'(a)^2 - (y_0 - h(a))\,h''(a)]/r_0^2} \tag{125a}$$

$$1/\sigma_0^2 = 1/\sigma^2 + [h'(a)^2 - (y_0 - h(a))\,h''(a)]/r_0^2 \tag{125b}$$

Assume that

$$p(x_i \mid y^i) \doteqdot \text{const}\exp\left(-\frac{(x_i - \mu_i)^2}{2\sigma_i^2}\right) \tag{126}$$

where μ_i and σ_i are generally functions of y^i. From (121) we have

$$p(x_{i+1} \mid x_i) = \text{const}\exp\left(-\frac{[x_{i+1} - f(x_i)]^2}{2q_i^2}\right) \tag{127}$$

and

$$p(y_{i+1} \mid x_{i+1}) = \text{const}\exp\left(-\frac{[y_{i+1} - h(x_{i+1})]^2}{2r_{i+1}^2}\right) \tag{128}$$

In order to carry out the integration with respect to x_i in the numerator of (122), expand $f(x_i)$ about μ_i as a Taylor series:

$$f(x_i) \doteqdot f(\mu_i) + f'(\mu_i)\,(x_i - \mu_i) + \tfrac{1}{2}f''(\mu_i)\,(x_i - \mu_i)^2 + o((x_i - \mu_i)^2) \tag{129}$$

From (126), (127), and (128),

$$\int p(x_i \mid y^i)\, p(x_{i+1} \mid x_i)\, dx_i \doteq \text{const} \exp(-\tfrac{1}{2} E_i)$$

where

$$E_i = \frac{(x_{i+1} - f(\mu_i))^2}{q_i^2} \left[1 - \frac{f'(\mu_i)^2/q_i^2}{1/\sigma_i^2 + [f'(\mu_i)^2 - (x_{i+1} - f(\mu_i)) f''(\mu_i)]/q_i^2}\right]$$
$$= \frac{1/\sigma_i^2 - (x_{i+1} - f(\mu_i)) f''(\mu_i)/q_i^2}{q_i^2[1/\sigma_i^2 + (f'(\mu_i)^2 - (x_{i+1} - f(\mu_i)) f''(\mu_i))/q_i^2]} (x_{i+1} - f(\mu_i))^2 \tag{130}$$

To carry out the integral with respect to x_{i+1} in the denominator of (122), expand $h(x_{i+1})$ into a Taylor series about

$$\hat{x}_{i+1} \triangleq f(\mu_i) \tag{131}$$

to obtain

$$h(x_{i+1}) = h(\hat{x}_{i+1}) + h'(\hat{x}_{i+1})(x_{i+1} - \hat{x}_{i+1}) + \tfrac{1}{2}h''(\hat{x}_{i+1})(x_{i+1} - \hat{x}_{i+1})^2$$
$$+ o[(x_{i+1} - \hat{x}_{i+1})^2] \tag{132}$$

The exponent in (128) can be written as

$$[y_{i+1} - h(x_{i+1})]^2 = [y_{i+1} - h(\hat{x}_{i+1})]^2 - 2(y_{i+1} - h(\hat{x}_{i+1}))\, h'(\hat{x}_{i+1})(x_{i+1} - \hat{x}_{i+1})$$
$$+ [h'(\hat{x}_{i+1}) - (y_{i+1} - h(\hat{x}_{i+1}))\, h''(\hat{x}_{i+1})](x_{i+1} - \hat{x}_{i+1})^2$$
$$+ O[(x_{i+1} - \hat{x}_{i+1})^2] \tag{133}$$

Combining (130) and (133), after the denominator in (122) is computed, we obtain

$$p(x_{i+1} \mid y^{i+1}) \doteq \text{const} \exp\left(-\frac{(x_{i+1} - \mu_{i+1})^2}{2\sigma_{i+1}^2}\right) \tag{134}$$

where

$$\mu_{i+1} = \hat{x}_{i+1} + \frac{(y_{i+1} - h(\hat{x}_{i+1}))\, h'(\hat{x}_{i+1})/r_{i+1}^2}{1/\sigma_{i+1}^2} \tag{135a}$$

where $\hat{x}_{i+1}$ is given by (131), and where

$$\frac{1}{\sigma_{i+1}^2} = \frac{1/\sigma_i^2}{q_i^2[1/\sigma_i^2 + f'(\mu_i)^2/q_i^2]} + \frac{h'(\hat{x}_{i+1})^2 - (y_{i+1} - h(\hat{x}_{i+1}))\, h''(\hat{x}_{i+1})}{r_{i+1}^2} \tag{135b}$$

provided $1/\sigma_{i+1}^2$ turns out positive.

From (135b), the variance is seen to depend on the observation data. This effect is not observed if the nonlinear equations are linearized first and the Kalman filter is constructed for the linearized systems.

Comments similar to those in Section 1,E can be made about negative variances which may occur in using this method. In short, a negative variance, when it occurs, is an indication that some of the assumptions of the Section are no longer valid and that the sequential estimation procedure of (135a) should be restarted.

b. *Higher-Order Estimator*

In order to increase the accuracy of the filter, it may be necessary to include the effects of the moments higher than the second.

Namely, instead of approximating $p(x_i \mid y^i)$ by $N(\mu_i, \sigma_i^2)$, it may be necessary to include the effect of the third moment, i.e., the skewness[39] of the probability distribution, in approximating $p(x_i \mid y^i)$ by

$$p(x_i \mid y^i) \doteqdot \text{const} \left[1 - \frac{\gamma_i}{6}\left\{3\left(\frac{x_i - \mu_i}{\sigma_i}\right) - \left(\frac{x_i - \mu_i}{\sigma_i}\right)^3\right\}\right] \exp\left(-\frac{(x_i - \mu_i)^2}{2\sigma_i^2}\right)$$

where

$$\gamma_i \triangleq E[(x_i - \mu_i)^3 \mid y^i]/\sigma_i^3$$

is the index of the skewness of the distribution.

Then proceeding quite analogously to the previous section, assuming now that f and h are differentiable at least three times, and retaining more terms in Taylor series expansions of f and h, a set of recursion equations for μ_i, σ_i, and γ_i are obtained. Then μ_{i+1} is given as a function of μ_i, σ_i, γ_i, and y_{i+1} among others.

Of course, this approach can be extended to include the effects of fourth or higher moments to increase the accuracy of approximation at the expense of added complexities of computation.

The method suggested in this section and some variations have been examined in some detail and performances of these nonlinear filters, as well as that of the Wiener-Kalman filter applied to the linearized system (method of Section F), have been investigated numerically. See Ph. D. Thesis by H. Sorensens for computational results. The preliminary numerical experiments seem to indicate that the method of Section F is quite good if the nominal $\bar{x}(i)$, about which the system equations are linearized, is taken to be the current optimal estimate $x^*(i)$, and that it is usually necessary to include more than the first two moments to achieve a comparable or a slightly better result than that obtainable by the method of Section F.

Another approach would be to use a density function from a class of probability density functions specified by a finite number of parameters, such as a Pearson type density function,[39] to approximate $p(x_i \mid y^i)$. This approach may be more advantageous since the approximating functions are always true probability density functions.

For a more general discussion of nonlinear estimation problems, see, for example, Balakrishnan.[18] See also Ref. 46.

Appendix. Completion of Squares

The procedure of completing squares of expressions involving matrices and vectors has already been discussed in detail in Appendixes C and D, Chapter II.

Since Appendix C contains many other topics, we excerpt here the portion on completing the matrices for easy reference. With regard to (83), define

$$
\begin{aligned}
E = {} & (x - \bar{x})'P_0^{-1}(x - \bar{x}) + (y - Hx)'R^{-1}(y - Hx) \\
& - (y - H\bar{x})'(R + HP_0H')^{-1}(y - H\bar{x})
\end{aligned}
$$

Note that R and P_0 are symmetric since they are covariance matrices. Collecting terms which are quadratic in x, linear in x, and independent of x, we have

$$
\begin{aligned}
E = {} & (x - \bar{x})'P_0^{-1}(x - \bar{x}) + [y - H\bar{x} - H(x - \bar{x})]'R^{-1}[y - H\bar{x} - H(x - \bar{x})] \\
& - (y - H\bar{x})(R^{-1} - R^{-1}HPH'R^{-1})(y - H\bar{x}) \\
= {} & (x - \bar{x})'(P_0^{-1} + H'R^{-1}H)(x - \bar{x}) - 2(x - \bar{x})'H'R^{-1}(y - H\bar{x}) \\
& + (y - H\bar{x})'[R^{-1} - (R + HP_0H')^{-1}](y - H\bar{x})
\end{aligned}
$$

Define

$$
P^{-1} = P_0^{-1} + H'R^{-1}H
$$

From the matrix identity in Appendix D, Chapter II,

$$
\begin{aligned}
(R + HP_0H')^{-1} &= R^{-1} - R^{-1}H(P_0^{-1} + H'R^{-1}H)^{-1}H'R^{-1} \\
&= R^{-1} - R^{-1}HPH'R^{-1}
\end{aligned}
$$

or

$$
R^{-1} - (R + HP_0H')^{-1} = R^{-1}HPH'R^{-1}
$$

Therefore,

$$
\begin{aligned}
E &= (x - \bar{x})'P^{-1}(x - \bar{x}) - 2(x - \bar{x})'H'R^{-1}(y - H\bar{x}) \\
&\quad + [H'R^{-1}(y - Hx)]'PH'R^{-1}(y - H\bar{x}) \\
&= (x - x^*)'P^{-1}(x - x^*)
\end{aligned}
$$

where

$$x^* = \bar{x} + PH'R^{-1}(y - H\bar{x})$$

Chapter VI

Convergence Questions in Bayesian Optimization Problems

1. Introduction

We have adopted the Bayesian approach in this book in studying the optimal control problems.

The Bayesian approach for adaptive control problems is characterized by the assumption that there exists an a priori distribution of the unknown parameter vector θ, $\theta \in \Theta$, where Θ is a known parameter space, which specifies the system parameter and/or the distribution functions of the random variables affecting the system. This a priori distribution is updated by the Bayes rule to obtain the a posteriori distribution of θ when a new set of information (observation data) becomes available. The Bayesian approach is widely used not only for optimal control problems but also for many other situations involving estimation of parameters in communication theory, statical theory of learning, operations research, and so on.

Because of the widespread use and the importance of the Bayesian approach in applications, it is important to investigate several related questions on the Bayesian approach such as:

(1) When can the search for optimal policies be restricted to the class of Bayesian policies?

(2) How do we choose a priori distribution for θ?

(3) When do the sequences of a posteriori distributions computed by the Bayes rule converge to the true distributions?

(4) Do two different choices of a priori distribution converge necessarily eventually to the same distribution?

(5) What is the effect of a particular choice of a priori distribution on the performance index of the system?

Answers to these questions will help us see whether the Bayesian approach is reasonable or applicable in any given problem.

The first question really asks for the conditions for the completeness of a class of Bayesian policies, i.e., the conditions under which optimal policies are guaranteed to be Bayesian, in a given problem. This question has been answered in Chapters II–IV and is not pursued any further here. See also Sworder.[133,136]

The second question has been a source of various criticisms against the Bayesian approach. So far no rational procedure has been put forth to choose a priori distributions. Spragins pointed out the desirableness of choosing self-reproducing-type a priori distribution functions.[128] It is sometimes suggested to choose a priori distributions which maximize the entropy, subject to some constraints such as fixed means of a priori distributions.[77]

In case the same decision problems occur repeatedly and independently with the same $p(y \mid \theta)$ and the same $p_0(\theta)$, the empirical Bayes approach may be used.[117,118,138] In this approach no specific a priori probability density $p_0(\theta)$ is assumed. Under certain conditions, the empirical Bayes control policies can be shown to approach asymptotically to the optimal but unknown Bayes control policies, which would be used if $p_0(\theta)$ is known. Question (2) is intimately connected with Questions (3), (4), and (5), because if it is true that different a priori distributions do converge to the same true distributions eventually then the arbitrariness associated with the initial choice of distribution functions becomes largely immaterial except for questions related to transient behaviors such as Question (5).

Investigation of Question (5) will give, for example, upper and/or lower bounds on additional costs of control or losses in the performance indexes due to "ignorance" on the part of controllers. Needless to say, such bounds are useful in many engineering problems.[12,134]

In Section 1, Chapter VII, we investigate some problems related to Question (5). For a class of linear control systems with quadratic criterion function we derive expressions giving approximate costs of control for parameter adaptive systems, as functions of control costs for the related stochastic systems, of a priori probability distributions and of the state vectors.

Questions (3) and (4), which are questions of convergence of a posteriori distributions, are discussed in Section 4 of this chapter. It turns out that answers to such convergence questions are already available in the existing mathematical and statistical literature in various forms as martingale convergence theorems.[47a,102] After an elementary discussion of convergence in Section 2, more precise statements of Questions (3) and (4) are given and some pertinent theorems are collected and stated in forms convenient for our purposes in Section 4. Since stochastic processes known as martingales are unfamiliar to most control engineers, we digress from the convergence questions and discuss martingales in Section 3. The problem of observability of stochastic and adaptive systems is intimately related to the convergence questions. This point is only touched upon in the last section of this chapter.

2. Convergence Questions: A Simple Case

Although the questions of convergence of a posteriori probability distributions will be treated generally in the next two sections, it is instructive to consider a simple example using heuristic arguments and elementary techniques. The following discussions of this example is based on Fukao.[62]

A particular problem considered in this section is the problem where the parameter space Θ contains a finite number of elements, i.e., the value of the unknown parameter θ is assumed to be one of θ_i, $1 \leqslant i \leqslant s$, and where the observations y are discrete and assumed independent for each θ in Θ. Suppose an a priori probability for θ is given by

$$z_{0,i} = \Pr[\theta = \theta_i], \qquad 1 \leqslant i \leqslant s \tag{1}$$

The a priori probability $z_0 = (z_{0,1}, \ldots, z_{0,s})$ is transformed by Bayes' rule into the a posteriori probability given an observation y. After $y_0, y_1, \ldots, y_n$ have been observed, the a posteriori probability, $z_{n+1} = (z_{n+1,1}, \ldots, z_{n+1,s})$, is given by

$$z_{n+1,i} = \frac{p(y^n \mid \theta_i)\, z_{0,i}}{\sum_{j=1}^{s} p(y^n \mid \theta_j)\, z_{0,j}} \tag{2}$$

where by the independence assumption of y's

$$p(y^n \mid \theta_i) = \prod_{j=0}^{n} p(y_j \mid \theta_i), \qquad 1 \leqslant i \leqslant s \tag{3}$$

Note that if $z_{i,k} = 0$ at some i, then $z_{j,k} = 0$ for all $j \geqslant i$, that if $z_{i,k} = 1$ at some i, then $z_{j,k} = 1$ for all $j \geqslant i$ and consequently $z_{j,l} = 0, \quad j \geqslant i, \quad l \neq k$

For example, given i, if $p(y_m \mid \theta_i) = 0$ for some m, then $z_{m+1,i} = 0$ from (2) and $z_{n,i} = 0$ for $n \geqslant m + 1$.

Assume now that y can take only a finite number of values $a_1, \ldots, a_I$ each time, with probability

$$\Pr[y = a_i] = p_i, \qquad \sum_1^k p_i = 1, \qquad 1 \leqslant i \leqslant I \tag{4}$$

where

$$p(y = a_i \mid \theta_j) > 0$$

for all $1 \leqslant i \leqslant I$ and $1 \leqslant j \leqslant s$. From the comments following (3), one can take $z_{0,i} > 0$, $1 \leqslant i \leqslant s$, without loss of generality. After a large number, N, of independent observations, a_i will be observed approximately Np_i times with probability close to one. Then

$$\begin{aligned} z_{N+1,i} &\doteqdot \frac{\prod_{j=1}^{I} [p(y = a_j \mid \theta_i)]^{Np_j} z_{0,i}}{\sum_{k=1}^{s} \prod_{j=1}^{I} [p(y = a_j \mid \theta_k)]^{Np_j} z_{0,k}} \\ &= 1 \Big/ \left\{ 1 + \sum_{j \neq i} \frac{z_{0,j}}{z_{0,i}} \left[\prod_{k=1}^{I} \left[\frac{p(y = a_k \mid \theta_j)}{p(y = a_k \mid \theta_i)} \right]^{p_k} \right]^N \right\} \end{aligned} \tag{5}$$

Equation (5) will now be used to discuss the limiting behavior of $z_{N,i}$ as N tends to infinity.

(a) If

$$\prod_{k=1}^{I} \left[\frac{p(y = a_k \mid \theta_j)}{p(y = a_k \mid \theta_i)} \right]^{p_k} > 1$$

for at least one j, then clearly, from (5),

$$\lim_{N \to \infty} z_{N,i} = 0$$

(b) If, on the other hand,

$$\prod_{k=1}^{I} \left[\frac{p(y = a_k \mid \theta_j)}{p(y = a_k \mid \theta_i)} \right]^{p_k} < 1$$

for all $j \neq i$, then

$$\lim_{N \to \infty} z_{N,i} = 1$$

(c) We may have an intermediate situation where

$$\prod_{k=1}^{I} \left[\frac{p(y = a_k \mid \theta_j)}{p(y = a_k \mid \theta_i)} \right]^{p_k} = 1 \qquad \text{for some} \quad j \neq i$$

and

$$\prod_{k=1}^{I} \left[\frac{p(y = a_k \mid \theta_l)}{p(y = a_k \mid \theta_i)}\right]^{p_k} < 1 \qquad \text{for all other} \quad l$$

then

$$\lim_{N\to\infty} z_{N,i} = \frac{1}{1 + z_{0,j}/z_{0,i}} = \frac{z_{0,i}}{z_{0,i} + z_{0,j}}$$

(d) If

$$\prod_{k=1}^{I} \left[\frac{p(y = a_k \mid \theta_j)}{p(y = a_k \mid \theta_i)}\right]^{p_k} = 1 \qquad \text{for all} \quad j \in J$$

where J is some subset of $\{1, 2, \ldots, I\}$ containing i and

$$\prod_{k=1}^{I} \left[\frac{p(y = a_k \mid \theta_j)}{p(y = a_k \mid \theta_i)}\right]^{p_k} < 1 \qquad \text{for all} \quad j \notin J$$

then

$$\lim_{N\to\infty} z_{N,i} = \frac{z_{0,i}}{\sum_{j\in J} z_{0,j}}$$

As can be seen from these four special cases, the ratio R,

$$R = \prod_{k=1}^{I} \left[\frac{p(y = a_k \mid \theta_j)}{p(y = a_k \mid \theta_i)}\right]^{p_k} \tag{6}$$

plays an important role in deciding the limiting behaviors of $z_{N,i}$ as N tends to infinity.

The condition $R \gtreqless 1$ is equivalent to that of

$$\sum_k p_k \log p(y = a_k \mid \theta_j) \gtreqless \sum_k p_k \log p(y = a_k \mid \theta_i) \tag{7}$$

It is easy to see that

$$H = -\sum_{k=1}^{I} p_k \log p(y = a_k \mid \theta_i) \tag{8}$$

is minimal with respect to the probability p_k, $1 \leqslant k \leqslant I$, when

$$p_k = p(y = a_k \mid \theta_i), \qquad 1 \leqslant k \leqslant I \tag{9}$$

Thus

$$-\sum_{k=1}^{I} p_k \log p(y = a_k \mid \theta_i) \geqslant -\sum_{k=1}^{I} p_k \log p_k\,, \qquad \text{for all} \quad 1 \leqslant i \leqslant s \tag{10}$$

Given p_j, $1 \leqslant j \leqslant I$, of the probability that $y = a_j$, suppose that $p(y = a_j \mid \theta_i) = p_j$ for all j and $p(y = a_j \mid \theta_k) \neq p_j$ for all $k \neq i$, then, from (9) and (10),

$$-\sum_j p_j \log p(y = a_j \mid \theta_i) = -\sum_j p_j \log p_j < -\sum p_j \log p(y = a_j \mid \theta_k)$$

hence, from (7),

$$R = \prod_{j=1}^{k} \left[\frac{p(y = a_j \mid \theta_k)}{p(y = a_j \mid \theta_i)}\right]^{p_j} < 1$$

This corresponds to Case (b) and $\lim_{N-\infty} z_{N\,i} = 1$. More generally, given p_j, $1 \leqslant j \leqslant I$, if

$$\min\left[-\sum p_j \log p(y = a_j \mid \theta_1), -\sum p_j \log p(y = a_j \mid \theta_2), \ldots\right]$$

is realized for a unique θ_j, then

$$-\sum_k p_k \log p(y = a_k \mid \theta_j) < -\sum_k p_k \log p(y = a_k \mid \theta_i) \qquad \text{for all} \quad i \neq j$$

and, from Case (b), $\lim_{N-\infty} z_{N,i} = 1$.

3. Martingales

As a preparation to our general discussions of convergence problems in Section 4, an introductory account of a special kind of stochastic process, martingales, will be presented in this section. Also see Appendix I at the end of this book.

Consider a discrete-time stochastic process $\{z_k; k = 0, 1, 2,\ldots\}$. It may be a sequence of state vectors $\{x_k ; k = 0, 1,\ldots\}$ of a given stochastic system or a sequence of observation vectors of the initial condition of a system $\{y_n ; n = 0, 1,\ldots\}$ contaminated by noise. A stochastic process $\{z_k ; k = 0, 1,\ldots\}$ is called a martingale if $E \mid z_k \mid < \infty$ for all $k \geqslant 0$ and, for any n subscripts, $0 \leqslant k_1 \leqslant k_2 < \cdots < k_n$,

$$E(z_{k_n} \mid z_{k_i}, 1 \leqslant i \leqslant n-1) = z_{k_{n-1}} \qquad \text{with probability} \quad 1 \tag{11}$$

For example, z_k is such that the expectation of z_{n+1} conditioned on the $n + 1$ preceding realization of z's, z_0, z_1,..., z_n, is equal to z_n. Before we discuss the meanings of (11), let us mention two other stochastic processes closely related to martingales. When the equality sign in (11) is replaced by an inequality sign $\leqslant(\geqslant)$ we call the stochastic process a semimartingale, or an expectation-decreasing (increasing) martingale.

At first sight of (11), one may think that martingales are too special to arise in many engineering problems. This suspicion turns out to be unfounded and actually there are many ways in which martingales arise in optimization problems.

One classical example of martingales is a fair gambling situation.[47a] By a slight change of terminology, this example can be rephrased as a control system with the plant and observation equations

$$x_{i+1} = x_i + f_i(\xi_i, u_i) \quad \text{and} \quad y_i = x_i$$

Assume that its control policy is given by $u_i = \phi_i(x_i)$. Suppose that ξ_i's are independent and that $Ef_i[\xi_i, \phi_i(x_i) \mid x_i] = 0$ for all x_i. Then $E(x_{i+1} \mid x^i) = x_i$ and $\{x_i\}$ is a martingale.

There are other, less trivial, examples. We discuss next the maximum likelihood estimation problem of an unknown parameter. We know from Chapters II–VI that, for some optimal adaptive control problems, the optimal control policy synthesis can be separated from the optimal estimation process of the unknown plant parameters and/or noise statistics. Maximum likelihood estimates are often used when exact Bayesian conditional expectation estimates are not available or are too cumbersome to work with. If the random variables are Gaussian, these two kinds of estimates coincide.

Suppose we have a system where its unknown parameter θ is assumed to be either θ_1 or θ_2.[47a] Consider a problem of constructing the maximum likelihood estimate of θ given a set of $(n+1)$ observed state vectors at time n, y^n. Suppose that $p(y^n \mid \theta_i)$ is defined for all $n = 0, 1,\ldots$ and $i = 1, 2$.

Form the ratio

$$z_n = \frac{p(y^n \mid \theta_2)}{p(y^n \mid \theta_1)} \tag{12}$$

The probability density $p(y^n \mid \theta)$, when regarded as a function of θ for fixed y^n, is a likelihood function mentioned in Section 2, Chapter V. Hence z_n is called the likelihood ratio.

Since $\theta = \theta_1$ or θ_2 in the example, the maximum likelihood estimate of θ is θ_2 if $z_n > 1$, θ_1 if $z_n < 1$, and undecided for $z_n = 1$. Thus, the stochastic process $\{z_n\}$ of (12) describes the time history of estimate of θ. To study the behavior of the sequential estimate of θ, one must study the behavior of $\{z_n\}$ as $n \to \infty$. Since p is a density function, the denominator is nonzero with probability one. Let us assume that

$p(y^n \mid \theta_2) = 0$ whenever $p(y^n \mid \theta_1) = 0$ since otherwise we can decide θ to be θ_2 immediately.

Suppose θ_1 is the true parameter value. Then

$$p(y_{n+1} \mid y^n) = \frac{p(y^{n+1} \mid \theta_1)}{p(y^n \mid \theta_1)}$$

and

$$\begin{aligned} E(z_{n+1} \mid y^n) &= \int z_{n+1}\, p(y_{n+1} \mid y^n)\, dy_{n+1} \\ &= \int \frac{p(y^{n+1} \mid \theta_2)}{p(y^n \mid \theta_1)}\, dy_{n+1} \\ &= \frac{p(y^n \mid \theta_2)}{p(y^n \mid \theta_1)} = z_n \qquad \text{with probability } 1 \end{aligned}$$

Then, since z^n are random variables which are functions of y^n,

$$E(z_{n+1} \mid y^n) = E(z_{n+1} \mid y^n, z^n) = z_n \qquad \text{with probability } 1 \tag{13}$$

Taking the conditional expectation of (13) with respect to z^n,

$$\begin{aligned} E(E(z_{n+1} \mid y^n) \mid z^n) &= E(E(z_{n+1} \mid y^n, z^n) \mid z^n) \\ &= E(z_{n+1} \mid z^n) \\ &= E(z_n \mid z^n) \\ &= z_n \end{aligned}$$

Thus, it is seen that the sequence of likelihood ratios, $\{z_n\}$, is a martingale. For more practical engineering examples, see, for example, Daly,[42,43] Kallianpur[83], Raviv.[116]

4. Convergence Questions: General Case

A. Problem Statement

We now make precise statements made in Section 1. This section is based on Blackwell and Dubins.[31]

A common frame of reference used in this book in judging system performances of control systems is the expected values of some scalar-valued functions J. In case of adaptive control systems, their expected values EJ depend, among others, on the unknown parameters θ taking their values in some known parameter spaces Θ.

There are many other systems, not necessarily control systems, whose performances are judged using this common frame of reference. A sequence of measurements $y_0, y_1, \ldots$ is made while a given system is in operation where the measurement mechanisms are assumed to be designed so that y's are functions, among others, of θ; i.e., joint conditional probability density $p(y^n \mid \theta)$ is assumed given for each $\theta \in \Theta$. An a priori probability density for θ, $p_0(\theta)$, is also assumed given.

The a posteriori probability density $p(\theta \mid y^n)$ is computed by the Bayes rule

$$p(\theta \mid y^n) = \frac{p_0(\theta)\, p(y^n \mid \theta)}{\int d\theta\, p_0(\theta)\, p(y^n \mid \theta)}$$

Now we formulate (from the questions on p. 197 and 198)

Question 3′. Under what conditions does $p(\theta \mid y^n)$ converge as $n \to \infty$?

Question 4′. Given two a priori probability densities $p_0(\theta)$ and $q_0(\theta)$, under what conditions do they approach the same density?

In Questions 3′ and 4′, the closeness or the distance of any two probabilities P_1 and P_2, defined for the same class of observable (i.e., measurable) events, is measured by the least upper bound of the absolute differences of the probabilities assigned to all such events by P_1 and P_2. Denote the distance of the two probabilities by $\rho(P_1, P_2)$ and the class of observable events by $\mathscr{F}$:

$$\rho(P_1, P_2) \triangleq \sup_{A \in \mathscr{F}} | P_1(A) - P_2(A)|$$

In the language of the theory of probability, Ω is a sample space, $\mathscr{F}$ is the σ field of subsets of Ω, and P_1 and P_2 are two probability measures so that $P_1(A)$ and $P_2(A)$ are the probabilities assigned to A, for every $A \in \mathscr{F}$. Some of the definitions and facts from the probability theory are summarized in Appendix I at the end of this book.

Question 3′ asks for the conditions for $\rho(P^n, P^*) \to 0$ as $n \to \infty$ for some probability P^* where P^n is the nth a posteriori probability.

Question 4′, therefore, asks for the conditions under which

$$\rho(P^n, Q^n) \to 0 \quad \text{as} \quad n \to \infty$$

where P^n and Q^n are the nth a posteriori probabilities starting from the a priori probabilities P_0 and Q_0, respectively.

B. Martingale Convergence Theorems

Both Questions 3′ and 4′ of Section 4,A are answered by straightforward applications of martingale convergence theorems. The forms in which we will use them are stated here without the proofs: The proofs can be found, for example, in Refs. 31, 47a. See also Appendix I at the end of this book.

Theorem 1. Let z_n be a sequence of random variables such that $\sup_n |z_n|$ has a finite expectation, converges almost everywhere to a random variable z, and let $y_0, y_1, \ldots$ be a sequence of measurements. Then

$$\lim_{n\to\infty} E(z_n \mid y^n) = E(z \mid y_0, y_1, \ldots)$$

Theorem 2. Let f_n be any sequence of random variables that converges to 0 with probability 1. Then, with probability 1 and for all $\epsilon > 0$,

$$P[|f_n| > \epsilon \mid y^n]$$

converges to 0 as $n \to \infty$.

We also note here that zero-one laws in their various versions,[47a,102] although they can be proved directly, can also be proved by applying Theorem 1.

Let $z = I_B$, where I_B is the indicator of the event B, i.e.,

$$I_B(\omega) = \begin{cases} 1, & \omega \in B \\ 0, & \omega \notin B \end{cases}$$

where the event B is defined on the sequence of the measurements $y_0, y_1, \ldots$.

Then, from Theorem 1, one has

Theorem 3. $P(B \mid y^n) \to I_B$ with probability 1, where B is defined on the y_n's.

C. Convergence

We now consider the convergence of the a posteriori probability densities $p(\theta \mid y^n)$ to the true value of θ, θ_0.

It is assumed that there exists:

(i) an a priori probability density which assigns a positive probability to some neighborhood of θ_0;

(ii) a subset B in Θ such that the event $\theta_0 \in B$ is defined on the y_n's; namely, with nonzero probability, there is a realization of measurements $y_0, y_1, \ldots$ such that the sequence of functions of $y_0, y_1, \ldots$ computed according to the Bayes rule converges to θ_0.

Then, by Theorem 3,

$$P(B \mid y^n) = \int_B d\theta \, p(\theta \mid y^n) \to 1 \quad \text{or} \quad 0$$

depending on

$$\theta_0 \in B \quad \text{or} \quad \theta_0 \notin B$$

This is equivalent to saying

$$p(\theta \mid y^n) \to \delta(\theta - \theta_0)$$

D. Mutual Convergence

For the sake of convenience in writing, let $w = (y^n)$ be the measurements that have been performed and let $v = (y_{n+1}, y_{n+2}, \ldots)$ be the future measurements. Let A be a measurable set in the product space $\mathscr{B}_{n+1} \times \mathscr{B}_{n+2} \times \cdots$, where $\mathscr{B}_k$ is a σ field of subsets of Y_k, the space of outcomes for the kth measurement y_k.

Let B be a measurable set in $\mathscr{F}$, a σ field of subsets of Θ.

Let $P^n(A, B \mid w)$ be the conditional probability of v being in A and θ being in B, given w, when the probability density $p_0(\theta)$ is adopted as the a priori density function on Θ. The conditional probability $Q^n(A, B \mid w)$ is similarly defined with $q_0(\theta)$ as its a priori probability density. $q_0(\theta)$ is assumed to be absolutely continuous with respect to $p_0(\theta)$. Namely it is assumed that a nonnegative function of θ, $f(\theta) \geq 0$, exists such that $q_0(\theta) = p_0(\theta) f(\theta)$.

The main result can be stated that except for the measurement sequence with Q-probability (i.e., the probability constructed from $q_0(\theta)$) zero, $\rho(P^n, Q^n) \to 0$.

The convergence to zero of distance $\sup_B \rho[P^n(B \mid w), Q^n(B \mid w)]$ as $n \to \infty$ is implied by the convergence to zero of $\sup_{A,B} \rho(P^n(A, B \mid w), Q^n(A, B \mid w))$. Therefore, the proof for this latter is sketched in this section. See Ref. 31 for details.

Because of the absolute continuity assumption, we can write

$$Q(C) = \int_C \phi(w, v, \theta) \, dP(w, v, \theta)$$

where C is a set of points (w, v, θ), i.e., $C \in \mathscr{F} \times \mathscr{B}_0 \times \mathscr{B}_1 \times \cdots \times \mathscr{B}_n \times \mathscr{B}_{n+1} \times \cdots$.

Define

$$\phi_n(w) = \int \phi(w, v, \theta)\, dP^n(v, \theta \mid w)$$

where the integration ranges over the whole space, i.e.,

$$\phi_n(w) = E_{v,\theta}(\phi(w, v, \theta) \mid w)$$

with respect to P measure. Define

$$d_n(w, v, \theta) = \begin{cases} \dfrac{\phi(w, v, \theta)}{\phi_n(w)}, & \phi_n \neq 0 \\ 1, & \phi_n = 0 \end{cases}$$

Then, from Theorem 1,

$\phi_n \to \phi$, almost surely with respect to P probability i.e., with probability 1 when the probability is given by P

Consequently,

$\overline{\lim_n}\, d_n \leqslant 1$, almost surely with respect to P measure and $d_n \to 1$ almost surely with respect to Q measure

Define

$$Q^n(w, D) = \int_D d_n(w, v, \theta)\, dP^n(v, \theta \mid w)$$

for all

$$D \in \mathscr{F} \times \mathscr{B}_{n+1} \times \cdots$$

Then Q^n is a conditional probability of future measurements and θ given the past measurements. Now

$$\begin{aligned} \rho(P^n(w), Q^n(w)) &= \sup_D \rho(P^n(w, D), Q^n(w, D)) \\ &= \int_{d_n - 1 > 0} dP^n(v, \theta \mid w) - \int dQ^n(v, \theta \mid w) \\ &= \int_{d_n - 1 > 0} [d_n(w, v, \theta) - 1]\, dP^n(v, \theta \mid w) \end{aligned}$$

$$= \int_{d_n - 1 > \epsilon} (d_n - 1)\, dP^n(v, \theta \mid w)$$

$$+ \int_{0 < d_n - 1 \leqslant \epsilon} (d_n - 1)\, dP^n(v, \theta \mid w) \leqslant \epsilon$$

$$+ \int_{d_n - 1 > \epsilon} (d_n - 1)\, dP^n(v, \theta \mid w) \leqslant \epsilon + \int_G d_n\, dP^n(v, \theta \mid w)$$

$$= \epsilon + Q^n(G \mid w)$$

where

$$G = \{(v, \theta) : d_n(w, v, \theta) - 1 > \epsilon\}$$

Thus

$$\rho(P^n(w), Q^n(w)) \leqslant \epsilon + Q[d_n - 1 > \epsilon \mid w] \leqslant 2\epsilon$$

The last step comes from Theorem 2. Thus, if given a priori density function for θ, $p_0(\theta)$, any other choices of a priori density functions also converge to the same density function eventually so long as they are absolutely continuous with respect to $p_0(\theta)$.

5. Stochastic Controllability and Observability

A. Introduction

In deterministic dynamical systems the concepts of controllability and observability[87–89,100,142] play a very important theoretical role in characterizing possible system behaviors.

As pointed out in Section 1, the corresponding concepts of observability and controllability of stochastic systems exist and are intimately connected with the convergence questions of a posteriori probability density functions such as $p(x_i \mid y^i)$ or $p(x_0 \mid y^i)$ as $i \to \infty$.

We will define these concepts in terms of the covariance matrices associated with these a posteriori density functions.* We have discussed in Chapters II–V the procedure for generating these a posteriori density functions for general systems with nonlinear plant and observation equations. Therefore, their definitions will in principle be applicable

* By the duality principle discussed in Section 3,C, Chapter II, the results of this section can be translated into the corresponding results on the asymptotic behaviors of regulator systems or vice versa. See Ref 89a.

The independent investigation of the asymptotic behaviors of the error covariance matrices is of interest since it sheds additional light on the subject.

to general nonlinear stochastic systems even though they are developed for stochastic systems with linear plant and observation equations in this section.

Let us illustrate by simple examples how the question of observability arises in stochastic control systems. Consider a system with the plant equation

$$x_{i+1} = Ax_i\,, \qquad A \text{ nonsingular} \tag{14}$$

and with the observation equation

$$y_i = H_i x_i + \eta_i \tag{15}$$

where the matrix A is assumed known, where $H_i = A^{-i}$, and where η's are some observation noises.

Then, from (14) and (15),

$$y_i = A^{-i}A^i x_0 + \eta_i = x_0 + \eta_i$$

showing that y_i observes a noisy version of x_0 for all $i = 0, 1,\ldots$.

In this case, since (14) is deterministic, x_i for any $i > 0$ can be constructed if x_0 is known exactly.

Thus assuming the existence of $p(x_0 \mid y^n)$, if $p(x_0 \mid y^n)$ converges as $n \to \infty$ to a delta function then so does the density function for x_i, at least for stable systems, since $x_i = A^i x_0$.

Instead of (14) consider now a system

$$x_{i+1} = Ax_i + C_i\xi_i \quad \text{and} \quad y_i = Hx_i + \eta_i \tag{16}$$

Then

$$x_i = A^i x_0 + \sum_{j=0}^{i-1} A^{i-1-j}C_i\xi_j$$

and

$$y_i = HA^i x_0 + \sum_{j=0}^{i-1} HA^{i-1-j}C_i\xi_j + \eta_i$$

If $HA^i = 0$ for some i_0, then $HA^k = 0$ for all $k \geqslant i_0$. Therefore, no matter how many observations are made, y_k does not contain x_0 for $k \geqslant i_0$. It is not possible to get more precise information on x_0 than that contained in $y_0,\ldots, y_{i_0-1}$. Similarly, if the density function for x_0 is not completely known, for example if the distribution function of x_0 contains an unknown parameter θ_1, then the observation scheme of (16) is such that $p(\theta_1 \mid y^n)$ remains the same for $n \geqslant i_0$. Then we cannot hope to improve our knowledge of θ_1 beyond that at time i_0 no matter how many observations are taken. Therefore, we may want to call the system with (14) and (15) stochastically observable and the system with (16) stochastically unobservable or observable in a weaker or wider sense.

Observability of stochastic systems is then defined as the existence condition of the system state vector estimates with certain specified asymptotic behaviors, where the class of the state vector estimates of x_i is taken to be functions of y^i. Such observability may be called on-line observability.

There is another type of observability concept which may be called off-line observability. The class of state vector estimates of x_i is no longer restricted to be functions of y^i but is taken to be of $y_j, y_{j+1}, \ldots, y_{j+k}$, where $j > i$ or $j < i$. The behavior in some probability sense of such estimates as $k \to \infty$ is then investigated.

Both are of interest in system applications. In this book, the on-line observability is developed using the convergence in the mean.

We now make these preliminary remarks more precise. Given two square matrices of the same dimension, A and B, we use the notation $A \geqslant B$ when $(A - B)$ is nonnegative definite and $A > B$ when $(A - B)$ is positive definite.

B. Observability of Deterministic Systems

Consider a deterministic system described by

$$x_{i+1} = A_i x_i$$

$$y_i = H_i x_i$$

where x's are n vectors and y's are m vectors and where A_i^{-1} exists for all i. The problem is to determine the x_i's from a sequence of observations $y_0, y_1, \ldots$.

Because of the deterministic plant equation, the problem is equivalent to determining x at any one particular time, say x_0, from a sequence of observations $y_0, y_1, \ldots$. Of course, the problem is trivial if $m \geqslant n$ and H_0 has rank n. Then x_0 is determined from y_0 alone by

$$x_0 = (H_0' H_0)^{-1} H_0 y_0$$

More interesting situations arise when $m < n$. Let us determine x_i from y^i. Defining the $(i + 1)m \times n$ augmented H matrix by

$$\mathbf{H}_i = \begin{bmatrix} H_0 \phi_{0,i} \\ H_1 \phi_{1,i} \\ \vdots \\ H_i \end{bmatrix}$$

where $\phi_{k,j}$ is the transition matrix from x_j to x_k and an augmented y vector by

$$\mathbf{y}_i = \begin{pmatrix} y_0 \\ y_1 \\ \vdots \\ y_i \end{pmatrix}$$

we can write

$$\mathbf{y}_i = \mathbf{H}_i x_i$$

Now if $(\mathbf{H}_i'\mathbf{H}_i)$ is nonsingular, then

$$x_i = (\mathbf{H}_i'\mathbf{H}_i)^{-1}\mathbf{H}_i'\mathbf{y}_i$$

i.e., if $\mathbf{H}_i$ has rank n, then x_i can be determined from y^i. By changing the definition of $\mathbf{H}_i$ to

$$\mathbf{H}_i = \begin{bmatrix} H_0 \\ H_1\phi_{1,0} \\ \vdots \\ H_i\phi_{i,0} \end{bmatrix}$$

we obtain

$$x_0 = (\mathbf{H}_i'\mathbf{H}_i)^{-1}\mathbf{H}_i'\mathbf{y}_i$$

Such a system is called observable. The condition that the rank of $\mathbf{H}_i$ is n is the observability condition of a deterministic system.[142] This concept has been introduced by Kalman.[87–89] Physically speaking, when a system is observable the observation mechanism of the system is such that all modes of the system response become available to it in a finite time. In other words, when the system is observable it is possible to determine any x_i , $i = 0, 1, \ldots$, exactly from only a finite number of observations y.

C. Stochastic Observability of Deterministic Plant with Noisy Measurements

Let us now consider a deterministic plant with noisy observations:

$$x_{i+1} = A_i x_i \tag{17}$$

$$y_i = H_i x_i + \eta_i \tag{18}$$

where x_0 is a Gaussian random variable with a covariance matrix Σ_0, where noises are independent Gaussian random variables with

$$
\begin{aligned}
E(\eta_i) &= 0 \\
E(\eta_i \eta_j') &= R_i \delta_{ij}
\end{aligned}
\tag{19}
$$

and where R_i is nonsingular, $i = 0, 1, \ldots$.

Here again, if we can determine (or estimate) the state vector x at any one time, such as x_0, then from (17) we can determine all other x's.

Because of the noisy observations, it is no longer possible to determine x_i from a finite number of observations.

We compute, instead, the probability density function $p(x_i \mid y^i)$ as our knowledge of x_i, or compute the least-squares estimate of x_i from y^i if noises are not Gaussian.

Since

$$x_n = \phi_{n,i} x_i$$

and

$$x_i = \phi_{i,n} x_n$$

where $\phi_{n,i}$ is the state transition matrix from time i to n,

$$\phi_{n,i} \triangleq A_{n-1} \cdots A_i, \qquad \phi_{i,i} \triangleq I \tag{20}$$

$$\phi_{i,n} \triangleq \phi_{n,i}^{-1} \tag{21}$$

from (18),

$$y_i = H_i \phi_{i,n} x_n + \eta_i \tag{22}$$

Define

$$\tilde{H}_i = H_i \phi_{i,n} \tag{23}$$

The best Wiener–Kalman estimate of x_n, x_n^*, is obtained by minimizing

$$J_n \triangleq \sum_0^n \| y_i - \tilde{H}_i x_n \|^2_{R_i^{-1}} \tag{24}$$

with respect to x_n. Then, from Chapter V, we know that

$$x_n^* = \left(\sum_0^n \tilde{H}_i' R_i^{-1} \tilde{H}_i\right)^+ \left(\sum_0^n \tilde{H}_i' R_i^{-1} y_i\right) \tag{25}$$

From (22) and (25),

$$\Gamma_n \triangleq \operatorname{cov}(x_n^* \mid y^n) = \left(\sum_0^n \tilde{H}_i' R_i^{-1} \tilde{H}_i\right)^+$$

a. *Stochastic Observability Matrix*

Define an $(n \times n)$ matrix, called the stochastic observability matrix, by

$$\mathcal{O}_n = \sum_0^n \tilde{H}_i' R_i^{-1} \tilde{H}_i$$

$$= \sum_{i=0}^n (\phi_{i,n}' H_i' R_i^{-1} H_i \phi_{i,n}) \tag{26}$$

when $\sum_0^{-1}$ is null. This matrix is nonnegative definite. It satisfies the recursion equation

$$\mathcal{O}_{n+1} = \phi_{n,n+1}' \mathcal{O}_n \phi_{n,n+1} + H_{n+1}' R_{n+1}^{-1} H_{n+1}$$

$$= (A_n^{-1})' \mathcal{O}_n A_n^{-1} + H_{n+1}' R_{n+1}^{-1} H_{n+1} \tag{27}$$

If $\mathcal{O}_n$ is positive definite, then the first term can be written as $(A_n \mathcal{O}_n^{-1} A_n')^{-1}$.

Thus, from Chapters II and V, we see that $\mathcal{O}_n^{-1}$ satisfies the same recursion equation as the error-covariance matrix of the Kalman filter, when Σ_0^{-1} is taken to be null matrix. When Σ_0^{-1} is not null $\mathcal{O}_0$ must be replaced by $\Sigma_0^{-1} + \tilde{H}_0' R_0^{-1} \tilde{H}_0$.

Since the second term of (27) is nonnegative definite, we see that $\mathcal{O}_j$ is positive definite for all $j \geqslant i_0$ when $\mathcal{O}_{i_0}$ is positive definite.

b. *Definition of Stochastic Observability* (*Strict Sense*)

The system with (17) and (18) is said to be stochastically observable in the strict sense if and only if the covariance matrices associated with the conditional probability density function of x_k given y^k goes to zero as $k \to \infty$, or equivalently the stochastic observability matrix $\mathcal{O}_k$ is positive definite for some k and its error-covariance matrix, Γ_k, converges to the null matrix as $k \to \infty$.*

* It is possible to define the observability by behavior of the variance of $p(x_0 \mid y^n)$. Thus, if x_0 is more and more accurately known as the number of observations increases, then the system is observable in the strict sense. The stochastic process (z_n), defined by

$$z_n = E(x_0 \mid y^n)$$

is a martingale.

If $E|\, x_0 \,| < \infty$, then, by the martingale convergence theorem,

$$E(x_0 \mid y^n) \to E(x_0 \mid y_0, y_1, \ldots)$$

with probability 1 as $n \to \infty$, i.e., the associated covariance matrices converge to the null matrix. For observable systems this limit is x_0.

By the Chebychev inequality, the stochastic observability, therefore, implies that the estimation errors of the state vectors converge to zero in probability as the number of observations increases.

Thus, with Σ_0^{-1} being null, if $\mathcal{O}_{i_0}$ is positive definite then

$$\Gamma_k = \mathcal{O}_k^{-1} \qquad \text{for all} \quad k \geqslant i_0 \tag{28a}$$

When Σ_0^{-1} is not null, we have

$$\Gamma_k^{-1} = \phi_{0,k}' \Sigma_0^{-1} \phi_{0,k} + \mathcal{O}_k \tag{28b}$$

A sufficient condition for stochastic observability is now derived. The sufficient condition must insure that $\mathcal{O}_k$ is positive definite for some k and that $\| \mathcal{O}_k \|$ increases indefinitely as $k \to \infty$. For this purpose it is convenient to modify $\mathcal{O}_k$ as

$$\tilde{\mathcal{O}}_k = \sum_{i=0}^{k} (\phi_{i,0}' H_i' R_i^{-1} H_i \phi_{i,0}) \tag{29}$$

Then, from (26) and (29),

$$\mathcal{O}_k = \phi_{0,k}' \tilde{\mathcal{O}}_k \phi_{0,k} \tag{30}^*$$

The matrix $\tilde{\mathcal{O}}_k$ satisfies the recursion equation

$$\tilde{\mathcal{O}}_{k+1} = \tilde{\mathcal{O}}_k + \phi_{k+1,0}' H_{k+1}' R_{k+1}^{-1} H_{k+1} \phi_{k+1,0} \tag{31}$$

c. *Sufficient Condition for Stochastic Observability (Strict Sense)*

The sufficient condition for stochastic observability is that there exists a positive integer q such that the partial sum of $H_i' R_i^{-1} H_i$ over any q consecutive time intervals is positive definite and that $\| \mathcal{O}_k^{-1} \|$ decreases in such a way that

$$\| \phi_{k,0} \|^2 \, \| \mathcal{O}_k^{-1} \| \to 0 \quad \text{as} \quad k \to \infty$$

Since $\phi_{i,0}$ is nonsingular, the partial sum of $\phi_{i,0}' H_i' R_i^{-1} H_i \phi_{i,0}$ over any q consecutive time intervals is positive definite and we have

$$\tilde{\mathcal{O}}_{k+j} > \tilde{\mathcal{O}}_k \qquad \text{for any} \quad j \geqslant q, \quad k \geqslant i_0$$

* The two observability matrices of (26) and (29) differ only in that time 0 or current time is used as the time of reference.

where $\tilde{\mathcal{O}}_{i_0}$ is positive definite. Then, from (28a) and (30),

$$\| \Gamma_k \| < \| \phi_{k,0} \|^2 \| \tilde{\mathcal{O}}_k^{-1} \|$$

when Σ_0^{-1} is null. When Σ_0^{-1} is not null, from (28b) and (30),

$$\| \Gamma_k \| < \| \phi_{k,0} \|^2 \| (\Sigma_0^{-1} + \tilde{\mathcal{O}}_k)^{-1} \| \tag{32}$$

For large enough k we have $\| \tilde{\mathcal{O}}_k \| \gg \| \Sigma_0^{-1} \|$ and

$$\| \Gamma_k \| \leqslant \| \phi_{k,0} \|^2 \| \tilde{\mathcal{O}}_k^{-1} \| \tag{33}$$

Thus in both cases $\| \Gamma_k \| \to 0$ as $k \to \infty$.

D. Stochastic Observability of General Dynamical Systems: I

As a next class of systems, consider

$$x_{i+1} = A_i x_i + C_i \xi_i \tag{34}$$

$$y_i = H_i x_i + \eta_i \tag{35}$$

where ξ's and η's are independent Gaussian random variables with

$$E(\xi_i) = E(\eta_i) = 0$$
$$E(\xi_i \xi_j') = Q_i \delta_{ij}$$
$$E(\eta_i \eta_j') = R_i \delta_{ij}$$

where Q_i and R_i are nonsingular, $i, j = 0, 1, \ldots$.

The initial state vector x_0 is taken to be random, independent of ξ's and η's with

$$\operatorname{cov}(x_0) = \Sigma_0$$

In the previous section, the stochastic observability matrix is shown to be related to the inverse of the error-covariance matrix.

Because of the plant noise, it is no longer possible to hope that any x_i will be learned eventually from $y_0, y_1, \ldots$, nor that the knowledge of x_i at any i suffices to determine x_j exactly, $j \neq i$. A reasonable definition of observability, then, is to focus our attention on the error-covariance matrix of the state vector estimate and define the systems to be stochastically observable in the wide sense when the error-covariance matrices remain bounded in some sense.*

Definition of Stochastic Observability (Wide Sense)

A system is stochastically observable in the wide sense if the covariance matrix associated with $p(x_i \mid y^i)$ remains bounded as $i \to \infty$.

In the process of obtaining a sufficient condition for this wide sense stochastic observability we need a concept of controllability of stochastic systems which is a companion or dual of the concept of observability. This concept is discussed in Section E and was also introduced by Kalman.[87–89] We will return to the topic of this section in Section F.

E. Controllability of Stochastic Systems

Consider a dynamical system with the plant equation

$$x_{i+1} = A_i x_i + C_i \xi_i$$

where ξ_i are independent random variables with

$$E(\xi_i) = 0, \qquad E(\xi_i \xi_j') = Q_i \delta_{ij}$$

Because of the noise disturbances the state vector at time n, x_n, differs from $\phi_{n,0} x_0$, the state vector at time n with no disturbances by

$$d_n \triangleq x_n - \phi_{n,0} x_0$$

$$= \sum_{i=0}^{n-1} \phi_{n,i+1} C_i \xi_i$$

The random variable d_n is such that

$$E(d_n) = 0$$

and

$$\operatorname{cov}(d_n) = \sum_{0}^{n-1} \phi_{n,i+1} C_i Q_i C_i' \phi_{n,i+1}'$$

$$\triangleq \mathscr{C}_n \tag{36}$$

If the matrix $\mathscr{C}_n$ is such that $\| \mathscr{C}_n \|$ remains bounded for all n, where $\| \cdot \|$ is a norm in an Euclidean space, then $\| d_n \|$ will remain bounded

* By Chebychev's inequality, the observability in the wide sense enables one to establish an upper bound on the probability of the estimation error exceeding a given threshold.

for all n. In other words, the effects of the random disturbances remain bounded. Therefore, $\mathscr{C}_n$ is called the stochastic controllability matrix of the dynamical system (34).

The system (34) is called stochastically controllable if its stochastic controllability matrix is positive definite for some n, and remains bounded for all n.

We are now ready to discuss the observability of the general system (34) and (35).

F. Stochastic Observability of General Dynamical Systems: II

The stochastic observability of the general system given by (34) and (35) is now discussed by applying the results of Sections C and E to its subsystems to be defined shortly.

Since

$$x_n = \phi_{n,0} x_0 + \sum_{0}^{n-1} \phi_{n,i+1} C_i \xi_i$$

it is easy to obtain an upper bound on Γ_n, the error-covariance matrix of the state vector x_n of the Wiener–Kalman filter, as

$$\Gamma_n \leqslant \phi_{n,0} \operatorname{cov}(x_0 \mid y^n) \, \phi'_{n,0} + \mathscr{C}_n \tag{37}$$

If the system is stochastically observable, then, given a positive integer i_0, there exists $N(i_0) > 0$ such that $\phi_{n,0} \operatorname{cov}(x_0 \mid y^n) \, \phi_{n,0} \leqslant \mathcal{O}_{i_0}^{-1}$ for all $n > N(i_0)$. Therefore,*

$$\Gamma_n \leqslant \mathcal{O}_{i_0}^{-1} + \mathscr{C}_n \qquad \text{for all} \quad n \geqslant N(i_0) \tag{37a}$$

This is essentially the bound obtained by Kalman.[88]

Let us also obtain a lower bound on Γ_n and improve on the upper bound given by (37a). For this purpose, it is convenient to write the vectors x_i and y_i as the sums of other vectors defined as follows:

$$x_i = x_i^1 + x_i^2 \tag{38}$$

$$y_i = y_i^1 + y_i^2 \tag{39}$$

* The conditioning variables y^n in (37) are more complicated than y^n used in defining the observability matrix, since the former is a function of ξ^{n-1} and η^n while the latter is simply a function of η^n. However, if the system is observable then $E(x_0 \mid y^n) \to 0$, even when y^n are functions of ξ and η. See Appendix I for detail. Hence the error-covariance matrix converges to the null matrix and can be bounded as in (37).

where

$$x_{i+1}^1 = A_i x_i^1 + C_i \xi_i, \qquad x_0^1 = 0, \qquad y_i^1 = H_i x_i^1 \tag{40a}$$

and

$$x_{i+1}^2 = A_i x_i^2, \qquad x_0^2 = x_0, \qquad y_i^2 = H_i x_i^2 + \eta_i \tag{40b}$$

The subsystem (40a) therefore has a stochastic plant with no measurement errors. The other subsystem, (40b), has a deterministic plant with noisy measurements. Assume that the subsystem (40a) is stochastically controllable and the subsystem (40b) is stochastically observable (strict or wide sense). Assume that the state vector x_i^2 is estimated by

$$\hat{x}_{i+1}^2 = A_i \hat{x}_i^2 + K_{i+1}^2 [y_{i+1}^2 - H_{i+1} A_i \hat{x}_i^2] \tag{41}$$

where K_{i+1}^2 is the gain of the filter, and that the estimation of the state vector x_i^1 is done by

$$\hat{x}_{i+1}^1 = A_i \hat{x}_i^1 + K_{i+1}^1 [y_{i+1}^1 - H_{i+1} A_i \hat{x}_i^1] \tag{42}$$

where K_{i+1}^1 is the gain of the filter. It is easy to see that the estimate of x_i given by

$$\hat{x}_i = \hat{x}_i^1 + \hat{x}_i^2$$

will be optimal if

$$K_{i+1}^1 = K_{i+1}^2 = K_{i+1}^* \tag{43}$$

where K_{i+1}^* is the optimal filter gain for the Wiener–Kalman filter for the system of (34) and (35).

The error-covariance matrix associated with $\hat{x}_i$ is given by

$$\begin{aligned} \Gamma_i &= E(x_i - \hat{x}_i)(x_i - \hat{x}_i)' \\ &\triangleq \hat{\Gamma}_i^1 + \hat{\Gamma}_i^2 \end{aligned} \tag{44}$$

where

$$\hat{\Gamma}_i^1 \triangleq E(x_i^1 - \hat{x}_i^1)(x_i^1 - \hat{x}_i^1)'$$

and

$$\hat{\Gamma}_i^2 \triangleq E(x_i^2 - \hat{x}_i^2)(x_i^2 - \hat{x}_i^2)'$$

The cross product terms disappear in (44) because of the particular choice of initial state vectors for the two subsystems.

The lower limit for Γ_i will now be established.

Since $\hat{\Gamma}_i^2$, the second term of (44), is the error-covariance matrix for the filter (41) with the nonoptimal gain K_{i+1}^*, we have

$$\Gamma_i^{*2} \leqslant \hat{\Gamma}_i^2$$

where Γ_i^{*2} is the error-covariance matrix of $\hat{x}_i^2$ with the optimal gain. By assumption, the subsystem of (40b) is stochastically observable. From (28b),

$$\Gamma_i^{*2} = \left(\phi_{0,i}'\Sigma_0^{-1}\phi_{0,i} + \mathcal{O}_i\right)^{-1} \tag{45}$$

In obtaining the estimate for $\hat{\Gamma}_i^1$, the first term in (43), we will encounter the controllability condition for the subsystem (40a). From (42),

$$x_{i+1}^1 - \hat{x}_{i+1}^1 = (I - K_{i+1}^1 H_{i+1})A_i(x_i^1 - \hat{x}_i^1) + C_i\xi_i \tag{46}$$

Defining the state transition matrix for (46) by $\psi_{i,j}^1$,

$$\begin{aligned}(x_i^1 - \hat{x}_i^1) &= \psi_{i,0}^1(x_0^1 - \hat{x}_0^1) + \sum_{j=0}^{i-1} \psi_{i,j+1}^1 C_j\xi_j \\ &= \sum_{j=0}^{i-1} \psi_{i,j+1}^1 C_j\xi_j\end{aligned}$$

where

$$x_0^1 - \hat{x}_0^1 = 0$$

is used. Thus,

$$\begin{aligned}\hat{\Gamma}_i^1 &= \sum_{j=0}^{i-1} \psi_{i,j+1}^1 C_j Q_j C_j' \psi_{i,j+1}^{1\prime} \\ &\triangleq \tilde{\mathscr{C}}_i\end{aligned} \tag{47}$$

where

$$\psi_{i,j}^1 = (I - K_i^1 H_i)A_{i-1}(I - K_{i-1}^1 H_{i-1})A_{i-2} \cdots (I - K_{j+1}^1 H_{j+1})A_j$$

By comparing (47) with (36), we see that when ψ's are substituted for ϕ's in (36) we obtain $\tilde{\mathscr{C}}_n$. This matrix is defined as the modified stochastic controllability matrix with the gain given by (43). $\mathscr{C}_i$ results from $\tilde{\mathscr{C}}_i$ by $K_i = 0$.

The matrix $\tilde{\mathscr{C}}$ is not simple to compute since the optimal gain for the Kalman filter for the original system is used. See Sorenson[125] for more detailed computations.

From (44), (45), and (47), we obtain a lower bound on Γ_i as

$$\left(\phi_{0,i}'\Sigma_0^{-1}\phi_{0,i} + \mathcal{O}_i\right)^{-1} \leqslant \left(\phi_{0,i}'\Sigma_0^{-1}\phi_{0,i} + \mathcal{O}_i\right)^{-1} + \tilde{\mathscr{C}}_i \leqslant \Gamma_i \tag{48}$$

To get a sharper upper bound on Γ_i, we compute $E[(x_i^2 - \hat{x}_i^2)(x_i^2 - \hat{x}_i^2)']$ using the gain

$$K_i^2 = (H_i' R_i^{-1} H_i)^+ H_i R_i^{-1} \tag{49}$$

From (40b) and (41),

$$x_{i+1}^2 - \hat{x}_{i+1}^2 = (I - K_{i+1}^2 H_{i+1}) A_i (x_i^2 - \hat{x}_i^2) - K_{i+1}^2 \eta_{i+1} \tag{50}$$

Defining the state transition matrix for (50) by $\psi_{i,j}^2$ analogously to $\psi_{i,j}^1$, we have

$$(x_i^2 - \hat{x}_i^2) = \psi_{i,0}^2 (x_0^2 - \hat{x}_0^2) - \sum_{j=0}^{i-1} \psi_{i,j+1}^2 K_j^2 \eta_j \tag{51}$$

In view of (51), define

$$\hat{\hat{\Gamma}}_i^2 = \psi_{i,0}^2 \Sigma_0 \psi_{i,0}^{2\prime} + \sum_{j=0}^{i-1} \psi_{i,j+1}^2 K_j^2 R_j K_j^{2\prime} \psi_{i,j+1}^{2\prime}$$

Then, substituting (49) as K_j^2,

$$\hat{\hat{\Gamma}}_i^2 = \psi_{i,0}^2 \Sigma_0 \psi_{i,0}^{2\prime} + \sum_{j=1}^{i} \psi_{i,j}^2 (H_j' R_i^{-1} H_j)^+ \psi_{i,j}^{2\prime} \tag{52}$$

Since the gain (49) is not optimal for the system (34) and (35)

$$\Gamma_i \leq \tilde{\tilde{\mathscr{C}}}_i + \hat{\hat{\Gamma}}_i^2 \tag{53}$$

where $\tilde{\tilde{\mathscr{C}}}_i$ is defined analogously to $\tilde{\mathscr{C}}_i$ with K_i^1 replaced by K_i^2 (49). Since

$$\tilde{\tilde{\mathscr{C}}}_i \leq \tilde{\mathscr{C}}_i$$

we have, from (45) and (53),

$$\left(\psi_{0,i}' \Sigma_0^{-1} \phi_{0,i} + \mathcal{O}_i\right)^{-1} \leq \Gamma_i < \tilde{\mathscr{C}}_i + \hat{\hat{\Gamma}}_i^2 \tag{54}$$

Thus, the system given by (34) and (35) is stochastically observable in the wide sense if the subsystem (40b) is stochastically observable (either in the strict or wide sense) and if the subsystem (40a) is stochastically controllable.

G. Identifiability of Stochastic Systems

Consider the system described by

$$x_{i+1} = A x_i$$
$$y_i = H x_i + \xi_i$$

where A is now assumed to be unknown.

To date, several iterative procedures to identify A have been proposed.[62,72a] The system is said to be identifiable when $\lim_{k\to\infty} \hat{A}_k = A$ in some probabilistic sense such as in quadratic mean or in probability, where $\hat{A}_k$ is some estimate of A given $y_0, \ldots, y_k$ i.e., the system is identifiable when the error covariance matrix of $\hat{A}_k$ converges to a null matrix.

The proof of this convergence[62a,72a] is adapted from the convergence proof of the stochastic approximation.[51] Thus, the condition of the identifiability is essentially that of the convergence of the stochastic approximation and not of observability.

It can be shown, however, that the Kalman observability criterion in Section 3 is sufficient for the identifiability.[62a,72a,100] This can also be inferred from the fact[62a] that the convergence proof of the identification procedure is essentially the same for systems with or without the inverse of H. This observability criterion is, however, not necessary. This can be seen by considering the next example.*

Consider a system described by

$$\begin{pmatrix} x_{i+1} \\ z_{i+1} \end{pmatrix} = \begin{pmatrix} a & 0 \\ 0 & a \end{pmatrix} \begin{pmatrix} x_i \\ z_i \end{pmatrix} + \begin{pmatrix} 0 \\ \xi_i \end{pmatrix}$$

$$y_i = (1, 0) \begin{pmatrix} x_i \\ z_i \end{pmatrix}$$

where the state vector has two components x and z, where z's are independent Gaussian random variables with means 0 and known finite variances.

Even without the plant noise, this system is not observable since it does not satisfy the rank condition, but is identifiable since

$$a = y_{i+1}/y_i \qquad \text{if} \quad y_i \neq 0$$

Even when the observation equation is modified to

$$y_i = (1, 0) \begin{pmatrix} x_i \\ \xi_i \end{pmatrix} + \eta_i$$

where η_i's are observation noises of known probability distribution function, it is still possible to identify a under certain conditions.[62a]

* This example is due to T. Fukao (private communication).

Chapter VII

Approximations

We come to realize very quickly that various optimal control formulations derived in Chapters II–IV do not generally admit closed-form analytic solutions. Even if we restrict our attention to a class of control systems with linear plant equations and quadratic performance indices, we can obtain optimal Bayesian control policies in analytically closed form only for special cases.

As pointed out repeatedly, it is usually the rule rather than the exception that we must solve optimal control problems approximately. We have mentioned some approximation schemes in discussing Example c, Section 3,B, Chapter III, when the gain of the system is unknown. In this chapter, we discuss several other approximation schemes.

There are many ways to approximately obtain optimal control policies: approximations in policy spaces,[4,9,11,20] linear or nonlinear programmings including gradient techniques of various kinds,[11,59,68,69,71,139] stochastic approximation[51] and separation of optimization from estimation with possibly additional approximations being made for control and/or estimation parts,[63,64,105,129] to name only a few possibilities. The subject of this Chapter could indeed be a basis for an entire book. We have chosen five topics somewhat arbitrarily, all of which, however, have to do with the question of how to reduce the amount of computations involved in obtaining optimal control policies.

The first topic discusses a method of approximate synthesis of optimal closed-loop control policies for a class of linear adaptive systems from the knowledge of optimal closed-loop control policies for a corresponding class of purely stochastic control systems.[5,62]

As will be discussed in detail in Section 1, under certain conditions, optimal policies for adaptive systems can even be synthesized exactly, in this manner. Since the amount of computations involved in deriving optimal closed-loop policies for adaptive systems are usually several orders of magnitude larger than that for purely stochastic systems, the saving in computational work could sometimes be very significant.

The second topic discusses an approximate control method which employs what is sometimes denoted as open-loop feedback control policies instead of closed-loop feedback control policies.[49,126,127]

The remaining three topics are devoted to the problems of approximate estimations of state vectors and/or unknown parameters. After performing some sensitivity and error analysis of Wiener–Kalman filter[82] in Section 3, we discuss two particular methods of approximate state vector estimation: by constructing an observer of state vectors to supplement the available measurements on the state vector in Section 4,[17,103] and by partitioning state vectors in Sections 5 and 6.[81,104,104a,112]

1. Approximately Optimal Control Policies for Adaptive Systems

A. Introduction

The problems of obtaining optimal control policies are generally much harder for adaptive systems than for purely stochastic systems. We have seen many examples testifying to this fact. It is natural and important to ask, therefore, if it is possible to construct approximate optimal control policies for adaptive systems from the knowledge of optimal control policies for purely stochastic systems. For brevity, the former will be referred to as optimal adaptive control policy and the latter as optimal stochastic control policy. Before we make this idea more precise, it is instructive to examine the relation between optimal adaptive and stochastic policies for a simple control problem. The system we consider is the same one used in Section 5 of Chapter III.

B. One-Dimensional Example[5]

The system to be considered is governed by the plant and observation equations

$$x_{i+1} = ax_i + u_i + r_i$$

$$y_i = x_i\,, \qquad 0 \leqslant i \leqslant N-1, \qquad u_i \in (-\infty, \infty)$$

where x, a, u, r, and y are all scalar quantities and where r_i is the independently and identically distributed random variable with

$$r_i = \begin{cases} c & \text{with probability } \theta \\ -c & \text{with probability } 1 - \theta \end{cases} \tag{1}$$

We take the usual criterion function

$$J = \sum_1^N W_i(x_i, u_{i-1})$$

When θ in (1) is assumed known, we have a purely stochastic control problem. When θ is not known we have an adaptive control problem.

Here, for the sake of simplicity, we consider the adaptive system to be such that

$$\begin{aligned} \Pr[\theta = \theta_1] &= z_0 \\ \Pr[\theta = \theta_2] &= 1 - z_0 \end{aligned} \tag{2}$$

where z_0 is the given a priori probability. The a posteriori probability that θ be equal to θ_1 at time i is denoted by z_i.

We will see that when W_i is quadratic the optimal adaptive control policy can be synthesized exactly by knowing the optimal stochastic control policies with $\theta = \theta_i$, $i = 1, 2$. Thus, with about twice the labor of solving a purely stochastic optimal control problem, an exact solution for the corresponding adaptive optimal control problem is obtained for this example. This is a large saving of labor compared with solving the adaptive problem exactly. Some idea of the degrees of saving may be obtained by the analogy with the difference in labor of integrating a function of one variable for two different parameter values and one function of two variables. In the next section we will see that for more general adaptive problems approximations to optimal adaptive control policies can be made with a similar savings of labor.

For the adaptive problem of this section the augmented state vector $\{(x_i, z_i)\}$ forms a first-order Markov sequence.

The minimum of the expected cost of control for the adaptive system at time i, γ_i^*, is therefore a function of (x_{i-1}, z_{i-1}). The equation for γ_N^* is already given by minimizing (144) of Chapter III.

The general recursion equation for γ_i^* is given as

$$\gamma_i^*(x_{i-1}, z_{i-1}) = \min_{u_{i-1}}[\lambda_i + E(\gamma_{i+1}^* \mid x_{i-1}, z_{i-1})] \tag{3}$$

where, from the definition of λ_i,

$$\begin{aligned} \lambda_i &= E(W_i(x_i, u_{i-1}) \mid x_{i-1}, z_{i-1}) \\ &= z_{i-1} E(W_i \mid x_{i-1}, \theta_1) + (1 - z_{i-1}) E(W_i \mid x_{i-1}, \theta_2) \end{aligned} \tag{4}$$

where

$$E(W_i \mid x_{i-1}, \theta_j) = \theta_j \, W_i(x_{i-1}^+, u_{i-1}) + (1 - \theta_j) \, W_i(x_{i-1}^-, u_{i-1}) \qquad j = 1, 2 \tag{5}$$

and where

$$x_{i-1}^{\pm} \triangleq ax_{i-1} + u_{i-1} \pm c \tag{6}$$

In (3) we can write

$$E(\gamma_{i+1}^* \mid x_{i-1}, z_{i-1}) = z_{i-1} \, E(\gamma_{i+1}^* \mid x_{i-1}, \theta_1) + (1 - z_{i-1}) \, E(\gamma_{i+1}^* \mid x_{i-1}, \theta_2) \tag{7}$$

where

$$E(\gamma_{i+1}^* \mid x_{i-1}, z_{i-1}, \theta_j) = \theta_j \, \gamma_{i+1}^*(x_{i-1}^+, z_{i-1}^+) + (1 - \theta_j) \, \gamma_{i+1}^*(x_{i-1}^-, z_{i-1}^-) \qquad j = 1, 2 \tag{8}$$

and where

$$\begin{aligned} z_{i-1}^+ &= \frac{z_{i-1}\theta_1}{z_{i-1}\theta_1 + (1 - z_{i-1})\theta_2} \\ z_{i-1}^- &= \frac{z_{i-1}(1 - \theta_1)}{z_{i-1}(1 - \theta_1) + (1 - z_{i-1})(1 - \theta_2)} \end{aligned} \tag{9}$$

are the a posteriori probabilities that $\theta = \theta_1$, given that $r_{i-1} = +c$ and $r_{i-1} = -c$, respectively.

From (4) and (8) we can write (3) as

$$\gamma_i^*(x_{i-1}, z_{i-1}) = \min_{u_{i-1}} [z_{i-1} \langle W_i + \gamma_{i+1}^* \rangle_1 + (1 - z_{i-1}) \langle W_i + \gamma_{i+1}^* \rangle_2] \tag{10}$$

where

$$\langle W_i + \gamma_{i+1}^* \rangle_j \triangleq E(W_i + \gamma_{i+1}^* \mid x_{i-1}, z_{i-1}, \theta_j), \qquad j = 1, 2 \tag{11}$$

for $1 \leqslant i \leqslant N$ and

$$\gamma_{N+1}^* = 0$$

Note that the variable z_{i-1} which expresses our ignorance about the precise value of θ appears linearly in the inside of the minimization operation of the recursion equation (10). Note also that the purely stochastic problem with $\theta = \theta_1$ corresponds to the problem with the a priori probability $z_0 = 1$ and the problem with $\theta = \theta_2$ to $z_0 = 0$. The recursion equation for the corresponding stochastic system where $\theta = \theta_1$ therefore is obtained by putting $z_{i-1} = 1$ for $1 \leqslant i \leqslant N$ in (10).

Denoting by $\gamma^*_{i,j}$ the optimal control cost for the stochastic problem with $\theta = \theta_j$, $j = 1, 2$, it satisfies the recursion equation:

$$\gamma^*_{i,j}(x_{i-1}) = \min_{u_{i-1}} \langle W_i(x_i, u_{i-1}) + \gamma^*_{i+1,j}(x_i) \rangle_j$$

$$= \min_{u_{i-1}} [\theta_j \{ W_i(x^+_{i-1}, u_{i-1}) + \gamma^*_{i+1,j}(x^+_{i-1}) \}$$

$$+ (1 - \theta_j)\{ W_i(x^-_{i-1}, u_{i-1}) + \gamma^*_{i+1,j}(x^-_{i-1}) \}], \qquad j = 1, 2 \quad (12)$$

where

$$x^{\pm}_{i-1} = a x_{i-1} + u_{i-1} \pm c, \qquad i = 1, 2, \ldots, N$$

Now suppose $W_i(x, u)$ is quadratic in x and u:

$$W_i(x_i, u_{i-1}) = v_i x_i^2 + t_{i-1} u_{i-1}^2$$

Then the optimal control at the last stage for the stochastic system with $\theta = \theta_j$, denoted as $u^*_{N-1,j}$, is given by

$$u^*_{N-1,j} = -\frac{v_N[a x_{N-1} + c(2\theta_j - 1)]}{v_N + t_{N-1}}, \qquad j = 1, 2 \quad (13)$$

The optimal control at $N - 1$ for the adaptive system, denoted as u^*_{N-1}, is given from (10) by

$$u^*_{N-1} = -\frac{v_N[a x_{N-1} + c(2\hat{\theta}_{N-1} - 1)]}{v_N + t_{N-1}} \quad (14)$$

where

$$\hat{\theta}_{N-1} \triangleq z_{N-1}\theta_1 + (1 - z_{N-1})\theta_2 \quad (15)$$

By comparing (13) with (15), we see that the optimal adaptive control is given by a linear combination of the optimal stochastic controls

$$u^*_{N-1} = z_{N-1} u^*_{N-1,1} + (1 - z_{N-1}) u^*_{N-1,2} \quad (16)$$

where z_{N-1} is the a posteriori probability that $\theta = \theta_1$ at the $(N - 1)$th stage, i.e., after $x_0, x_1, \ldots, x_{N-1}$ have been observed. Thus, at least for this example, the last optimal adaptive control is obtained once the last optimal stochastic controls for $\theta = \theta_1$ and θ_2 are known.

We can show from (10) and (12) that the inequality

$$\gamma_i^*(x, z) \geqslant z\, \gamma^*_{i,1}(x) + (1 - z)\, \gamma^*_{i,2}(x) \quad (17)$$

holds. Furthermore, W_i need not be quadratic for (17) to be true.[5] More precisely, we will show later on that

$$\gamma_i^*(x, z) = z\, \gamma_{i,1}^*(x) + (1 - z)\, \gamma_{i,2}^*(x) + \Delta\gamma_i(z) \tag{18}$$

where $\Delta\gamma_i(z)$ depends only on z.

Numerical experiments done for some stable final-value control problems show that $\Delta\gamma_i$ is small compared with $\gamma_{i,1}^*$ and $\gamma_{i,2}^*$ for i of

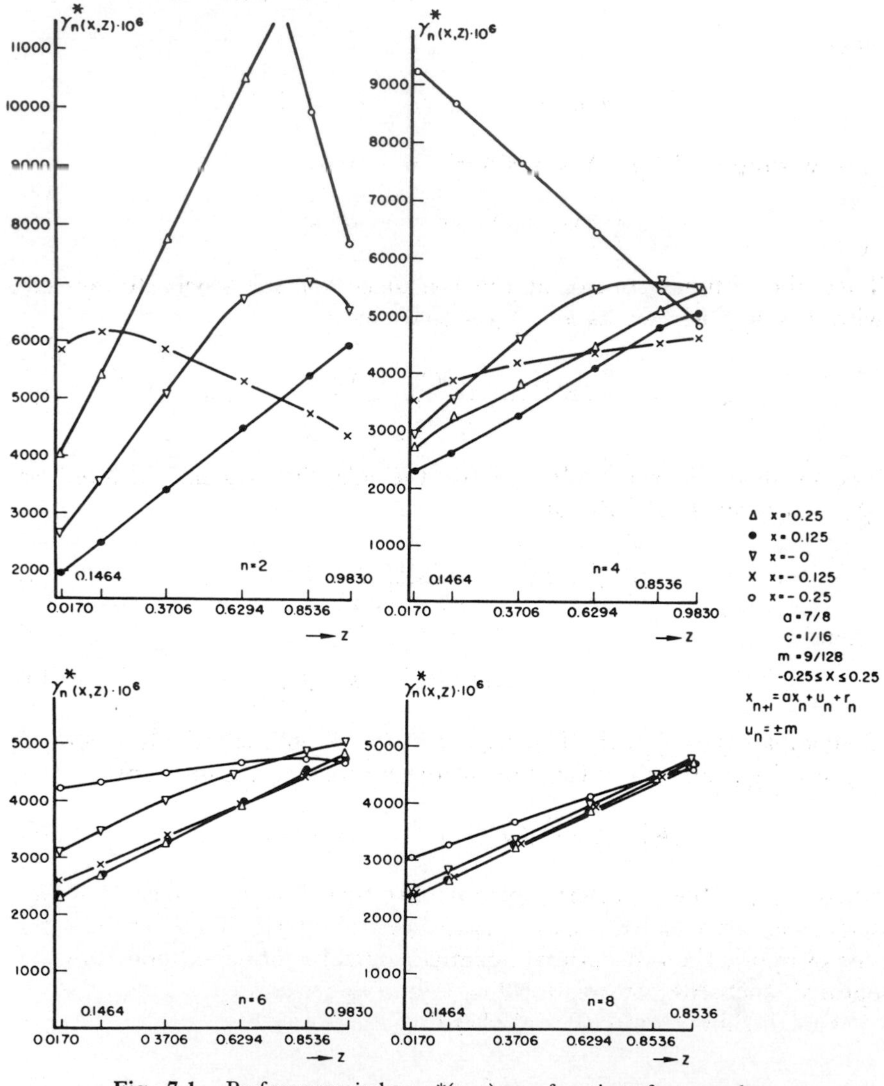

Fig. 7.1. Performance index $\gamma_n^*(x, z)$ as a function of x, z, and n.

order 10. Thus, for the example under consideration, not only the optimal adaptive control is obtainable exactly from the corresponding optimal stochastic controls but also (17) gives a good approximation for $\gamma_i^*(x, z)$ as well. See Fig. 7.1 for some computation results.[5]

C. Derivation of Approximate Relations of Optimal Control Policies for Adaptive and Stochastic Systems

We now generalize the above observation and discuss the relation of the optimal adaptive and stochastic control policies for linear systems with quadratic criterion function and with exact state vector measurements. The following developments are based in part on Fukao.[62] When the state vector measurements are noisy, the problem of approximating adaptive policies becomes much more difficult and requires further analytical and computational investigation.

The system is now assumed given by

$$x_{i+1} = A_i x_i + B_i u_i + C_i \xi_i \tag{19}$$

$$y_i = x_i \tag{20}$$

where x_i is n vector, u_i is r vector, ξ_i is m-dimensional random vector, A is $n \times n$ matrix, B is $n \times r$ matrix, and C is $n \times m$ matrix.

Let us use R_i as a generic symbol of the random variables. We consider the problems such that, at time $j + 1$, $R_0, \ldots, R_j$ will be known exactly from the known collection of the state vectors $x_0, \ldots, x_{j+1}$.

In Section D, we consider two examples, one with $R_i = \xi_i$ and the other with $R_i = A$.

Since the problem to be considered is adaptive, the probability distribution function for R will not be completely known. Let us assume that a parameter θ characterizes the probability distribution function for R and the a priori information on θ is given as

$$\Pr[\theta = \theta_i] = z_{0,i}, \qquad 1 \leqslant i \leqslant S$$

where

$$\sum_1^S z_{0,i} = 1$$

and where the first subscript 0 of $z_{0,i}$ refers to time 0 and the second subscript i indicates that it is the probability of θ being equal to θ_i. In other words, when θ is specified to be θ_i, the random variables R^j, $j = 0, 1, \ldots$, are distributed with known probability distribution function $F(R^j \mid \theta_i)$.

We will use the notation $\langle \cdot \rangle_k$ introduced by (11) to indicate the expectation operation when the distribution function involved has the parameter value θ_k. For example, $\langle \Phi(R) \rangle_k = \int \Phi(R) \; p(R \mid \theta_k) \, dR$ when the indicated integral exists.

In keeping with the notation introduced above, we denote the a posteriori probability that $\theta = \theta_i$ at time j by $z_{j,i}$.

By the Bayes rule, when R's are independent for each θ, the recursion relation for $z_{i,j}$ is given by

$$z_{j+1,i} = \frac{p(R_j \mid \theta_i) \, z_{j,i}}{\sum_{i=1}^{S} p(R_j \mid \theta_i) \, z_{j,i}}, \qquad = 0, 1, \ldots, \quad 1 \leqslant i \leqslant S \tag{21}$$

where $p(R_j \mid \theta_i)$ is the probability density function of R_j when θ is θ_i.

Let $z_i = (z_{i,1}, z_{i,2}, \ldots, z_{i,S})$. Then the augmented state vector (x_i, z_i) forms a first-order Markov sequence.

We now state a series of four observations which will serve as a basis of our approximation scheme. The notations used are summarized here. $\gamma_i^*(x, z)$ is the minimum of $E[\sum_{j=i}^{N} W_j(x_j, u_{j-1}) \mid x, z]$ when $x_{i-1} = x$ and the probability of the parameter at time i is given by z. $\gamma_{i,k}^*(x) \equiv \gamma_i^*(x, z)$ where $z = (0, \ldots, 0, 1, 0, \ldots, 0)$ where the only nonzero component of z is the kth component which is one.

Thus, $\gamma_{i,k}^*(x)$ is the minimum of $E[\sum_{j=1}^{*} W_j(x_j, u_{j-1}) \mid x]$ when θ is known to be θ_k. Let us call γ_i^* the adaptive control cost and $\gamma_{i,k}^*$ the stochastic control cost.

a. *Observation* 1

Assume that if $\gamma_{i+1}^*(x, z)$ is separable in x and in the components of z. Then the adaptive control cost is expressible as

$$\gamma_{i+1}^*(x, z_i) = \sum_{k=1}^{S} \mu_k(z_{i,k}) \, \nu_k(x) \tag{22}$$

Assume further that $\mu_k(z_{i,k})$ is proportional to $z_{i,k}$, where

$$\mu_k(1) \neq 0, \qquad \mu_k(0) = 0, \qquad 1 \leqslant k \leqslant S \tag{23}$$

Then

$$\gamma_{i+1}^*(x, z_i) = \sum_{k=1}^{S} z_{i,k} \, \gamma_{i+1,k}^*(x) \tag{24}$$

Remember that

$$\gamma_{i+1,k}^*(x) \triangleq \gamma_{i+1}^*(x, z_i = (0, \ldots, 0, 1, 0, \ldots, 0)) \tag{25}$$

where only the kth component of z_i is nonzero and is equal to one in (25). Thus (24) shows that, if the adaptive control cost is a separable function of x and components of z, then it is a linear combination of the stochastic control cost. This is a useful fact in approximating the adaptive control policy by those of the stochastic control systems.

Before proving Observation 1, let us note that (10) and the ensuing discussions show that the adaptive control cost of a final-value control problem satisfies approximately the assumption of Observation 1, where $\mu_k(z)$ is proportional to z.

Proof of Observation 1. Let

$$z = (0, 0, \dots, 0, 1)$$

then, from (23) and (25),

$$\gamma_i^*(x, z) = \gamma_{i,S}^*(x) = \mu_S(1)\nu_S(x) \tag{26}$$

for some μ_S and ν_S.

Let

$$z_{i,k} = 1, \qquad 1 \leqslant k \leqslant S \tag{27}$$

then

$$\gamma_{i+1}^*(x, z) = \gamma_{i+1,k}^*(x) = \mu_k(1)\nu_k(x) \tag{28}$$

for some μ_k and ν_k.

Therefore, from (26) and (28),

$$\gamma_{i+1}^*(x, z_i) = \sum_{k=1}^{S} \frac{\mu_k(z_{i,k})}{\mu_k(1)} \gamma_{i+1,k}^*(x) \tag{29}$$

If $\mu_k(z)$ is proportional to z, then

$$\mu_k(z_{i,k})/\mu_k(1) = z_{i,k} \tag{30}$$

and we obtain (24).

b. *Observation* 2

As one of the components in z_i approaches 1,

$$\gamma_{i+1}^*(x, z_i) \to \sum_{k=1}^{S} z_{i,k}\, \gamma_{i+1,k}^*(x) \tag{31}$$

This shows that, if the a priori probability of θ being equal to one of $\theta_1, \ldots, \theta_S$ is close to 1, or if the a posteriori probability z_i is such that most of the probability mass is concentrated on one of S possible values for θ (i.e., when one is fairly sure which value θ is), then the adaptive control cost will approach the form assumed in Observation 1.

Proof of Observation 2.

Expand $\gamma_i^*(x, z)$ about $z_i^* = (0, \ldots, 1(j\text{th}), 0, \ldots, 0)$ retaining only linear terms in the components of z and use Observation 1.

c. *Observation* 3

Suppose

$$\gamma_{i+1}^*(x, z_i) = \sum_1^S z_{i,k}\, \gamma_{i+1,k}^*(x) \tag{32}$$

Then the recursion equation for the adaptive control cost is given by

$$\gamma_i^*(x_{i-1}, z_{i-1}) = \min_{u_{i-1}} \sum_{k=1}^S z_{i-1,k} \langle W_i(x_i, u_{i-1}) + \gamma_{i+1,k}^*(x_i) \rangle_k \tag{33}$$

where the notation introduced earlier by (11) is used to write the conditional expectation

$$\langle W_i(x_i, u_{i-1}) + \gamma_{i+1,k}^*(x_i) \rangle_k \triangleq \int [W_i(x_i, u_{i-1}) + \gamma_{i+1,k}^*(x_i)] \times p(x_i \mid x, z_{i-1}, \theta_k)\, dx_i$$

where

$$x_i = A_{i-1}x + B_{i-1}u_{i-1} + C_{i-1}\xi_{i-1}$$

and where the random variable R_{i-1} is assumed to have the probability distribution with the parameter $\theta = \theta_k$. Thus, by knowing the stochastic control cost $\gamma_{i+1,k}^*$ for $1 \leqslant k \leqslant S$, the optimal adaptive control variable u_{i-1}^* can be obtained from (33) if γ_{i+1}^* has the assumed form (32). (33) shows that, even if γ_{i+1}^* is linear homogeneous in z, γ_i^* is not necessarily linear homogeneous in z.

Proof of Observation 3. The recursion equation for γ_i^* is given by

$$\gamma_i^*(x, z_{i-1}) = \min_{u_{i-1}} \sum_{k=1}^S z_{i-1,k} \langle W_i(x', u_{i-1}) + \gamma_{i+1}^*(x', z_{i-1}') \rangle_k \tag{34}$$

where

$$x' = A_{i-1}x + B_{i-1}u_{i-1} + C_{i-1}\xi_{i-1}$$

and z'_{i-1} is the a posteriori probability when the a priori probability is given by z_{i-1}. Its components are given by

$$z'_{i-1,j} = \frac{p(R_{i-1} \mid \theta_j)\, z_{i-1,j}}{\sum_{k=1}^{S} p(R_{i-1} \mid \theta_k)\, z_{i-1,k}}$$

By Assumption (32),

$$\gamma^*_{i+1}(x', z'_{i-1}) = \sum_{1}^{S} z'_{i-1,j}\, \gamma^*_{i+1,k}(x')$$

Thus in (34)

$$\sum_{k=1}^{S} z_{i-1,k} \sum_{j=1}^{S} \langle z'_{i-1,j}\, \gamma^*_{i+1,j}(x') \rangle_k$$

$$= \sum_{j=1}^{S} \sum_{k=1}^{S} z_{i-1,k} \int \frac{p(R_{i-1} \mid \theta_j)\, z_{i-1,j}\, \gamma^*_{i+1,j}(x')}{[\sum_{k=1}^{S} p(R_{i-1} \mid \theta_k)\, z_{i-1,k}]}\, p(R_{i-1} \mid \theta_k)\, dR_{i-1}$$

$$= \sum_{j=1}^{S} \int z_{i-1,j}\, \gamma^*_{i+1,j}(x')\, p(R_{i-1} \mid \theta_j)\, dR_i$$

$$= \sum_{j=1}^{S} z_{i-1,j} \langle \gamma^*_{i+1,j}(x') \rangle_j$$

establishing (33).

The optimal adaptive control u^*_{i-1} is therefore obtained from (33). If we have assumed

$$\gamma^*_{i+1}(x, z_i) = \sum_{1}^{S} z_{i,k}\, \gamma^*_{i+1,k}(x) + \Delta\gamma_{i+1}(z_i)$$

instead of (32), then u^*_{i-1} is still obtained by

$$\min_{u_{i-1}} \sum_{1}^{S} z_{i,k} \langle W_i + \gamma^*_{i+1,k} \rangle_k$$

since the contribution $\Delta\gamma_{i+1}$ is independent of u_{i-1}.

Thus, in view of our discussion in Section B and of Observations

2 and 3, we may define a measure of increase in control cost due to the imprecise knowledge of θ by

$$\Delta\gamma_i \triangleq \gamma_i^*(x, z_{i-1}) - \sum_{k=1}^{S} z_{i-1,k}\, \gamma_{i,k}^*(x) \tag{35}$$

when the system is in the state $(x_{i-1} = x, z_{i-1})$ at time $i - 1$.

When γ_i^* is expressible as (33), the right-hand side of (35) can be written as

$$\delta\gamma_i \triangleq \min_{u_{i-1}} \sum_{k=1}^{S} z_{i-1,k}\langle W_i + \gamma_{i+1,k}^*\rangle_k$$

$$- \sum_{k=1}^{S} z_{i-1,k} \min_{u_{i-1}}\langle W_i + \gamma_{i+1,k}^*\rangle_k \tag{35a}$$

i.e., $\delta\gamma_i$ is the special case of $\Delta\gamma_i$ where γ_i^* has the form (33) as the result of the assumed form (32).

Note that the operations of the minimization and the averaging with respect to z are interchanged in (35a). We may therefore say in this case the increase in the cost of adaptive control over the cost of stochastic control is given by the interchange of the summation and the minimization operations.

The relation of the optimal policies for adaptive and purely stochastic systems is established by Observation 4.

d. *Observation* 4

If

$$\gamma_i^*(x, z_{i-1}) = \min_{u_{i-1}} \sum_{k=1}^{S} z_{i-1,k}\langle W_i + \gamma_{i+1,k}^*\rangle_k \tag{36}$$

if $\langle W_i + \gamma_{i+1,k}^*\rangle_k$ is quadratic in u, and if no constraints are imposed on u and x (i.e., state vector and control vectors are not constrained in any way), then the optimal control vector for the adaptive system at time $i - 1$ is given by a linearly weighted sum of the optimal control vector of the corresponding S stochastic problems at time $i - 1$. Under the same set of assumptions, $\delta\gamma_i$ of (35a) is, at most, quadratic in the optimal control vector for the stochastic problems.

Proof of Observation 4. Since the dependence of $\langle W_i + \gamma_{i+1,k}^*\rangle_k$ on u is quadratic by assumption, by completing the square, if necessary, and recalling the recursion formula for $\gamma_{i,k}^*$ and that the notation $u_{i-1,k}^*$

is used to denote the optimal control for the purely stochastic problem with $\theta = \theta_k$ at time i, we can write it as

$$\langle W_i + \gamma^*_{i+1,k} \rangle_k = (u - u^*_{i-1,k})' \Phi_{i,k} (u - u^*_{i-1,k}) + \phi_{i,k} \tag{37}$$

where $\Phi'_{i,k} = \Phi_{i,k}$ and where $\Phi_{i,k}$ and $\phi_{i,k}$ generally depend on x. Note that $u^*_{i-1,k}$ will generally depend on θ_k.

Substituting (37) into (36), the optimal control u^*_{i-1} for the adaptive problem is given by performing the minimization

$$\min_{u_{i-1}} \sum_{k=1}^{S} z_{i-1,k}[(u - u^*_{i-1,k})' \Phi_{i,k} (u - u^*_{i-1,k}) + \phi_{i,k}]$$

i.e.,

$$u^*_{i-1} = \left(\sum_{k=1}^{S} z_{i-1,k} \Phi_{i,k} \right)^{-1} \left(\sum_{k=1}^{S} z_{i-1,k} \Phi_{i,k} u^*_{i-1,k} \right) \tag{38}$$

proving Observation 4 when the indicated inverse exists.

Equation (38) shows that the adaptive optimal control policy is obtainable by solving S purely stochastic control problems.

Knowing optimal control vectors for the stochastic problems $u^*_{i-1,k}$, $k = 1,\ldots, S$, we can obtain the difference of the adaptive and the stochastic control cost when the assumptions of Observations 4 are met. From (35a) and (37),

$$\begin{aligned}
\delta\gamma_i &= \sum_{k=1}^{S} z_{i-1,k}[\langle W_i + \gamma^*_{i+1,k} \rangle_k]_{u^*_{i-1}} \\
&\quad - \sum_{k=1}^{S} z_{i-1,k}[\langle W_i + \gamma^*_{i+1,k} \rangle_k]_{u^*_{i-1,k}} \\
&= \sum_{k=1}^{S} z_{i-1,k}(u^*_{i-1} - u^*_{i-1,k})' \Phi_{i,k} (u^*_{i-1} - u^*_{i-1,k}) \\
&= \sum_{k=1}^{S} (u^*_{i-1,k})' z_{i-1,k} \Phi_{i,k} u^*_{i-1,k} - \left(\sum_{k=1}^{S} z_{i-1,k} \Phi_{i,k} u^*_{i-1,k} \right)' \\
&\quad \times \left(\sum_{k=1}^{S} z_{i-1,k} \Phi_{i,k} \right)^{-1} \left(\sum_{k=1}^{S} z_{i-1,k} \Phi_{i,k} u^*_{i-1,k} \right)
\end{aligned} \tag{39}$$

As a special case, if the quadratic part of $\gamma^*_{i,k}$ is independent of θ_k, i.e., if

$$\Phi_{i,k} = \Phi_i, \qquad 1 \leqslant k \leqslant S$$

then, from (38), the adaptive optimal control is related to $u_{i-1,k}^*$, $1 \leqslant k \leqslant S$, by

$$u_{i-1}^* = \sum z_{i-1,k} u_{i-1,k}^* \tag{40}$$

Namely the optimal adaptive control is a weighted average of the corresponding stochastic optimal control. For this special case, (39) reduces to

$$\delta\gamma_i = \sum_{k=1}^{S} (u_{i-1,k}^*)' z_{i-1,k} \Phi_i u_{i-1,k}^* - \left(\sum_{k=1}^{S} z_{i-1,k} u_{i-1,k}^*\right)' \Phi_i \left(\sum_{k=1}^{S} z_{i-1,k} u_{i-1,k}^*\right) \tag{41}$$

Even in the general case, by defining

$$\bar{\Phi}_i \triangleq \sum_{k-1}^{S} z_{i-1,k} \Phi_{i,k} \tag{42}$$

and

$$\bar{z}_{i,k} \triangleq z_{i,k} \bar{\Phi}_i^{-1} \Phi_{i,k} \tag{43}$$

We can express u_{i-1}^* and $\delta\gamma_i$ in forms similar to (40) and (41), respectively. We have, from (40), (42), and (43),

$$u_{i-1}^* = \sum_{k=1}^{S} \bar{z}_{i-1,k} u_{i-1,k}^* \tag{44}$$

and, from (39), (42), and (43),

$$\delta\gamma_i = \sum_{k=1}^{S} (u_{i-1,k}^*)' \bar{\Phi}_i \bar{z}_{i-1,k} u_{i-1,k}^* - \left(\sum_{k=1}^{S} \bar{z}_{i-1,k} u_{i-1,k}^*\right)' \bar{\Phi}_i \left(\sum_{k=1}^{S} \bar{z}_{i-1,k} u_{i-1,k}^*\right) \tag{45}$$

The difference in control cost $\delta\gamma_i$ generally depends on x. If $\bar{\Phi}_k$ is independent of the state vector x and if the stochastic optimal control vector $u_{i,k}^*$ can be expressed as a sum of functions of x_i only and of θ_k only, then $\delta\gamma_i$ will be independent of x. To see this we express, by assumption, $u_{i,k}^*$ as

$$u_{i,k}^* = a(x_i) + b_k \qquad (46)^*$$

* Equation (13) shows that the system of Section B satisfies (46), at least for $i = N - 1$.

Then, substituting (46) into (44) and (45), we obtain

$$u_i^* = a(x_i) + \sum_{k=1}^{S} \bar{z}_{i,k} b_k \tag{47}$$

and

$$\delta\gamma_{i+1} = \sum_{k=1}^{S} b_k' \bar{\Phi}_{i+1} \bar{z}_{i,k} b_k - \left(\sum_{k=1}^{S} \bar{z}_{i,k} b_k\right)' \Phi_{i+1} \left(\sum_{k=1}^{S} \bar{z}_{i,k} b_k\right) \tag{48}$$

Equation (48) shows that $\delta\gamma_i$ is independent of x, when the stochastic problems are such that Φ_k is independent of x and when their optimal control are given by (46).

Let us now consider two examples of adaptive control systems with quadratic performance indices and illustrate the usefulness of these observations for the systems described by (19) and (20).

D. Examples

a. *Adaptive Systems with Unknown Plant Noise*

If we identify R_i with ξ_i in the development of Section C, then we have an adaptive control problem where the probability distribution function for the plant disturbance random variable contains unknown parameter θ. Assume that ξ_i are the only random variables in (19), that they are independent in time, and that their common distribution function is given by $F(z \mid \theta)$, where θ is chosen from $\theta_1, ..., \theta_S$. Thus,

$$\begin{aligned} \lambda_N(x_{N-1}, z_{N-1}) &= \int W_N(x, u_{N-1})\, p(x \mid x_{N-1}, z_{N-1}, u_{N-1})\, dx \\ &= \int W_N(x, u_{N-1})\, p(x \mid x_{N-1}, \xi_{N-1}, u_{N-1}) \\ &\quad \times p(\xi_{N-1} \mid z_{N-1})\, d(x, \xi_{N-1}) \end{aligned} \tag{49}$$

We take W_N to be

$$W_N(x, u) = (x, V_N x) + (u, P_{N-1} u)$$

where

$$x = A_{N-1} x_{N-1} + B_{N-1} u_{N-1} + C_{N-1} \xi_{N-1}$$

and where

$$p(\xi_{N-1} \mid z_{N-1}) = \sum_{k=1}^{S} p(\xi_{N-1} \mid \theta_k)\, z_{N-1,k} \tag{50}$$

Thus

$$\gamma_N^*(x_{N-1}, z_{N-1}) = \min_{u_{N-1}} \sum_{k=1}^{N} z_{N-1,k} \langle W_N \rangle_k \tag{51}$$

where, dropping the subscript $N-1$ from A, B, and C,

$$\begin{aligned}\langle W_N\rangle_k &= \langle W_N(Ax_{N-1} + Bu_{N-1} + C\xi_{N-1}, u_{N-1})\rangle_k \\ &= W_N(Ax_{N-1} + Bu_{N-1}, u_{N-1}) \\ &\quad + 2\{C\langle\xi_{N-1}\rangle_k, V_N(Ax_{N-1} + Bu_{N-1})\} \\ &\quad + \langle(C\xi_{N-1}, V_N C\xi_{N-1})\rangle_k\end{aligned}$$

Therefore, $u^*_{N-1,k}$ is obtained by

$$\min_{u_{N-1}}[W_N(Ax_{N-1} + Bu_{N-1}, u_{N-1}) + 2(C\langle\xi_{N-1}\rangle_k, V_N(Ax_{N-1} + Bu_{N-1}))]$$

where $\langle\xi_{N-1}\rangle_k$ is the mean of the distribution function $F(\xi_{N-1} \mid \theta_k)$. Thus Φ_N defined in (37) is seen to be independent of x and k:

$$\Phi_{N,k} = \Phi_N = B'_{N-1}V_N B_{N-1} + P_{N-1} \tag{52}$$

From (52),

$$\begin{aligned}u^*_{N-1,k} &= -(P_{N-1} + B'_{N-1}V_N B_{N-1})^{-1}B'_{N-1}V_{N-1}(A_{N-1}x_{N-1} + C_{N-1}\langle\xi_{N-1}\rangle_k) \\ &= a_{N-1}x_{N-1} + b_{k,N-1}\end{aligned} \tag{53}$$

where

$$a_{N-1} \triangleq -(P_{N-1} + B'_{N-1}V_N B_{N-1})^{-1}B'_{N-1}V_{N-1}A_{N-1} \tag{54a}$$

$$b_{k,N-1} \triangleq -(P_{N-1} + B'_{N-1}V_N B_{N-1})^{-1}B'_{N-1}V_{N-1}C_{N-1}\langle\xi\rangle_k \tag{54b}$$

From (53) the corresponding stochastic control cost is given by

$$\begin{aligned}\gamma^*_{N,k} = \{&x_{N-1}, (A'V_N A - A'V_N B(P_{N-1} + B'V_N B)^{-1}B'V_N A)x_{N-1}\} \\ &- 2\langle\xi\rangle_k' C'V_N B(P_{N-1} + B'V_N B)^{-1}B'V_N A x_{N-1} \\ &- \langle\xi\rangle_k' C'V_N B(P_{N-1} + B'V_N B)^{-1}B'V_N A C\langle\xi\rangle_k \\ &+ \langle\xi_{N-1}, C'V_N C\xi_{N-1}\rangle_k\end{aligned} \tag{55}$$

The optimal adaptive control u^*_{N-1} is obtained by

$$\min_{u_{N-1}}[W_N(Ax_{N-1} + Bu_{N-1}, u_{N-1}) + 2(C\bar{\xi}, V_N(Ax_{N-1} + Bu_{N-1}))]$$

where

$$\bar{\xi} \triangleq \sum_{k=1}^{S} z_{N-1,k}\langle\xi\rangle_k$$

From (42)–(44), and (45)

$$u^*_{N-1} = a_{N-1}x_{N-1} + \sum_{1}^{S} z_{N-1,k}b_{k,N-1}$$

Thus

$$\gamma_N^*(x_{N-1}, z_{N-1}) = \sum_{k=1}^{S} z_{N-1,k}\, \gamma_N^*(x_{N-1}) + \Delta\gamma_N(z_{N-1}) \tag{56}$$

where $\Delta\gamma_N$ is given from (35), (52), (54a), and (54b), and is independent of x_{N-1} since $\bar{\Phi}$ and b's are independent of x.

If $\langle \xi \rangle_k$ is the same for all $k = 1,\ldots, S$ (for example, zero for all k), then $u_{N-1,k}$ is the same for all k and u_{N-1}:

$$u_{N-1}^* = u_{N-1,k}^*$$

for any k. By employing the argument similar to those in the proof of Observation 3, we can show that u_{i-1}^* is obtained from

$$\min_{u_{i-1}} \sum_{k=1}^{S} z_{i-1,k} \langle W_i + \gamma_{i+1,k}^* \rangle_k \tag{57}$$

and

$$\gamma_{i+1}^*(x_i, z_i) = \sum_{k-1}^{S} z_{i,k}\, \gamma_{i+1,k}^*(x_i) + \Delta\gamma_{i+1} \tag{58}$$

where $\Delta\gamma_{i+1}$ is independent of x and is the solution to the recursion equation

$$\begin{aligned} \Delta\gamma_i(z_{i-1}) &= \delta\gamma_i(z_{i-1}) + \sum_{k=1}^{S} z_{i-1,k} \langle \Delta\gamma_{i+1}(z_{i-1}') \rangle_k \\ \Delta\gamma_{N+1} &= 0 \end{aligned} \tag{59}$$

where $\delta\gamma_i(z_{i-1})$ is defined by (35a).

In the system just discussed $\Delta\gamma_i$ turned out to be a function of z only. Hence we could synthesize u_i^* from $u_{i,k}^*$, $1 \leqslant k \leqslant S$ exactly. If $\Delta\gamma_i$ is a function of x, however, then we can no longer synthesize u_i^* so simply. When the random variable R_i contains A_i, B_i, and/or C_i in addition to or instead of ξ_i, $\Delta\gamma_i$ will, in general, be functions of u, x, and ξ. Such an example is briefly discussed next.

b. *Adaptive System with Unknown Transition Matrix*

Suppose A of (19) is an unknown constant matrix with S possible values $A^{(1)},\ldots, A^{(S)}$. The random variable ξ's are assumed to be independently and identically distributed with $E\xi_i = 0$ and assumed to have finite second moments. Assume $C = I$ in (19) for the sake of simplicity. Now,

$$\gamma_N(x_{N-1}, z_{N-1}) = \sum_{k=1}^{S} z_{N-1,k}\langle W_N\rangle_k \tag{60}$$

where $\langle\cdot\rangle_k$ now stands for the expected value for the system with $A^{(k)}$ since

$$p(x_N \mid x_{N-1}, z_{N-1}) = \sum z_{N-1,k}\, p(\xi_{N-1} = x_N - A^{(k)}x_{N-1} - B_{N-1}u_{N-1})$$

One can write

$$\langle W_N\rangle_k = (u_{N-1} - u^*_{N-1,k})'\Phi_{N,k}(u_{N-1} - u^*_{N-1,k}) + \phi_{N,k} \tag{61}$$

where

$$\Phi_{N,k} = \Phi_N \triangleq (B'_{N-1}V_N B_{N-1} + P_{N-1}) \tag{62a}$$

$$\begin{aligned} u^*_{N-1,k} &= -(B'_{N-1}V_N B_{N-1} + P_{N-1})^{-1}B'_{N-1}V_N A^{(k)}x_{N-1} \\ &\triangleq a_{N-1,k}x_{N-1} \end{aligned} \tag{62b}$$

$$\begin{aligned} \phi_{N,k} \triangleq\ & x'_{N-1}(A^{(k)})'(V_N^{-1} + B'_{N-1}P_{N-1}B_{N-1})^{-1}A^{(k)}x_{N-1} \\ &+ E[\xi'_{N-1}(V_N^{-1} + B'P_{N-1}B)^{-1}\xi_{N-1}] \end{aligned} \tag{62c}$$

when the indicated inverses exist. From (42),

$$\bar{\Phi}_N = \Phi_N$$

From (43),

$$\bar{z}_{N-1,k} = z_{N-1,k}$$

From (44),

$$u^*_{N-1} = \sum_{k=1}^{S} z_{N-1,k}u^*_{N-1,k}$$

From (45),

$$\begin{aligned} \delta\gamma_N &= \sum_{k=1}^{S} (a_{N-1,k}x_{N-1})'\Phi_N\, z_{N-1,k}(a_{N-1,k}x_{N-1}) \\ &\quad - \left(\sum_{k=1}^{S} z_{N-1,k}a_{N-1,k}x_{N-1}\right)' \Phi_N \left(\sum_{k=1}^{S} z_{N-1,k}a_{N-1,k}x_{N-1}\right) \\ &= x'_{N-1}\left[\sum_{k=1}^{S} z_{N-1,k}(a'_{N-1,k}\Phi_N a_{N-1,k}) \right. \\ &\quad \left. - \left(\sum_{k=1}^{S} z_{N-1,k}a_{N-1,k}\right)' \Phi_N \left(\sum_{k=1}^{S} z_{N-1,k}a_{N-1,k}\right)\right] x_{N-1} \end{aligned} \tag{63}$$

Thus, unlike the previous example, $\delta\gamma_N$ is a quadratic function of x_{N-1}.

Hence Assumption (36) of Observation 4 is true only for $i = N$ and, in general,

$$\gamma_{i+1}^*(x, z_i) = \sum z_{i,k}\, \gamma_{i+1,k}^*(x) + \Delta\gamma_{i+1}(x, z_i)$$

where $\Delta\gamma_i$ satisfies the recursion equation (59).

Thus the control constructed from the stochastic controls by (38) is no longer an optimal adaptive control but becomes its approximation which is equivalent to neglecting $\Delta\gamma$ terms in the recursion equation for γ^*.

From (59) and (63), it can be seen that such an approximation will be good so long as

$$\left(\sum_{k=1}^{S} z_{i,k} a_{i,k}' \Phi_{i+1} a_{i,k}\right) - \left(\sum_{k=1}^{S} z_{i,k} a_{i,k}\right)' \Phi_{i+1} \left(\sum_{k=1}^{S} z_{i,k} a_{i,k}\right)$$

remains small; in other words, if the norm of

$$\sum_{k=1}^{S} z_{i,k} (A^{(k)})' A^{(k)} \qquad \left(\sum z_{i,k} (A^{k})\right)' \left(\sum z_{i,k} A^{(k)}\right)$$

is small either by having $z_{i,k}$ close to zero except for one k(i.e., when the learning on the value of A is almost complete) or if $A^{(1)}, \ldots, A^{(k)}$ are very close together.

2. Approximation with Open-Loop Feedback Control Policies

In the previous section, we have discussed the method which approximately synthesizes optimal closed-loop control policies for adaptive systems from optimal closed-loop policies for the corresponding purely stochastic systems.

In this section we will discuss a scheme which approximates optimal closed-loop control policies with what is sometimes called optimal open-loop feedback control policies for the same systems.[49]

An open-loop control policy specifies the sequence of control decisions to be followed from a given initial point, i.e., all control decisions are given as functions of the initial point and time. An open-loop feedback control policy computes the current and all future control variables u_j, $i \leqslant j \leqslant N-1$, at time i from the past and current observed state variables of the system y^i but incorporates feedback in that only u_i

is actually used, and the new observation y_{i+1} on the attained state variable x_{i+1} is used to recompute the open-loop control u_{i+1} as the functions of y^{i+1} at time $i + 1$.

The discussion will be for systems whose state vectors are exactly observable. This assumption of exact measurements is not essential for the development of this section. The systems with measurement noise can be treated similarly but with added complexities in the derivation. The method discussed in this section is essentially a stochastic version of Merriam's parametric expansion method[104b] for deterministic systems and adapted from the method proposed by Spang.[126] For computer study of the effectiveness of the open-loop feedback control policies, also see Spang.[127]

One starts from the assumption of the plant equation given by

$$x_{k+1} = Ax_k + Bu_k + C\xi_k, \qquad k = 0, 1, \ldots, N-1 \tag{64}$$

where x_k is the state vector, u_k is the control vector, and ξ_k is the random disturbance vector. The matrices A, B, and C are assumed unknown, with given a priori joint probability density function $p_0(A, B, C)$. The matrix C is assumed nonsingular.* The assumption of unknown C amounts to the assumption that the variance of the noise to the system is unknown.

The joint probability density function of $\xi_0, \xi_1, \ldots, \xi_{N-1}$ is assumed to exist and to be known.

It is a straightforward extension of the method of this section to include the case where the joint probability density function is parametrized by an unknown parameter. As before, optimal closed-loop u_k is to depend only on y^k and u^{k-1}. The criterion function J is taken to be quadratic:

$$J = \sum_1^N W_i \tag{65}$$

where

$$W_i = x_i' V_i x_i + u_{i-1}' T_{i-1} u_{i-1}$$

and where V_i and T_{i-1} are positive symmetric matrices, $1 \leqslant i \leqslant N$. The contribution to J from the present and the future at time k is given by

$$J_k \triangleq \sum_k^N W_i \tag{66}$$

---

* If C is singular, it can be shown that a certain number of coefficients can be learned exactly in a finite time.

Equation (66) can be rewritten as

$$J_k = x_k' V_k x_k + u_{k-1}' T_{k-1} u_{k-1} + J_{k+1} \tag{67}$$

Here we will make use of the extension of Merriam's idea of parametric expansion for the deterministic systems. This difference equation for J_k is satisfied by a quadratic form in x_{k-1}, u_{k-1}, $u_k, \ldots, u_{N-1}$, and ξ_{k-1}, $\xi_k, \ldots, \xi_{N-1}$. Therefore, we write

$$\begin{aligned} J_k = a_k &+ 2 \sum_{i=k-1}^{N-1} b_i(k)\, u_i + \sum_{i=k-1}^{N-1} \sum_{j=k-1}^{N-1} u_i' \, K_{ij}(k)\, u_j \\ &+ 2C_k x_{k-1} + x_{k-1}' L_k x_{k-1} + 2 \sum_{i=k-1}^{N-1} g_i(k)\, \xi_i \\ &+ \sum_{i=k-1}^{N-1} \sum_{j=k-1}^{N-1} \xi_i' \, N_{ij}(k)\, \xi_j + 2 \sum_{j=k-1}^{N-1} u_j' \, f_j(k)\, x_{k-1} \\ &+ 2 \sum_{i=k-1}^{N-1} \xi_i' \, M_i(k)\, x_{k-1} + 2 \sum_{i=k-1}^{N-1} \sum_{j=k-1}^{N-1} \xi_i' \, O_{ij}(k)\, u_j \end{aligned} \tag{68}$$

where a_k, $b(k)$'s, etc., are matrices of appropriate dimensions. Substituting Eq. (68) into Eq. (67), we obtain a set of recursion equations for the coefficients of the expansion. They are derived in Appendix A at the end of this Chapter. They are, then, solved for all k off-line.

We know from our discussions in Chapters II–IV that an optimal closed-loop feedback policy is such that it minimizes

$$\begin{aligned} \gamma_{k+1} &= E\left(\sum_{k+1}^{N} W_i \mid x^k\right) \\ &= \int J_{k+1}\, p(A, B, C, \xi_k, \xi_{k+1}, \ldots, \xi_{N-1} \mid x^k) \\ &\quad \times d(A, B, C, \xi_k, \ldots, \xi_{N-1}) \\ &= \int J_{k+1}\, p(\xi_k, \ldots, \xi_{N-1} \mid A, B, C, x^k)\, p(A, B, C \mid x^k) \\ &\quad \times d(A, B, C, \xi_k, \ldots, \xi_{N-1}) \end{aligned} \tag{69}$$

with respect to u_i, $k \leqslant i \leqslant N-1$, where u_i is a function of x^i and u^{i-1}.

Define

$$\Gamma_{ij}^k = \int \xi_i' \xi_j \, p(\xi_k, \xi_{k+1}, ..., \xi_{N-1} \mid A, B, C, x^k) \, d(\xi_k, ..., \xi_{N-1}) \tag{70a}$$

$$\mu_j^k = \int \xi_j \, p(\xi_k, \xi_{k+1}, ..., \xi_{N-1} \mid A, B, C, x^k) \, d(\xi_k, ..., \xi_{N-1}), \tag{70b}$$
$$k \leqslant i, \quad j \leqslant N-1$$

Using a bar to indicate the conditional expectation operation with respect to A, B, C, Eq. (69) becomes approximately equal to

$$\begin{aligned}
E(J_{k+1} \mid x^k) \approx\ & a_{k+1} + 2 \sum_{i=k}^{N-1} \overline{b_i(k+1)u_k} + \sum_{i=k}^{N-1} \sum_{j=k}^{N-1} u_k' \overline{K_{ij}(k+1)} u_j \\
& + 2\overline{C}_{k+1} x_k + x_k' \overline{L_{k+1}} x_k + 2 \sum_{i=k}^{N-1} \overline{g_i'(k+1)\mu_i^k} \\
& + \sum_{i=k}^{N-1} \sum_{j=k}^{N-1} \overline{\mathrm{tr}(N_{ij}(k+1)\Gamma_{ij}^k)} + 2 \sum_{j=k}^{N-1} u_j' \overline{f_j(k+1)} x_k \\
& + 2 \sum_{i=k}^{N-1} \overline{\mu_i^{k\prime} M_i(k+1)} x_k + 2 \sum_{i=k}^{N-1} \sum_{j=k}^{N-1} \overline{\mu_i^{k\prime} O_{ij}(k+1)} u_j \\
=\ & a_{k+1} + 2 \sum_{i=k}^{N-1} \overline{g_i'(k+1)\mu_i^k} + \sum_{i=k}^{N-1} \sum_{j=k}^{N-1} \overline{\mathrm{tr}(N_{ij}(k+1)\Gamma_{ij}^k} \\
& + 2 \sum_{i=k}^{N-1} \left(b_i(k+1) + \sum_{j=i}^{N-1} \overline{\mu_j^{k\prime} O_{ji}(k+1)} \right) u_i \\
& + 2 \left(\overline{C}_{k+1} + \sum_{i=k}^{N-1} \overline{\mu_i^{k\prime} M_i(k+1)} \right) x_k \\
& + \sum_{i=k}^{N-1} \sum_{j=k}^{N-1} u_i' \overline{K_{ij}(k+1)} u_j + 2 \sum_{j=k}^{N-1} u_j' \overline{f_j(k+1)} x_k \\
& + x_k' L_{k+1} x_k
\end{aligned} \tag{71}$$

The approximation consists in replacing closed-loop control decisions with open-loop control decisions. For $i > k$, note the relations

$$\begin{aligned}
\overline{b_i(k+1)u_i} &\triangleq \int b_i(k+1) u_i \, p(A, B, C \mid x^k) \, d(A, B, C) \\
&\neq u_i \int b_i(k+1) \, p(A, B, C \mid x^k) \, d(A, B, C) \\
&= \overline{b_i(k+1)} u_i
\end{aligned}$$

Similarly

$$\overline{u_i' k_{ij}(k+1) u_j} \neq u_i' \overline{k_{ij}(k+1)} u_j, \quad \text{etc.}, \qquad i, j > k$$

Note that only when u_k is involved we can write

$$\overline{b_k(k+1) u_k} = \overline{b_k(k+1)} u_k$$

$$\overline{u_k' K_{kk}(k+1) u_k} = u_k' \overline{K_{kk}(k+1)} u_k$$

etc.

When $\overline{b_i(k+1) u_i}$, $\overline{u_i' K_{ij}(k+1) u_j}$, etc., are equated with $\overline{b_i(k+1)} u_i$, $u_i \overline{K_{ij}(k+1)} u_j$, etc., in the right-hand side of (71), the control variables $u_k, u_{k+1}, \ldots, u_{N-1}$ are all taken to be functions of x^k only, i.e., open-loop control variables are substituted for closed-loop control variables.

The optimal open-loop control variables u_k $u_{k+1}, \ldots, u_{N-1}$ which approximate the optimal closed-loop policy is then given by $u_k, \ldots, u_{N-1}$, which minimizes (71). Hence, by differentiating Eq. (71) with respect to u_j, $j = k, k+1, \ldots, N-1$, we obtain

$$\sum_{i=k}^{N-1} \overline{K_{ji}(k+1)} u_i^* = -\left(\overline{b_j(k+1)} + \sum_{i=k}^{N-1} \overline{\mu_i^{k\prime} O_{ij}(k+1)}\right)$$
$$- \overline{f_j(k+1)} x_k \qquad j = k, k+1, \ldots, N-1 \quad (72)$$

which, when solved, gives u_k^* among others.

When u_k^* is applied at time k and the time advances to $k+1$ from k, we have one more observation x_{k+1}. Therefore, rather than using $u_{k+1}^*, \ldots, u_{N-1}^*$ obtained by solving Eq. (72) at time k, we resolve Eq. (72) after μ's and I''s are re-evaluated conditioned on x^{k+1} rather than on x^k. In other words, only the immediate control u_k^* is used from (72).

Thus, at each time instant k we have a recursive procedure to obtain u_k^*.

This approximation generates an open-loop feedback control policy since a new observation x_{k+1} is incorporated in computing a new optimal open-loop policy based on the knowledge x^{k+1}.

It is easy to see that open-loop policies are much easier to compute than closed-loop policies.

The question of when optimal open-loop feedback policies are good approximations to optimal closed-loop policies must be carefully considered for each individual problem. See Spang[127] for computer studies for simple systems.

3. Sensitivity and Error Analysis of Kalman Filters

A. Introduction

If the description of a linear dynamic system is given exactly by the set of equations

$$x_{i+1} = A_i x_i + \xi_i \tag{73}$$

$$y_i = H_i x_i + \eta_i \tag{74}$$

$$E(\xi_i) = E(\eta_i) = 0 \tag{75a}$$

$$E(\xi_i \xi_j') = Q_i \delta_{ij} \tag{75b}$$

$$E(\eta_i \eta_i') = R_i \delta_{ij} \tag{75c}$$

$$E(\xi_i \xi_j') = 0 \tag{75d}$$

namely, when the matrices of the system A_i and H_i, the means and covariance matrices of the random noises, are given exactly as above, then the outputs of the Wiener-Kalman filter are the best linear estimates of the state vectors of the system. See Chapter V and Section 4 of Chapter II.

It is important to have some measures of the variations of the filter outputs when some of the underlying assumptions are not true, since the system parameters such as A_i and H_i or noise statistics such as Q_i and R_i will not be generally known exactly in real problems.

Such inaccuracy may arise as a result of numerically evaluating A_i and H_i (round-off errors and/or error in quadrature). For example the linear system given by (73) and (74) may be merely an approximate expression of a nonlinear dynamic and/or plant equations obtained by linearizing them about some nominal trajectories. Then, A_i and H_i are evaluated, perhaps numerically, by taking certain partial derivatives. See, for example, Section 3,F of Chapter V.

Another reason for such analysis is that, for problems with complex expressions for A and/or H, it is of interest to examine the effect of a simplified approximate expression for A and/or H on the accuracy of the estimation.

As for noise statistics, we usually have only their rough estimates. Therefore, it is important to evaluate the effects of inaccuracies in A_i, H_i, Q_i, and/or in R_i on the estimates, i.e., on the error covariance matrices of the outputs of the Wiener–Kalman filters.

It is also important to know the effects of nonoptimal filter gains on the error-covariance matrices. We are interested in nonoptimal gains: (1) to study the sensitivity of the estimates and of the error covariance matrices with respect to the filter gain and (2) to study the effects of the simplified suboptimal method of gain computation on the filter performance since the gain computation is the most time consuming operation in generating the estimates. For additional details see, for example, Joseph.[81,82]

We have derived, in Section 3 of Chapter II and elsewhere, the expressions for the error-covariance matrices for Kalman filter. They are given by

$$x_{i+1}^* = \hat{x}_{i+1} + K_{i+1}[y_{i+1} - H_{i+1}\hat{x}_{i+1}] \tag{76}$$

where

$$\hat{x}_{i+1} \triangleq E(x_{i+1} \mid y^i) = A_i x_i^* \tag{77a}$$

where

$$x_i^* \triangleq E(x_i \mid y^i) \tag{77b}$$

and where K_{i+1} is the optimal filter gain given by

$$K_{i+1} = M_{i+1}H'_{i+1}[H_{i+1}M_{i+1}H'_{i+1} + R_{i+1}]^{-1} \tag{77c}$$

where

$$\begin{aligned} M_{i+1} &\triangleq E[(x_{i+1} - \hat{x}_{i+1})(x_{i+1} - \hat{x}_{i+1})' \mid y^i] \\ &= A_i \Gamma_i A_i' + Q_i \end{aligned} \tag{78}$$

The error-covariance matrix of the optimal estimate is calculated by

$$\begin{aligned} \Gamma_i &\triangleq E[(x_i - x_i^*)(x_i - x_i^*)' \mid y^i] \\ &= (I - K_i H_i)M_i(I - K_i H_i)' + K_i R_i K_i' \end{aligned} \tag{79a}$$

or equivalently by

$$\Gamma_i = (I - K_i H_i)M_i \tag{79b}$$

The initial estimate x_0^* and its error-covariance matrix Γ_0 is assumed given from a priori information on the initial state of the system.

B. Gain Variation

Let us first consider the effects on Γ of the gain changes from its optimal values K_i by δK_i. Denoting by $\delta\Gamma_i$ the deviation of the error-covariance matrix from its optimal form Γ_i and dropping the subscripts,

$$\begin{aligned} \delta\Gamma &= [I - (K + \delta K)H]M[I - (K + \delta K)H]' + (K + \delta K)R(K + \delta K)' \\ &\quad - (I - KH)M(I - KH)' - KRK' \\ &\doteqdot \delta K\,[-HM(I - KH)' + RK'] + [(I - KH)MH' + KR]\,\delta K' \end{aligned} \tag{80}$$

where the second-order terms are neglected.

Since K is given by (77c), coefficients multiplying δK and $\delta K'$ vanish in (80) and we have

$$\delta \Gamma = 0$$

The alternate expression for optimal error-covariance (79b), obtainable by substituting (77c) into (79b), gives

$$\delta \Gamma = -\delta K H M$$

Therefore, in numerically evaluating Γ, the expression (79a) would be less sensitive than (79b) to small variation in K.

In Sections 4–6 we consider several suboptimal filters using non-optimal gains in the Wiener–Kalman filters. See also Section 3,E.

C. The Variation of the Transition Matrix

We now investigate the effects of changes in A_i on the accuracy of computing M_{i+1} from Γ_i. The noises are taken to be Gaussian random variables.

Denoting the small variation of A_i by δA_i and dropping subscripts, $\delta M = \delta A \Gamma A' + A \Gamma \, \delta A'$ from (78).

Since δM will be small compared with M, write $M + \delta M = M + \epsilon N$, where ϵ is a small positive constant.

Since M is symmetric, by appropriate linear transformation on x, M can be made diagonal, i.e., the components of the estimation error $x - \hat{x}$ after the linear transformation can be taken to be uncorrelated, hence independent. The variances of these independent errors are the eigenvalues of M. Therefore, the change in the eigenvalues of M due to a small change in A may be regarded approximately as the changes in the variances of the components of the estimation error $x - \hat{x}$. (This is only approximately true since δM will not be generally diagonal even if M is.)

We will now investigate the difference of the eigenvalues of M and of $M + \delta M$. Denote by λ_i the ith eigenvalue of M with its normalized eigenvector denoted by e_i. We define $\tilde{\lambda}_i$ and $\tilde{e}_i$ as the corresponding quantities for $M + \epsilon N$. Writing

$$\tilde{\lambda}_i = \lambda_i + \epsilon \lambda_{i1} + o(\epsilon)$$

$$\tilde{e}_i = e_i + \epsilon e_{i1} + o(\epsilon)$$

the relation $(M + \epsilon N)\tilde{e} = \tilde{\lambda}\tilde{e}$ yields, to the order ϵ,

$$\begin{aligned}\epsilon\lambda_{i1} &= e_i'\epsilon N e_i \\ &= e_i'(\delta A \Gamma A' + A\Gamma\,\delta A')e_i \\ &= 2e_i'\,\delta A \Gamma A' e_i \\ &= 2e_i'\,\delta A A^{-1}\,A\Gamma A' e_i \\ &= 2e_i'(\delta A A^{-1})(\lambda_i e_i - Q e_i)\end{aligned}$$

Therefore,

$$|\,\epsilon\lambda_{i1}\,| \leqslant 2\,|\,\lambda_i\,|\,\|\,\delta A_i A_i^{-1}\,\| + 2\,\|\,Q_i\,\|$$

or

$$\frac{|\,\epsilon\lambda_{i1}\,|}{|\,\lambda_i\,|} \leqslant 2\left(\|\,\delta A_i A_i^{-1}\,\| + \frac{\|\,Q_i\,\|}{\lambda_i}\right)$$

If a major contribution to M comes from $A\Gamma A'$ and not from Q, then $\|\,Q_i\,\|/\lambda_i \ll 1$, and one has approximately

$$|\,\epsilon\lambda_{i1}\,|/|\,\lambda_i\,| \leqslant 2\,\|\,\delta A_i A_i^{-1}\,\|$$

In computing M_N, Eq. (78) will be used N times starting from Γ_0. If each step of going from Γ_j to M_{j+1}, $0 \leqslant j \leqslant N-1$, satisfies the assumptions stated above, then the total percentage error in M_N is approximately given by

$$2\sum_{0}^{N-1} \|\,\delta A_i A_i^{-1}\,\|$$

or

$$2N\,\|\,\delta A A^{-1}\,\|$$

if A is a constant matrix.

Therefore, as a rule of thumb, one must have

$$\|\,\delta A A\,\| \ll \frac{1}{2N}$$

in such applications where N total number of estimates are generated.

D. Imprecise Noise Covariance Matrices

Since the statistics of the random noises are known only very roughly, the effects of large variations of Q and R, rather than their small variations on Γ, need be investigated. Such investigations must generally be done numerically in designing filters.

One may take the min-max point of view in evaluating the effect of different Q's and R's on Γ, using techniques similar to those in Aoki[12] where the effects of unknown gain (distribution) matrix on the performance index have been discussed.

See also Section 2,D of Chapter II, Section 2 of this chapter, and Refs. 64 and 129 for treatment of unknown covariance matrices.

E. Effects of Simplification

The amount of computations for implementing optimal Kalman filter is quite large for systems with high dimensions. In order to update x_i^* and Γ_i, i.e., to obtain x_{i+1}^* and Γ_{i+1} from x_i^* and Γ_i, the following steps are involved: (i) $\hat{x}_{i+1}$ is computed by x_i^* and A_i, (ii) M_{i+1} is computed from Γ_i by (78), (iii) K_{i+1} is computed by (77), (iv) x_{i+1}^* is computed by (76), and (v) Γ_{i+1} is computed by (79).

A rough calculation shows that the number of multiplications involved is of the order n^3 even without counting the number of multiplications necessary to invert an $(m \times m)$ matrix, where n is the dimension of the state vector.

In many problems, therefore, one is willing to use slightly inaccurate estimates if a significant reduction of the amount of computation results.

One such reduction is achieved by reducing the dimension of the state vectors, for example, by replacing correlated noises by uncorrelated noises, or by partitioning the state vectors.[81,104,104a,112]

Related approximation methods aimed at the reduction of the amount of computation are discussed in the next two sections.

In practice, any such approximation must be carefully evaluated to achieve a reasonable trade-off of accuracy versus the amount of computation.

4. Estimation of State Vectors by a Minimal-Order Observer

A. Introduction

When the problems of control are separated from those of estimation,* approximation may be made to the subproblems of control, to estimation, or to both. Approximate control schemes may, for example, use some

* This procedure is known to yield an over-all optimal control system for a class of linear systems with quadratic criterion. See Section 2 of Chapter II for detail.

statistics which are not sufficient to approximately summarize past and current observation data and use control policies which are functions of these statics.

In the next three sections, we will discuss effects on the performances of the optimal Kalman filters of various approximations which reduce the amount of computation required to generate estimates of the state vectors.

Consider the case of linear systems with additive noises. We have seen in Section 3 of Chapter II that for the linear observation scheme the best linear estimator of the state vector has the same dimension as the plant. For complex systems with large dimensions, therefore, the problem of constructing the optimal filter or computing the optimal state vector estimates is not trivial.

It is, therefore, important in practice to consider approximately optimal estimation procedures where constraints are imposed on the permissible complexities of the estimators or on the amount of computations. One approach is to partition the state vector into subvectors[81]; i.e., instead of constructing an optimal estimate for the entire state vector, one may partition the state vector and construct a suboptimal filter for the state vector by combining judiciously estimates of these partitioned components of the state vector. This method requires a smaller amount of computation because of the nonlinear dependence of the amount of computation on the dimension of the state vector. This will be the subject of Sections 5 and 6.

Another approach in limiting the complexities of an estimation scheme is to specify the dimension of the estimator. One such proposal has been made by Johansen.[78]

Consider a situation where the system is described by

$$x_{i+1} = Ax_i + Bu_i + \xi_i \tag{81}$$

$$y_i = Hx_i + \eta_i \tag{82}$$

where x is an n-dimensional state vector, y is an m-dimensional observation vector, u is a control vector, and ξ and η are Gaussian noises, and where we use

$$\mu_i = E(x_i \mid y^i), \qquad 0 \leqslant i \leqslant N-1$$

as the optimal estimate of x_i at time i.

The best estimate μ_{i+1} has been shown to be generated recursively as a linear function of μ_i and y_{i+1}. Note that μ has the same dimension as x. Johansen's proposal in discrete-time version is to generate approximate estimates of x_i, z_i, i.e., an approximation to μ_i, by

$$z_{i+1} = F_i z_i + D_i y_i \quad \text{or} \quad z_{i+1} = F_i z_i + D_i y_{i+1}$$

where the dimension of z_i is generally less than that of x_i, and to use control generated by

$$u_i = C_i z_i$$

in problems with quadratic criterion functions since we know that the optimal control u_i is proportional to μ_i. In this formulation, matrices C, D, and F are chosen to minimize a given criterion function. These matrices, however, are not determined uniquely and require further conditions and/or numerical experimentation to obtain satisfactory results.

Since the observation of the state vector y_i carries a certain amount of information on the state vector x_i, we will now consider a procedure for generating a vector z_i in such a way as to supplement the information carried by y_i so that z_i, together with y_i, can be employed to yield an approximation to μ_i.

This idea will be made more precise for the case of time-invariant linear sample data systems of (81) and (82).* We are particularly interested in this procedure where the dimension of the vector z_i is smaller than that of x_i, where z_k is the state vector of the dynamic system governed by

$$z_{k+1} = F_k z_k + D_k y_k, \qquad k = 0, 1, \ldots$$

where z_k is the p-dimensional vector at the kth time instant, $p \leqslant n$, F_k is the $(p \times p)$ matrix, and D_k is the $(p \times m)$ matrix. Typically, $p < n$. For example, one may take the estimate of x_k, $\hat{x}_k$, to be

$$\hat{x}_k = K z_k + N y_k$$

where K and N are to be chosen. The vector z_k, together with y_k, acts as the inputs to the estimator of x_k. Such a system will be called an observer in this section.

We now consider the problem of constructing an estimator z_i of $(n - m)$ dimensions so that x_i is estimated as some linear function of y_i and z_i.

B. Determination of the State Vector of a Deterministic System

Under some regularity conditions it is possible to generate z_i which, together with y_i, determines x_i exactly for deterministic linear systems.

---

*The following development is based on Aoki and Huddle.[17]

Namely, if an n-dimensional linear plant is completely observable, and if the observation on the system state vector produces m independent outputs ($m < n$), then it is possible to construct a device with $(n - m)$-dimensional state vector to supply the remaining $n - m$ components of the plant state vector. We will give a sketch of the method developed by Luenberger.[103] A more detailed discussion is given in Section C, where the basic idea is modified to estimate the state vectors of a stochastic system using a more constructive method.

Consider a linear system, the plant of which is governed by

$$x_{i+1} = Ax_i + Bu_i$$

where x_i is the n-dimensional state vector and the observation equation is given by

$$y_i = Hx_i$$

where y_i is m-dimensional, $m \leqslant n$, and H is an $(m \times n)$ matrix. Assume that the system is completely observable,[142] i.e., assume that the $m \cdot n$ column vectors of the matrices

$$\{(A')^k H', \qquad k = 0, 1, \ldots, n - 1\}$$

span the n-dimensional Euclidean space.

Then it is possible to design an observer with arbitrarily small time constant, such that x_i can be reconstructed exactly from y_i and z_i where z_i is the state vector of the observer.

The design of such an observer is based on the existence of a matrix T which relates the state vectors of the plant and the observer by

$$z_i = Tx_i\,, \qquad i = 0, 1, \ldots$$

The dynamic equation of the observer is given by

$$z_{i+1} = Fz_i + Dy_i + Gu_i$$

where T and F is related to A and C by the matrix equations

$$TA - FT = DH \tag{83}$$

and

$$G = TB \tag{84}$$

These equations are derived in Section C. Luenberger shows that if the original plant is observable then F can be chosen so that its norm is arbitrarily small and that T can be chosen in such a way that $\hat{T} = \begin{pmatrix} T \\ H \end{pmatrix}$ is nonsingular. Therefore,

$$x_i = \hat{T}^{-1} \begin{pmatrix} z_i \\ y_i \end{pmatrix}$$

His proof that T can be chosen to make T nonsingular, however, is not constructive. We will construct an $(n - m)$-dimensional observer for the stochastic system in such a way that the error-covariance matrices of the estimates of the plant state vector are minimized in a sense to be specified later.

C. Estimation of the State Vector of a Stochastic System

We will now extend the ideas discussed in Section B to linear stochastic systems and design an estimator of x_i using (y_i, z_i), where y_i is the system observation and z_i is the output of an observer with $(n - m)$ memory elements. If the system is such that nearly all the components of x_i are observed, i.e., if m is close to n, then the number of memory elements employed by the observer is much less than n. If the resultant error covariance matrix indicates that system performance is not much worse than that achieved using the optimal Wiener-Kalman filter, then the estimator considered here may have a practical application. See Section D and Ref. 17 for some numerical comparisons of the filter performances.

a. *The Stochastic Design Problem and the Estimation Error-Covariance Matrix*

In this section we consider the stochastic problem without control. The control term is introduced in Section 4,C,c.

The system whose state is to be estimated is shown in Fig. 7.2. The state vector satisfies the nth-order time-invariant linear difference equation

$$x_{i+1} = Ax_i + \xi_i \tag{85}$$

where ξ_i is a sequence of independent vector random variables representing disturbance noise. The observation equation of the state vector is assumed given by (82). We will assume here that H is an $(m \times n)$ matrix having rank m and in addition is such that the system

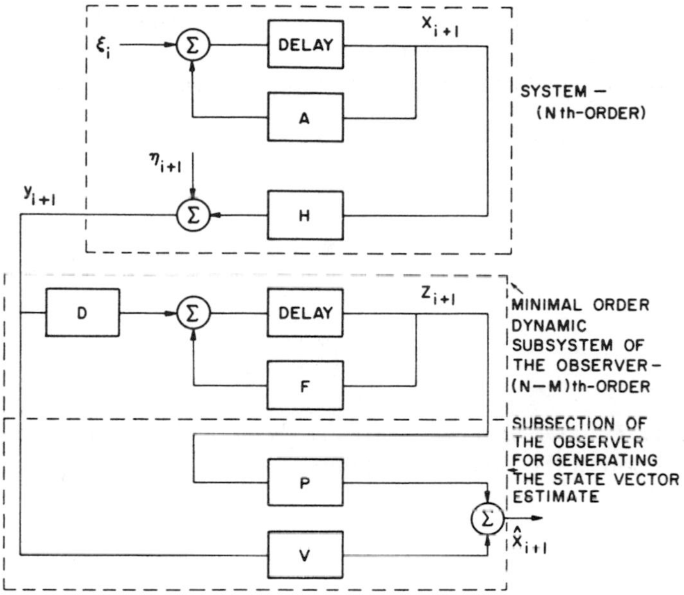

Fig. 7.2. Schematic diagram of $(n - m)$-dimensional observer and the state vector estimator.

is observable.* We denote by R and Q the covariance matrices of the independent noises ξ, η which are assumed here, for convenience, to be stationary:

$$E(\xi_i \xi_j') = Q\delta_{ij}$$
$$E(\eta_i \eta_j') = R\delta_{ij}$$
$$E(\xi_i \eta_j') = 0 \qquad \text{for all } i \text{ and } j$$

The state vector of the observer is assumed to satisfy the difference equation

$$z_{i+1} = Fz_i + Dy_i \tag{86}$$

where F and D are time-invariant $(n - m) \times (n - m)$ matrix and $(n - m) \times m$ matrix, respectively, yet to be specified.

From the discussion of the previous paragraphs, the observer system is seen to involve two distinct sections. The first is a dynamic subsystem whose output is to represent, under nonstochastic conditions and proper initialization, a linear transformation Tx of the observed system state vector.

* See Ref. 17 for discussions on unobservable systems.

The other section of the observer accomplishes the construction of the observer estimate of the system state vector by applying the inverse linear transformation $\hat{T}^{-1}$ to the partitioned state vector

$$\begin{bmatrix} z_i \\ y_i \end{bmatrix}$$

Denoting

$$\hat{T}^{-1} = (P \mid V) \tag{87a}$$

where

$$\hat{T} = \left(\frac{T}{H}\right) \tag{87b}$$

and where P is an $(n \times (n - m))$ matrix and V is an $(n \times m)$ matrix, we may express the observer output as

$$\hat{x}_i = Pz_i + Vy_i \tag{88}$$

which is as depicted in Fig. 7.2.

The central problem in the design of the observer for deterministic systems is to select the unspecified matrices such that the fundamental matrix equation (83) is satisfied while $\hat{T}$ remains nonsingular.[103] For the stochastic problem, these conditions must also be specified, but in addition we seek that solution which permits minimization of the elements of the estimation error-covariance matrix. To obtain this design solution we first derive a number of matrix relations involving the estimation error-covariance matrix which is defined as

$$C_i \triangleq E[(\hat{x}_i - x_i)(\hat{x}_i - x_i)'] \tag{89}$$

where $\hat{x}_i$ is the estimate of x_i provided by the observer at time i and where x_i is the true state of the system of (85) at time i.

The relations obtained will then be manipulated in such a way that a set of equations are obtained for elements of the covariance matrix C in terms of the given matrices A, H, Q, and R and one design matrix V of (87a). These relations may then be used by the designer to minimize certain elements of the error-covariance matrix C_i as desired. It should be emphasized that the constraints placed on observer design lead to a loss of freedom in the minimization process as should be expected. The central question, then, is whether or not these constraints allow a much cheaper estimator to be built which may have performance comparable to that of the (unconstrained) optimal estimator for the particular application considered. Throughout the ensuing discussion we shall use the following relations which, as shown in Appendix B at the end of this chapter, guarantee the existence of the observer:

$$F = TAP \tag{90}$$

$$D = TAV \tag{91}$$

$$PT + VH = I_n \tag{92}$$

$$\begin{aligned} HV &= I_m \\ TP &= I_{n-m} \\ HP &= 0 \\ TV &= 0 \end{aligned} \tag{93}$$

where I_k denotes the $(k \times k)$ identity matrix.

We begin by considering the error in the dynamic subsystem of the observer. We define it as

$$e_i = z_i - Tx_i \tag{94}$$

The dynamic equation for e_i may be written from (85) and (86) as

$$e_{i+1} = Fe_i + (DH - (TA - FT))x_i + \zeta_i$$

where

$$\zeta_i \triangleq D\eta_i - T\xi_i$$

But as T is taken to satisfy (83), (94) simplifies to

$$e_{i+1} = Fe_i + \zeta_i \tag{95}$$

We note that the augmented observation vector satisfies the equation

$$\begin{bmatrix} z_i \\ y_i \end{bmatrix} = \hat{T}x_i + \begin{bmatrix} e_i \\ \eta_i \end{bmatrix} \tag{96}$$

where

$$\begin{bmatrix} z_i \\ y_i \end{bmatrix}$$

is the observation of x_i which augments the originally available observation vector y_i. The noise e_i is not white however. Its mean and covariance matrices are given by

$$\begin{aligned} Ee_i &= 0 \\ S_{i+1} \triangleq Ee_{i+1}e_{i+1}' &= FS_i'F' + DRD' + TQT' \end{aligned} \tag{97}$$

Note that

$$E(e_i \eta_i') = 0$$

The estimate of x_i is constructed as the output of the observer and is given by (88). Expressing z_i and y_i as functions of x_i, we have from (96)

$$\hat{x}_i = (PT + VH)x_i + Pe_i + V\eta_i \tag{98}$$

Using (92) we see that the error-covariance matrix is expressed by

$$C_i = PS_iP' + VRV' \tag{99}$$

Using (93) and (99) we easily obtain

$$TC_iH' = 0 \tag{100}$$

The covariance Q of the plant disturbance noise does not enter relation (100) explicitly. To obtain an expression containing Q we reconsider the error propagation of the estimate.

Defining $\tilde{x}_i = \hat{x}_i - x_i$, we write $\hat{x}_{i+1}$ as

$$\hat{x}_{i+1} = x_{i+1} + \tilde{x}_{i+1} = Pz_{i+1} + Vy_{i+1} \tag{101}$$

Using (86) and (90)–(92), x_{i+1} can be rewritten as

$$\begin{aligned} \hat{x}_{i+1} &= Vy_{i+1} + P(Fz_i + Dy_i) \\ &= Vy_{i+1} + PTA(Pz_i + Vy_i) \\ &= Vy_{i+1} + PTA\hat{x}_i \\ &= Vy_{i+1} + (I - VH)A\hat{x}_i \end{aligned} \tag{102}$$

Therefore we have the difference equation for the estimation error as

$$\begin{aligned} \tilde{x}_{i+1} &= \hat{x}_{i+1} - x_{i+1} \\ &= V\eta_{i+1} + (I - VH)(A\tilde{x}_i - \xi_i) \end{aligned} \tag{103)*$$

From (103), the recursion equation for the error covariance matrix is given by

$$C_{i+1} = VR_{i+1}V' + (I - VH)(AC_iA' + Q_i)(I - VH)' \tag{104}$$

where V satisfies the constraint

$$HV = I_m \tag{105}$$

* Matrices VH and $PT = I - VH$ that appear in (103) and elsewhere, are projection operators since $(VH)(VH) = VH$.

Multiplying (104) by H' from right and making use of the relations of (93), we obtain

$$C_{i+1}H' = VR_{i+1} \tag{106}$$

b. *Optimal Design of an Estimator of Minimal Order*

In this section we modify the matrix relations involving the error-covariance matrix C, obtained in the previous section, and proceed to an optimal design solution in a rather unencumbered manner, while still satisfying the multiple constraints imposed on the observer structure.

The constraint (105) is explicit and can be applied with no difficulty at the outset of the design effort for a given observation matrix H. Since (92) alone is sufficient for the inverse $\hat{T}^{-1}$ to exist we employ the expression

$$PT = I - VH \tag{107}$$

(with $HV = I_m$ imposed) wherever useful in the ensuing discussion. From (106), we obtain

$$HC_{i+1}H' = R_{i+1} \tag{108}$$

From (104), we obtain

$$(I - VH)C_{i+1} = (I - VH)[AC_iA' + Q_i](I - VH)' \tag{109}$$

These two implicit relations involving C_{i+1} are sufficient with Eq. (101) to obtain an expression equivalent to (106):

$$(I - VH)C_{i+1}H' = 0$$

The constraint on C_{i+1} expressed by (108) is easily imposed at the outset of design, to specify the covariance C_{i+1} given C_i and the design matrix V.* Thus, if we address ourselves to the task of minimizing selected elements of C_{i+1} while (106), (108), and (109) are satisfied, by selection of the matrix V subject to the constraint $HV = I_m$, we will have optimized the design of the minimal-order estimator for the stochastic application. If this is done sequentially ($i = 1, \ldots$) we will derive a sequence of matrices $\{V_i\}$ which realize the optimal transient response of the filter. On the other hand, by assuming a steady-state condition,

$$C_{i+1} = C_i = C \tag{110}$$

* Although the conditions given by (104) and (105) and those given by (106), (108), and (109) are equivalent, the latter may be more convenient to employ directly.

we can use (108)–(110) to yield by the same procedure an estimator design which is optimal in the steady state.

c. *Control Systems*

Now suppose that instead of (85) we have the control system as originally given by (81):

$$x_{i+1} = Ax_i + Bu_i + \xi_i$$

The estimator is now taken, by adding a control term to (86), to be

$$z_{i+1} = Fz_i + Dy_i + Gu_i \tag{111}$$

Then, as before, in terms of T which satisfies $TA - FT = DH$, the difference e_i between z_i and Tx_i satisfies the equation

$$\begin{aligned} z_{i+1} - Tx_{i+1} &= Fz_i - TAx_i + DHx_i + D\eta_i + Gu_i - TBu_i - T\xi_i \\ &= F(z_i - Tx_i) + (G - TB)u_i + D\eta_i - T\xi_i \end{aligned}$$

Therefore, by choosing

$$G = TB \tag{112}$$

where T is previously chosen, the result of the previous section still holds true.

d. *Connection with Optimal Wiener–Kalman Filter*

The estimator described in this section generates the suboptimal estimate $\hat{x}_i$ of x_i by (88):

$$\hat{x}_{i+1} = Vy_{i+1} + Pz_{i+1} \tag{113}$$

where y_{i+1} is the observed state vector of the system given by (82), where z_{i+1} is the output of the observer (86), and where F and D are given by (89) and (90), respectively.

Therefore, from (102) we can see that

$$\begin{aligned} \hat{x}_{i+1} &= Vy_{i+1} + PTA\hat{x}_i \\ &= A\hat{x}_i + V(y_{i+1} - HA\hat{x}_i) \end{aligned} \tag{114}$$

where V must satisfy the constraint given by (105).

In this form, we can see clearly the relation with the Wiener-Kalman filter of the estimation scheme of this section. Instead of using optimal time-varying gains of the Kalman filter, the estimation scheme of this section uses a constant gain V which is chosen optimally in order to minimize the steady-state error-covariance matrix C of (110).

Figure 7.2 is the schematic diagram of the estimator showing how the observed state vector and the output of the observer is combined to generate the estimate of the state vector.

We next present an example of constructing an observer which is optimal in the steady state. For this example, the original plant is chosen to be observable.

D. Example. Observable System

Consider a two-dimensional system with the plant equation

$$x(i+1) = Ax(i) + Bu(i) + \xi(i)$$

where

$$x(i) = \begin{pmatrix} x_1(i) \\ x_2(i) \end{pmatrix}, \qquad A = \begin{pmatrix} -2 & 1 \\ 0 & -1 \end{pmatrix}, \qquad B = \begin{pmatrix} 0 \\ 1 \end{pmatrix}$$

and where x_1, x_2, u, and ξ are scalar quantities and with the observation equation

$$y(i) = Hx(i) + \eta(i)$$

where

$$H = (1, 0)$$

$$Q(i) = \begin{pmatrix} q_1 & 0 \\ 0 & q_2 \end{pmatrix}$$

$$R(i) = r$$

The observation y is taken on x_1, but x_2 is not observed. We will construct a first-order observer which estimates x_2 by

$$z_{i+1} = Fz_i + D\,y(i) + K\,u(i)$$

Let

$$T = (t_1\ t_2) \qquad \text{and} \qquad \hat{T}^{-1} = \begin{bmatrix} P_1 & v_1 \\ P_2 & v_2 \end{bmatrix}$$

The constraint equations (90)–(93) between $\hat{T}$ and $\hat{T}^{-1}$ yield

$$\begin{aligned} v_1 &= 1 \\ P_1 &= 0 \\ t_2P_2 &= 1 \\ t_1P_2 &= -v_2 \\ t_1 + t_2v_2 &= 0 \end{aligned} \tag{115}$$

We now compute the steady-state error-covariance matrix C:

$$C = \begin{bmatrix} c_{11} & c_{12} \\ c_{12} & c_{22} \end{bmatrix}$$

Imposing the constraints on the steady-state error-covariance matrices,

$$HCH' = R \qquad \text{yields} \quad c_{11} = r$$
$$(I - VH)CH' = 0 \qquad \text{yields} \quad c_{12} = v_2r$$

and

$$(I - VH)C = (I - VH)ACA' + Q(I - VH)'$$

yields

$$c_{22} = \frac{4rv_2^3 - v_2^2(r + q_1) - q_2}{v_2(v_2 + 2)} \tag{116}$$

We choose to minimize the variance of x_2, c_{22}, by selection of the free variable v_2. Thus we seek v_2 such that

$$\frac{\partial c_{22}}{\partial v_2} = 0$$

which yields

$$2rv_2^4 + 8rv_2^3 - (r + q_1)v_2^2 + v_2q_2 + q_2 = 0$$

Solving this equation with the additional simplifying assumption

$$r = q_1 = q_2 = \sigma^2 \tag{117}$$

we find

$$v_2 = -0.37 \tag{118}$$

and

$$\begin{aligned} c_{11} &= \sigma^2 \\ c_{22} &= 2.445\sigma^2 \\ c_{12} &= -0.37\sigma^2 \end{aligned} \tag{119}$$

To complete the design of the observer, we compute

$$\begin{aligned} F &= TAP = -0.63 \\ D &= TAV = -0.5t_2 \end{aligned} \tag{120}$$

and

$$K = t_2$$

where

$$\hat{T} = \begin{bmatrix} 0.37t_2 & t_2 \\ 1 & 0 \end{bmatrix}$$

and

$$\hat{T}^{-1} = \begin{bmatrix} 0 & 1 \\ 1/t_2 & -0.37 \end{bmatrix}$$

It is seen that t_2 remains unspecified in the optimization. This is due to the fact that the multiplication of the transformation

$$z = 0.37x_1 + x_2$$

by t_2 is irrelevant in reconstructing x, so long as it is nonzero, as passing z through the inversion $\hat{T}^{-1}$ cancels whatever effect t_2 may have.

The schematic diagram of the observer is given in Fig. 7.3.

In order to obtain some insight into the accuracy of the estimation method discussed in this section, the error-covariance matrices of the optimal Wiener–Kalman filter are computed for the system of the example for comparison.

Denoting the (i,j)th component of the optimal error-covariance matrix at time k by $\Gamma_{ij}(k)$, the following set of equations hold:

$$\begin{aligned} \Gamma_{11}(i+1) &= [q_1 + \Gamma_{11}(i) - 4\,\Gamma_{12}(i) + \Gamma_{22}(i)] \\ &\quad \times [1 - (q_1 + 4\,\Gamma_{11}(i) - 4\,\Gamma_{12}(i) + \Gamma_{22}(i))/\Delta_i] \\ \Gamma_{12}(i+1) &= [2\,\Gamma_{12}(i) - \Gamma_{22}(i)][1 - (q_1 + 4\,\Gamma_{11}(i) - \Gamma_{12}(i) + \Gamma_{22}(i))/\Delta_i] \\ \Gamma_{22}(i+1) &= q_2 + \Gamma_{22}(i) - (2\,\Gamma_{12}(i) - \Gamma_{22}(i))^2/\Delta_i \end{aligned}$$

where

$$\Delta_i \triangleq q_1 + r + 4\,\Gamma_{11}(i) - 4\,\Gamma_{12}(i) + \Gamma_{22}(i)$$

In particular, we are interested in $\Gamma_{11}(\infty)$, $\Gamma_{12}(\infty)$, and $\Gamma_{22}(\infty)$. These satisfy the algebraic equation

$$q_2^2 s^4 + q^2 s^3 - (q_1 + 5r^2) q_2^2 s^2 + 2 q_2^2 s + 4r^2 = 0$$

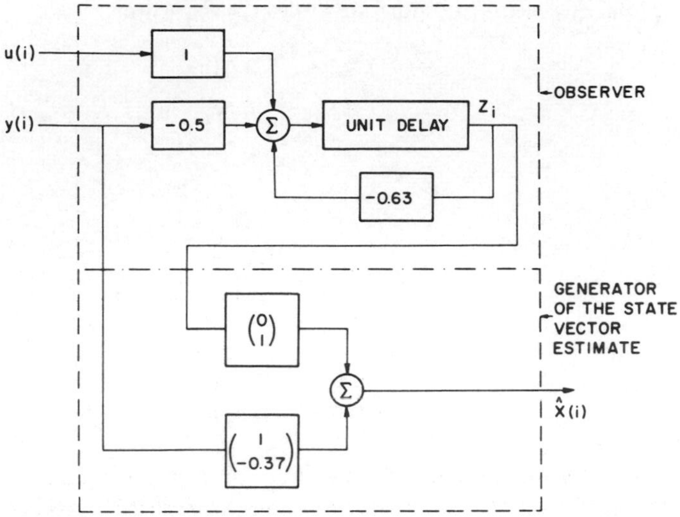

$$\left.\begin{aligned} X(i+1) &= \begin{pmatrix} -2 & 1 \\ 0 & -1 \end{pmatrix} X(i) + \begin{pmatrix} 0 \\ 1 \end{pmatrix} u(i) + \xi(i) \\ y(i) &= (1, 0)\, X(i) + \eta(i) \end{aligned}\right\} \text{SYSTEM}$$

$$E\xi = 0 , \quad E\eta = 0$$

$$E\xi\xi' = \begin{pmatrix} \sigma^2 & 0 \\ 0 & \sigma^2 \end{pmatrix}, \quad E\eta\eta' = \sigma^2$$

$$E\xi\eta' = 0$$

Fig. 7.3. Numerical example of the observer construction.

where

$$s \triangleq \frac{2\,\Gamma_{12}(\infty) - \Gamma_{22}(\infty)}{q_2}$$

In terms of s,

$$\Gamma_{11}(\infty) = r\left(1 - \frac{r}{q_2 s_2}\right)$$
$$\Gamma_{12}(\infty) = r/s$$
$$\Gamma_{22}(\infty) = 2r/s - q_2 s$$

Considering s for the same case of (117), we must solve

$$s^4 + s^3 - 6s^2 + 2s + 4 = 0$$

The required solution is

$$s = -3.055$$

which yields the optimal error covariances for the (unconstrained) Kalman filter as

$$\Gamma_{11}(\infty) = 0.89\sigma^2$$
$$\Gamma_{22}(\infty) = 2.4\sigma^2$$
$$\Gamma_{12}(\infty) = -0.33\sigma^2$$

Comparing these results with those obtained for the minimal-order filter, we see that performance appears very favorable while realizing simultaneously a reduction in memory elements.

5. Suboptimal Linear Estimation by State Vector Partition Method: Theory

We discuss in this section another approximate estimation scheme of state vectors of dynamical systems with linear plant and observation equations. The scheme is based on the observation made in Section 3,E that the amount of computation involved in generating an optimal estimate of the state vector of a linear dynamical system is a nonlinear function of the dimension of the state vector. For example, it requires a smaller amount of computations to generate k estimates of n/k-dimensional state vectors than to generate one estimate of the n-dimensional state vector.

After an introductory discussion of such a suboptimal estimation method in this section an approximate estimation problem will be discussed in Section 6 when a natural partitioning of the state vector is possible based on the difference of time responses of various modes[142] of the system.

The discussion of this section is done for the system given by (73)–(75d) of Section 3.

A. Construction of Suboptimal Filter

Suppose x_i is partitioned into k subvectors z_i^1, $z_i^2,\ldots, z_i^k$, where z_i^j is the value of the jth subvector at time i and where z^j has dimension n_j, $\sum_j n_j \geqslant n$.

The jth subvector is related to the state vector by a $(n_j \times n)$ matrix D_j:

$$z_i^j = D_j x_i, \qquad 1 \leqslant j \leqslant k \tag{121}$$

Although the matrices D_j could be taken to be time varying, they are assumed to be time invariant in order to avoid the resultant complexities of the filter construction. Therefore, the manner in which the state vector x is partitioned into k subvectors is fixed throughout the estimation process.

From (121),

$$z_i^{j*} \triangleq D_j x_i^* \qquad \hat{z}_i^j \triangleq D_j \hat{x}_i \tag{122}$$

where the notations * and ^ have the same meanings given by (77a) and (77b).

The estimates x_i^* and $\hat{x}_i$ are assumed to be reconstructed from the estimates for the partitioned subvectors by

$$x_i^* = \sum_{j=1}^{k} F_j z_i^{j*} \qquad \hat{x}_i = \sum_{j=1}^{k} F_j \hat{z}_i^j \tag{123}$$

where F's and D's must satisfy the relation

$$\sum_i^k F_j D_j = I \tag{124}$$

in order that the state vector is reconstructed from the partitioned subvectors.

Proceeding analogously with the optimal estimation procedure, we consider the sequential estimation equation for the subvectors given by

$$z_i^{j*} = \hat{z}_i^j + K_i^j G_j [y_j - H_i \hat{x}_i] \tag{125}$$

where K_i^j is the filter gain at time i and where the matrix G_j chooses the subvector of the y that is used in updating the estimate for z_i^j. The matrices G_j are also taken to be time invariant.

From (123) and (125),

$$\begin{aligned} x_i^* &= \sum_i^k F_j z_i^{j*} \\ &= \sum_i^k F_j \hat{z}_i^j + \sum_i^k F_j K_i^j G_j [y_i - H_i \hat{x}_i] \\ &= \hat{x}_i + \sum_i^k F_j K_i^j G_j [y_i - H_i \hat{x}_i] \end{aligned} \tag{126}$$

The comparison of (76) and (126) shows that the suboptimal estimation scheme implies that

$$K_i = \sum_{j=1}^{k} F_j K_i^j G_j \tag{127}$$

is the gain of the filter for the state vector x_i.

We choose K_i^j next in a manner analogous to (77c). From (121) and (122),

$$\begin{aligned} z_{i+1}^j - \hat{z}_{i+1}^j &= D_j(x_{i+1} - \hat{x}_{i+1}) \\ &= D_j(A_i x_i + \xi_i - A_i x_i^*) \\ &= D_j A_i(x_i - x_i^*) + D_j \xi_j \end{aligned}$$

Since $(x_i - x_i^*)$ is not available, it is approximated by

$$x_i - x_i^* \doteqdot D_j^+(z_i^j - z_i^{j*})$$

where the superscript plus indicates a pseudoinverse to yield

$$z_{i+1}^j - \hat{z}_{i+1}^j = D_j A_i D_j^+(z_i^j - \hat{z}_i^j) + D_j \xi_i \tag{128}$$

Then

$$\begin{aligned} E(z_{i+1}^j - \hat{z}_{i+1}^j)(z_{i+1}^j - \hat{z}_{i+1}^j)' = A_i^j E[(z_i^j - z_i^{j*})(z_i^j - z_i^{j*})'] A_i^{j\prime} \\ + D_j Q_i D_j' \end{aligned} \tag{129}$$

where

$$A_i^j \triangleq D_j A_i D_j^+$$

Proceeding analogously with the optimal estimation equations we construct a suboptimal filter by the following set of equations:

$$\begin{aligned} \Gamma_0^j &\triangleq E(z_0^j - z_0^{j*})(z_0^j - z_0^{j*})' \\ &= D_j \Gamma_0 D_j' \end{aligned} \tag{130}$$

where Γ_0 is assumed known,

$$P_{i+1}^j \triangleq A_i^j \Gamma_i^j A_i^{j\prime} + Q_i^j$$

where

$$A_i^j \triangleq D_j A_i D_j^+$$

and

$$
\begin{aligned}
Q_i^j &\triangleq D_j Q_i D_j' \\
H_i^j &\triangleq G_j H_i D_j^+ \\
R_i^j &\triangleq G_j R_i G_j' \\
K_i^j &\triangleq P_i^j H_i^j [H_i^j P_i^j H^{j\prime} + R_i^j]^{-1} \\
\Gamma_i^j &= [I - K_i^j H_i^j] P_i^j [I - K_i^j H_i^j]' + K_i^j R_i^j K_i^{j\prime}
\end{aligned}
\tag{131}
$$

$$
\begin{aligned}
\hat{x}_i &= A_{i-1} x_{i-1}^* \\
x_i^* &= \hat{x}_i + \sum_{j=1}^{k} F_j K_i^j G_j [y_i - H_i \hat{x}_i]
\end{aligned}
\tag{131a}
$$

where $\hat{x}_0$ is assumed known. Figure 7.4 is a schematic diagram of the suboptimal filter.

Computations in (131) involve manipulations of matrices of order less than $(n \times n)$ or $(m \times n)$. Of course, the above derivation does not give any unique partitions of the state vector. If the partition subvectors are not crosscoupled to any other subvectors, either through the plant or observation equations or through the random disturbances, then the present scheme would be optimal. Physical intuition based on the components of x plus a certain amount of numerical experimentation would be necessary to arrive at a reasonable partition.

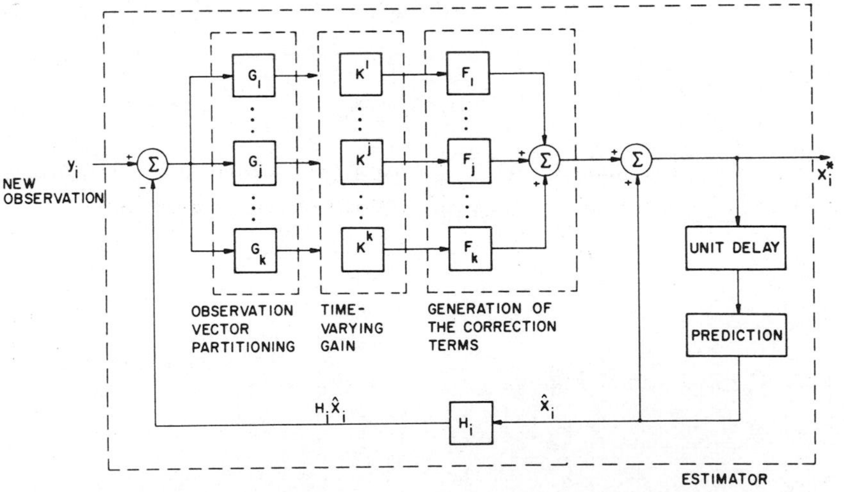

Fig. 7.4. Suboptimal filter by partitioning of the state vector.

B. Error Covariance of the Suboptimal Filter

Noting that the suboptimal filter based on the partitioned vector of Section B is equivalent to using the filter gain (127) in the Wiener–Kalman filter for x_i, the error-covariance matrices of this suboptimal filter can be computed as follows:

$$P_{i+1} = A_i \Gamma_i A_i' + Q_i$$

$$\Gamma_{i+1} = \left[I - \left(\sum_{j=1}^{k} F_j K_{i+1}^{j} G_j\right) H_{i+1}\right] P_{i+1} \left[I - \left(\sum_{j=1}^{k} F_j K_{i+1}^{j} G_j\right) H_{i+1}\right]'$$

$$+ \left(\sum_{j=1}^{k} F_j K_{i+1}^{j} G_j\right) R_{i+1} \left(\sum_{j=1}^{k} F_j K_{i+1}^{j} G_j\right)'$$

where Γ_0 is given and where K_i^j is computed by (131).

Comparing Γ thus generated with the optimal error covariance which results from using the optimal gain

$$K_i = P_i H_i'[H_i P_i H_i' + R_i]^{-1}$$

the degradation of the filter accuracy can be computed for this suboptimal filter.

See Pentecost[112] for an application to a navigation problem.

We will next consider in detail a particular partition that results from the certain assumed form of the plant transition matrix.

6. Suboptimal Estimation by State Vector Partition: An Example

A. Introduction

As an example of the subject of the last section, where the estimation of state vectors via partitioned substate vectors is treated, let us now consider a problem where the state vector can be grouped into two subvectors naturally in a sense to be mentioned below.

The system is given by (73) and (74). As before, x_i and ξ_i are n vectors and y_i and η_i are m vectors where

$$E(\xi_i) = E(\eta_i) = 0$$

$$E(\xi_i \xi_j') = \Lambda_i \delta_{ij}$$

$$E(\eta_i \eta_j') = \sum_i \delta_{ij}$$

$$E(\xi_i \eta_j') = 0$$

We use Λ and Σ instead of Q and R since we want to use Q and R to denote submatrices of Λ and Σ.

We have already discussed the desirability of reducing the amount of computations associated with optimal filterings by using some suboptimal filtering scheme, so long as the required accuracy of desired estimates is compatible with that of the suboptimal filters. Suppose that the system is stable and that eigenvalues of A_i can be grouped into two classes such that the real parts of eigenvalues in one group are much different from those of the other group.

Using Jordan canonical representation,[142] assume that the state vector x_i can be written as

$$x_i = \begin{pmatrix} z_i \\ \hline w_i \end{pmatrix}$$

where z_i is a q vector and w_i is an $(n - q)$ vector. The plant equation becomes

$$\begin{pmatrix} z_{i+1} \\ \hline w_{i+1} \end{pmatrix} = \left(\begin{array}{c:c} \Phi_i & 0 \\ \hdashline 0 & \Psi_i \end{array}\right) \begin{pmatrix} z_i \\ \hline w_i \end{pmatrix} + \begin{pmatrix} \mu_i \\ \hline \nu_i \end{pmatrix} \tag{132}$$

where it is assumed that $\| \psi_i \| \ll \| \phi_i \|$, $i = 0, 1, \ldots$ and where μ_i is a q vector and ν_i is an $(n - q)$ vector.

Define covariance submatrices Q_i, S_i, and R_i by

$$\Lambda_i = E\left[\begin{pmatrix} \mu_i \\ \hline \nu_i \end{pmatrix} (\mu_i' \mid \nu_i')\right] = \begin{pmatrix} Q_i & S_i \\ S_i' & R_i \end{pmatrix} \tag{133}$$

Assume that

$$\| \Phi_i \| = O(1)$$

and

$$\| \Psi_i \| = O(\epsilon)$$

where ϵ is a small positive quantity and where the notations $O(1)$ and $O(\epsilon)$ mean that $\| \Phi_i \|$ is of order 1 and $\| \Psi_i \|$ is of order ϵ, respectively.

Partition H_i as

$$H_i = (M_i \mid N_i) \tag{134}$$

where

$$M_i = (m \times q) \quad \text{matrix}$$
$$N_i = m \times (n - q) \quad \text{matrix}$$

Then, writing the Kalman filter equation for x_i^* in terms of its components z_i^* and w_i^*, the optimal estimates of z_i and w_i, they satisfy the equations

$$\begin{aligned} z_{i+1}^* &= \Phi_i z_i^* + K_{i+1}(y_{i+1} - M_{i+1}\Phi_i z_i^* - N_{i+1}\Psi_i w_i^*) \\ w_{i+1}^* &= \Psi_i w_i^* + L_{i+1}(y_{i+1} - M_{i+1}\Phi_i z_i^* - N_{i+1}\Psi_i w_i^*) \end{aligned} \tag{135}$$

where

$$K_{i+1} = (q \times m) \quad \text{matrix}$$
$$L_{i+1} = (n - q) \times m \quad \text{matrix}$$

are gains of the filters for the subvectors z and w.

Optimal gains of these two filters can be expressed as

$$K^*_{i+1} = \Lambda_1{}^*(i)'\, \Xi^{*-1}_{i+1}$$
$$L^*_{i+1} = \Lambda_2{}^*(i)'\, \Xi^{*-1}_{i+1} \tag{136}$$

where

$$\Xi^*_{i+1} \triangleq (M_{i+1}, N_{i+1})\, \hat{\Gamma}^*(i) \begin{pmatrix} M'_{i+1} \\ N'_{i+1} \end{pmatrix} + \Sigma_{i+1} \tag{137}$$

$$\hat{\Gamma}^*(i) \triangleq \begin{pmatrix} \Phi_i & 0 \\ 0 & \Psi_i \end{pmatrix} \Gamma^*(i) \begin{pmatrix} \Phi_i' & 0 \\ 0 & \Psi_i' \end{pmatrix} + \begin{pmatrix} Q_i & S_i \\ S_i' & R_i \end{pmatrix} \tag{138}$$

$$\Lambda_1{}^*(i) \triangleq M_{i+1}\, \hat{\Gamma}^*_{11}(i) + N_{i+1}\, \hat{\Gamma}^{*\prime}_{12}(i)$$
$$\Lambda_2{}^*(i) \triangleq M_{i+1}\, \hat{\Gamma}^*_{12}(i) + N_{i+1}\, \hat{\Gamma}^*_{22}(i) \tag{139}$$

The time index of Γ is now carried as the argument of Γ and the subscripts on Γ refer to the components of Γ. The asterisk indicates a quantity associated with the optimal filters.

Since

$$\begin{pmatrix} z_{i+1} - z^*_{i+1} \\ \hline w_{i+1} - w_{i+1} \end{pmatrix} = \left[I - \begin{pmatrix} K^*_{i+1} \\ \hline L^*_{i+1} \end{pmatrix} H_{i+1} \right] \left[\begin{pmatrix} \Phi_i & 0 \\ 0 & \Psi_i \end{pmatrix} \begin{pmatrix} z_i - z_i{}^* \\ \hline w_i - w_i{}^* \end{pmatrix} + \begin{pmatrix} \mu_i \\ \hline \nu_i \end{pmatrix} \right] - \begin{pmatrix} K^*_{i+1} \\ \hline L^*_{i+1} \end{pmatrix} \eta_{i+1}$$

the components of the optimal error-covariance matrices are given by

$$\Gamma^*_{11}(i+1) = \hat{\Gamma}^*_{11}(i) - \Lambda_1{}^*(i)'\, \Xi^{*-1}_{i+1}\, \Lambda_1{}^*(i)$$
$$\Gamma^*_{12}(i+1) = \hat{\Gamma}^*_{12}(i) - \Lambda_1{}^*(i)'\, \Xi^{*-1}_{i+1}\, \Lambda_2{}^*(i)$$
$$\Gamma^*_{22}(i+1) = \hat{\Gamma}^*_{22}(i) - \Lambda_2{}^*(i)'\, \Xi^{*-1}_{i+1}\, \Lambda_2{}^*(i) \tag{140}$$

When arbitrary nonoptimal gains K_{i+1} and L_{i+1} are used these components of the error-covariance matrices are related by

$$\Gamma_{11}(i+1) = \hat{\Gamma}_{11}(i) - K_{i+1}\, \Lambda_1(i) - \Lambda_1(i)'\, K_{i+1} + K_{i+1}\Xi_{i+1}K'_{i+1}$$
$$\Gamma_{12}(i+1) = \hat{\Gamma}_{12}(i) - \Lambda_1(i)'\, L'_{i+1} - K_{i+1}\, \Lambda_2(i) + K_{i+1}\Xi_{i+1}L'_{i+1} \tag{141}$$
$$\Gamma_{22}(i+1) = \hat{\Gamma}_{22}(i) - L_{i+1}\, \Lambda_2(i) - \Lambda_2(i)'\, L_{i+1} + L_{i+1}\Xi_{i+1}L_{i+1}$$

where Ξ_{i+1} is defined by

$$\Xi_{i+1} = H_{i+1}\,\hat{\Gamma}(i)\,H'_{i+1} + \Sigma_{i+1} \tag{142}$$

and where

$$\begin{aligned}
\hat{\Gamma}_{11}(i) &\triangleq Q_i + \Phi_i\,\Gamma_{11}(i)\,\Phi_i' \\
\hat{\Gamma}_{12}(i) &\triangleq S_i + \Phi_i\,\Gamma_{12}(i)\,\Psi_i' \\
\hat{\Gamma}_{22}(i) &\triangleq R_i + \Psi_i\,\Gamma_{22}(i)\,\Psi_i'
\end{aligned} \tag{143}$$

By our assumption on Φ_i and Ψ_i,

$$\|\hat{\Gamma}_{22}(i)\| = O(\|R_i\|) \tag{144}$$

and

$$\|\hat{\Gamma}_{12}(i)\| = O(\|S_i\|) \qquad \text{if} \quad \|S_i\| = O(1) \tag{145a}$$

$$\|\hat{\Gamma}_{12}(i)\| = O(\epsilon) \qquad \text{if} \quad \|S_i\| = O(\epsilon) \tag{145b}$$

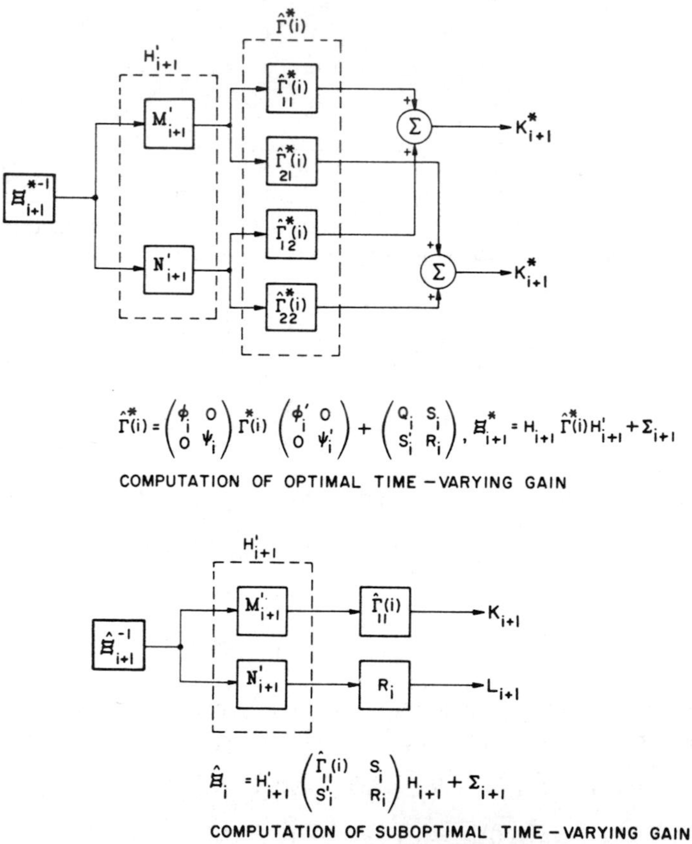

Fig. 7.5. Comparison of filter gain generations for optimal and suboptimal filters.

B. Suboptimal Filter

As an approximation, consider the filter gains which result from retaining submatrices of order 1 and neglecting those of order ϵ in $\hat{\Gamma}(i)$. Namely we use gains

$$K_{i+1} = \hat{\Gamma}_{11}(i)\, M'_{i+1}\hat{\Xi}_{i+1}^{-1}$$
$$L_{i+1} = R_i N'_{i+1}\hat{\Xi}_{i+1}^{-1} \tag{146}$$

where

$$\hat{\Xi}_{i+1} \triangleq H_{i+1}\begin{pmatrix}\hat{\Gamma}_{11}(i) & S_i \\ S_i' & R_i\end{pmatrix} H'_{i+1} + \Sigma_{i+1} \tag{147}$$

to generate estimates for z_{i+1} and w_{i+1}. The matrix $\hat{\Xi}_{i+1}^{*}$ is defined similarly with $\hat{\Gamma}_{11}^{*}(i)$ replacing $\hat{\Gamma}_{11}(i)$ in (142). Since we have made no assumptions on the magnitude of S_i, S_i is retained in the definition of $\hat{\Xi}_{i+1}$ at this point. Figure 7.5 shows diagrammatically the difference in the optimal and the suboptimal filter gains given by (136) and (146).

C. Error-Covariance Matrix of the Suboptimal Filter

We will now obtain an estimate of the magnitude of the differences

$$\Delta\Gamma(i) \triangleq \Gamma(i) - \Gamma^*(i)$$
$$\Delta\hat{\Gamma}(i) \triangleq \hat{\Gamma}(i) - \hat{\Gamma}^*(i) \tag{148}$$

which arise from the use of the suboptimal gain instead of the optimal gains.

Write

$$\Xi_{i+1} = \hat{\Xi}_{i+1} + \delta_{i+1}$$

Then, from (142) and (147),

$$\delta_{i+1} = H_{i+1}\begin{pmatrix}0 & \Phi_i\,\Gamma_{12}(i)\,\Psi_i' \\ \Psi_i\,\Gamma_{12}'(i)\,\Phi_i' & \Psi_i\,\Gamma_{22}(i)\,\Psi_i'\end{pmatrix} H'_{i+1} \tag{149}$$

Thus δ_{i+1} is of $o(\epsilon)$ while $\hat{\Xi}_{i+1}$ is of $O(1)$. From (141) and (146) the error-covariance matrix for the suboptimal filter is given by

$$\begin{aligned}\Gamma_{11}(i+1) = {} & \hat{\Gamma}_{11}(i) - \hat{\Gamma}_{11}(i)\, M'_{i+1}\hat{\Xi}_{i+1}^{-1}M_{i+1}\,\hat{\Gamma}_{11}(i) \\ & - \hat{\Gamma}_{11}(i)\, M'_{i+1}\hat{\Xi}_{i+1}^{-1}N_{i+1}(S_i + \Phi_i\,\hat{\Gamma}_{12}(i)\,\Psi_i') \\ & - (S_i + \Phi_i\,\Gamma_{12}(i)\,\Psi_i')N'_{i+1}\hat{\Xi}_{i+1}^{-1}M_{i+1}\,\hat{\Gamma}_{11}(i) \\ & + \hat{\Gamma}_{11}(i)\, M'_{i+1}\hat{\Xi}_{i+1}^{-1}\delta_{i+1}\hat{\Xi}_{i+1}^{-1}M_{i+1}\,\hat{\Gamma}_{11}(i)\end{aligned} \tag{150a}$$

$$\begin{aligned}\Gamma_{12}(i+1) = \hat{\Gamma}_{12}(i) &- \hat{\Gamma}_{11}(i)\, M'_{i+1}\hat{\Xi}^{-1}_{i+1}N_{i+1}R_i - \hat{\Gamma}_{12}(i)\, N'_{i+1}\hat{\Xi}^{-1}_{i+1}N_{i+1}R_i \\ &- \hat{\Gamma}_{11}(i)\, M'_{i+1}\hat{\Xi}^{-1}_{i+1}M_{i+1}\, \hat{\Gamma}_{12}(i) - \hat{\Gamma}_{11}(i)\, M'_{i+1}\hat{\Xi}_{i+1}N_{i+1}\, \hat{\Gamma}_{22}(i) \\ &+ \hat{\Gamma}_{11}M'_{i+1}\hat{\Xi}^{-1}_{i+1}N_{i+1}R_i + \hat{\Gamma}_{11}(i)\, M'_{i+1}\hat{\Xi}^{-1}_{i+1}\delta_{i+1}\hat{\Xi}^{-1}_{i+1}N_{i+1}R_{i+1} \qquad (150b)\end{aligned}$$

and

$$\begin{aligned}\Gamma_{22}(i+1) = \hat{\Gamma}_{22}(i) &- R_iN'_{i+1}\hat{\Xi}^{-1}_{i+1}(M_{i+1}\, \hat{\Gamma}_{12}(i) + N_{i+1}\, \hat{\Gamma}_{22}(i)) \\ &- (\hat{\Gamma}'_{12}(i)\, M'_{i+1} + \hat{\Gamma}_{22}(i)\, N'_{i+1})\hat{\Xi}^{-1}_{i+1}N_{i+1}R_i \\ &+ R_iN'_{i+1}\hat{\Xi}^{-1}_{i+1}N_{i+1}R_i + R_iN'_{i+1}\hat{\Xi}^{-1}_{i+1}\delta_{i+1}\hat{\Xi}^{-1}_{i+1}N_{i+1}R_i \qquad (150c)\end{aligned}$$

Define Δ_{i+1} by

$$\Xi^*_{i+1} = \hat{\Xi}_{i+1} + \Delta_{i+1}$$

From (137) and (147),

$$\Delta_{i+1} = H_{i+1}\begin{pmatrix} -\Delta\Gamma_{11}(i) & \Phi_i\, \Gamma^*_{12}(i)\, \Psi_i' \\ \Psi_i\, \Gamma^{*\prime}_{12}(i)\, \Phi_i' & \Psi_i\, \Gamma^*_{22}(i)\, \Psi_i' \end{pmatrix} H'_{i+1} \qquad (151)$$

Since Δ_{i+1} is of $O(\epsilon)$, the inverse of Ξ^*_{i+1} is approximately given by

$$\Xi^{-1}_{i+1} \doteqdot \hat{\Xi}^{-1}_{i+1} - \hat{\Xi}^{-1}_{i+1}\Delta_{i+1}\hat{\Xi}_{i+1} \qquad (152)$$

From (149) and (151),

$$\delta_{i+1} - \Delta_{i+1} = H_{i+1}\begin{pmatrix} \Delta\hat{\Gamma}_{11}(i) & \Phi_i\, \Delta\Gamma_{12}(i)\, \Psi_i' \\ \Psi_i\, \Delta\Gamma_{12}(i)\, \Phi_i' & \Psi_i\, \Delta\Gamma_{22}(i)\, \Phi_i' \end{pmatrix} H'_{i+1} \qquad (153)$$

Intuitively speaking, the suboptimal filter with gain (146) would be most accurate when the correlation between these subvectors is zero, i.e., when $S_i = 0$, $i = 0, 1, \ldots$. Therefore, we will investigate two cases: (i) when S_i is of small quantity of order ϵ and (ii) when S_i is not small. In Case (i) it is assumed that $\| S_i \| \approx \| \Psi_i \| = O(\epsilon)$.

a. *Case with Small* S_i

From (150a), to the order of ϵ,

$$\begin{aligned}\Delta\Gamma_{11}(i+1) \doteqdot \Delta\hat{\Gamma}_{11}(i) &- \Delta\hat{\Gamma}_{11}(i)\, M'_{i+1}\hat{\Xi}^{-1}_{i+1}M_{i+1}\, \hat{\Gamma}^*_{11}(i) \\ &- \hat{\Gamma}^*_{11}(i)\, M'_{i+1}\hat{\Xi}^{*-1}_{i+1}M_{i+1}\, \Delta\hat{\Gamma}_{11}(i) \\ &+ \Gamma^*_{11}M'_{i+1}\hat{\Xi}^{*-1}_{i+1}\begin{pmatrix} \Delta\hat{\Gamma}_{11} & 0 \\ 0 & 0 \end{pmatrix}\hat{\Xi}^{*-1}_{i+1}M_{i+1}\, \hat{\Gamma}^*_{11}(i) \qquad (154)\end{aligned}$$

The details of the following calculations are found in Appendix C at the end of this chapter.

Dropping the subscript $(i+1)$ from M, N, Σ, Ξ^*, Δ, and δ and removing the subscript i from R and S,

$$\Delta\Gamma_{12}(i+1) \doteq -\Delta\hat{\Gamma}_{11}\, M'\hat{\Xi}^{*-1}NR + \hat{\Gamma}_{11}^{*}M'\hat{\Xi}^{*-1}\begin{pmatrix}\Delta\hat{\Gamma}_{11} & 0\\ 0 & 0\end{pmatrix}\hat{\Xi}^{*-1}NR \quad (155)$$

$$\Delta\Gamma_{22}(i+1) \doteq RN'\hat{\Xi}^{*-1}\begin{pmatrix}\Delta\Gamma_{11} & 0\\ 0 & 0\end{pmatrix}\hat{\Xi}^{*}NR \quad (156)$$

Therefore,

$$\|\Delta\Gamma_{11}(i+1)\| \leqslant \alpha_i \,\|\Delta\Gamma_{11}(i)\| \quad (157)$$

where

$$\alpha_i \triangleq [2\,\|\tfrac{1}{2}I - M'_{i+1}\hat{\Xi}_{i+1}^{*-1}M_{i+1}\,\hat{\Gamma}_{11}^{*}(i)\| + \|\hat{\Gamma}_{11}^{*}(i)\, M'_{i+1}\hat{\Xi}_{i+1}^{*-1}\|^2]\,\|\Phi_i\|^2$$

$$\|\Delta\Gamma_{12}(i+1)\| \leqslant \beta_i \,\|\Delta\Gamma_{11}(i)\| \quad (158)$$

where

$$\beta_i \triangleq (\|M'_{i+1}\hat{\Xi}_{i+1}^{*-1}N_{i+1}R_i\| + \|\hat{\Gamma}_{11}^{*}(i)\, M'_{i+1}\hat{\Xi}_{i+1}^{-1}\|\,\|\hat{\Xi}_{i+1}^{*}N_{i+1}R_i\|)\,\|\Phi_i\|^2$$

and

$$\|\Delta\Gamma_{22}(i+1)\| \leqslant \gamma_i \,\|\Delta\Gamma_{11}(i)\| \quad (159)$$

where

$$\gamma_i \triangleq \|\hat{\Xi}_{i+1}^{*-1}N_{i+1}R_i\|^2\,\|\Phi_i\|^2$$

Hence,

$$\|\Delta\Gamma_{11}(i)\| \leqslant \left(\prod_{0}^{i-1} a_j\right)\|\Delta\Gamma_{11}(0)\| \quad (160)$$

b. *Case with* $S_i = O(1)$

Now $\Delta\Gamma_{12}$ is $O(1)$. From (150),

$$\begin{aligned}\Delta\Gamma_{11}(i+1) \doteq\ & \Delta\hat{\Gamma}_{11}(i)\,(\tfrac{1}{2}I - M'\hat{\Xi}^{*-1}M\hat{\Gamma}_{11}^{*} - M'\hat{\Xi}^{*-1}NS')\\ & + (\tfrac{1}{2}I - \hat{\Gamma}_{11}^{*}M'\hat{\Xi}^{*-1}M - SN'\hat{\Xi}^{*-1}M)\,\Delta\hat{\Gamma}_{11}(i) + SN'\hat{\Xi}^{*-1}NS'\\ & + (M\hat{\Gamma}_{11}^{*} + NS')\hat{\Xi}^{*-1}M\,\Delta\Gamma_{11}\,M'\hat{\Xi}^{*-1}(M\hat{\Gamma}_{11} + NS') \quad (161a)\end{aligned}$$

$$\begin{aligned}\Delta\Gamma_{12}(i+1) \doteq\ & -\Delta\hat{\Gamma}_{11}\,(M'\hat{\Xi}^{*-1}MS + M'\hat{\Xi}^{*-1}NR) + SN'\hat{\Xi}^{*-1}MS\\ & + (\hat{\Gamma}_{11}^{*}M' + SN')\hat{\Xi}^{*-1}\,\Delta\Gamma_{11}\,M'\hat{\Xi}^{*-1}(MS + NR) \quad (161b)\end{aligned}$$

and

$$\Delta\Gamma_{22}(i+1) \doteqdot SM'\hat{\Xi}^{*-1}MS + (S'M' + RN')\hat{\Xi}^{*-1}M\,\Delta\Gamma_{11}\,M'\hat{\Xi}^{*-1}(MS + NR) \tag{161c}$$

Therefore,

$$\|\,\Delta\Gamma_{11}(i+1)\| \leqslant a_i + \alpha_i \,\|\,\Delta\Gamma_{11}(i)\| \tag{162}$$

where

$$a_i \triangleq \|\, S_i N'_{i+1}\hat{\Xi}^{*-1}_{i+1} N_{i+1} S_i' \,\|$$

$$\alpha_i = \|\,\Phi_i\,\|^2\, [2\,\|\,\tfrac{1}{2}I - M'_{i+1}\hat{\Xi}^{*-1}_{i+1}M_{i+1}\,\hat{\Gamma}^*_{11}(i) - M'_{i+1}\hat{\Xi}^{*-1}_{i+1}N_{i+1}S_i'\,\|$$

$$+ \|(M_{i+1}\,\hat{\Gamma}^*_{11}(i) + N_{i+1}S_i')'\hat{\Xi}^{*-1}_{i+1}M_i\,\|^2]$$

$$\|\,\Delta\Gamma_{12}(i+1)\| \leqslant b_i + \beta_i \,\|\,\Delta\Gamma_{11}(i)\| \tag{163}$$

where

$$b_i \triangleq \|\, S_i N'_{i+1}\hat{\Xi}^{*-1}_{i+1} M_{i+1} S_i \,\|$$

$$\beta_i \triangleq \|\,\Phi_i\,\|^2\,\|\, M'_{i+1}\hat{\Xi}^{*-1}_{i+1}(M_{i+1}S_i + N_{i+1}R_i)\|\,(1 + \|(\hat{\Gamma}^*_{11}(i)\,M'_{i+1}$$

$$+ S_i N'_{i+1})\hat{\Xi}^{*-1}_{i+1}M_{i+1}\,\|)$$

and

$$\|\,\Delta\Gamma_{22}(i+1)\| \leqslant c_i + \gamma_i \,\|\,\Delta\Gamma_{11}(i)\| \tag{164}$$

where

$$c_i \triangleq \|\, S_i M'_{i+1}\hat{\Xi}^{*-1}_{i+1} M_{i+1} S_i \,\|$$

$$\gamma_i \triangleq \|\,\Phi_i\,\|^2\,\|\, M'_{i+1}\Xi^{*-1}_{i+1}(M_{i+1}S_i + N_{i+1}R_i)\|^2$$

Comparing (157)–(159) with (162)–(164), it is clear that that $\|\, S_i \,\|$ is the major source of error of this type of approximations as expected.

Appendix A. Derivation of the Recursion Formula for Open-Loop Feedback Control Policies (Section 2)

Substituting Eq. (68) into Eq. (67), one obtains

$$a_n + 2\sum_{k=n-1}^{N-1} b_k(n)\,u_k + \sum_k\sum_j u_k'\,K_{kj}(n)\,u_j$$

$$+ 2C_n x_{n-1} + x'_{n-1}L_n x_{n-1} + 2\sum_k g_k(n)\,\xi_k + \sum_k\sum_j \xi_k'\,N_{kj}(n)\,\xi_j$$

$$+ 2\sum_j u_j'\,f_j(n)\,x_{n-1} + 2\sum_k \xi_k'\,M_k(n)\,x_{n-1} + 2\sum_k\sum_j \xi_k'\,O_{kj}(n)\,u_j$$

$$
\begin{aligned}
&= x_n' V_n x_n + u_{n-1}' T_{n-1} u_{n-1} \\
&\quad + a_{n+1} + 2 \sum_k b_k(n+1)\, u_k + \sum_k \sum_j u_k'\, K_{kj}(n+1)\, u_j \\
&\quad + 2C_{n+1} x_n + x_n' L_{n+1} x_n + 2 \sum_k g_k(n+1)\, \xi_k \\
&\quad + \sum_k \sum_j \xi_k'\, N_{kj}(n+1)\, \xi_j + 2 \sum_j u_j'\, f_j(n+1)\, x_n \\
&\quad + 2 \sum \xi_k\, M_k(n+1)\, x_n + 2 \sum_k \sum_j \xi_k'\, O_{kj}(n+1)\, u_j
\end{aligned}
\tag{A1}
$$

where $x_n = Ax_{n-1} + Bu_{n-1} + C\xi_{n-1}$.

Since Eq. (A1) must hold for all values of the variables u, ξ, and x, one obtains

$$
\begin{aligned}
a_n &= a_{n+1} \\
b_{n-1}(n) &= C_{n+1}B \\
b_k(n) &= b_k(n+1), && k \neq n-1 \\
C_n &= C_{n+1}A \\
L_n &= A'(L_{n+1} + V_n)A \\
f_{n-1}(n) &= B'L_{n+1}A \\
f_k(n) &= f_k(n+1)\, A \\
k_{n-1,n-1}(n) &= B'L_{n+1}B + T_{n-1} \\
K_{k,n-1}(n) &= f_k(n+1)\, B, && k \neq n-1 \\
K_{k,j}(n) &= K_{k,j}(n+1), && k, j \neq n-1 \\
\text{with} \quad K_{k,j}(n) &= K_{j,k}'(n) \\
g_{n-1}(n) &= C_{n+1}C \\
g_k(n) &= g_k(n+1), && k \neq n-1 \\
M_{n-1}(n) &= C'L_{n+1}A \\
M_k(n) &= M_k(n+1)\, A, && k \neq n-1 \\
O_{n-1,n-1}(n) &= C'L_{n+1}B \\
O_{k,n-1}(n) &= M_k(n+1), && k \neq n-1 \\
O_{k,j}(n) &= O_{k,j}(n+1), && k, j \neq n-1 \\
O_{n,k}(n) &= C'\, M_k(n+1)', && k \neq n-1 \\
N_{k,j}(n) &= N_{k,j}(n+1), && k, j \neq n-1 \\
N_{k,n}(n) &= N_{n,k}(n)', && k \neq n-1 \\
N_{k,n-1}(n) &= M_k(n+1)\, C, && k \neq n-1 \\
N_{n-1,n-1}(n) &= C'L_{n+1}C
\end{aligned}
$$

Appendix B. Derivation of the Constraint Matrix Equations (Section 4)

As is evident from the discussion of Section 4,B, the existence of a minimal $(n - m)$th-order observer depends on the fact that the matrix T satisfies the matrix equation

$$TA - FT = DH \tag{B1}$$

while the matrix

$$\hat{T} = \left[\begin{array}{c} T \\ \hline H \end{array}\right] \tag{B2}$$

remains nonsingular.

In the matrix equation (B1), F and D are to be specified by the designer. It is well known that if A and F have no common eigenvalues a unique solution for T of (B1) exists for arbitrary DH. See, for example, R. Bellman "Introduction to Matrix Analysis." Since for the stochastic problem we are concerned with obtaining a solution which permits the minimization of certain elements of the error-covariance matrix C_i defined by (89), we present here a constructive procedure which specifies the design matrices F and D in such a manner that (B1) and (B2) are true. This approach is useful as it obtains the method of Section 4,C for minimizing the system error-covariance matrix in a straightforward way, even though a number of constraints need be simultaneously satisfied. We present the essentials of this approach in the form of a theorem.

Theorem. If

$$F = TAP$$

$$D = TAV$$

where

$$\hat{T} \triangleq \left[\begin{array}{c} T \\ \hline H \end{array}\right], \quad \begin{array}{l} T \text{ is an } (n - m) \times n \text{ matrix,} \\ H \text{ is an } m \times n \text{ matrix} \end{array}$$

$$L \triangleq [P \mid V], \quad \begin{array}{l} P \text{ is an } nx(n - m) \text{ matrix,} \\ V \text{ is an } n \times m \text{ matrix} \end{array}$$

are such that either

A. $L\hat{T} = PT + VH = I_n$, I_n is the $n \times n$ identity matrix,

or

B. $\hat{T}L = \left[\begin{array}{c|c} TP & TV \\ \hline HP & HV \end{array}\right] = \left[\begin{array}{c|c} I_{n-m} & 0 \\ \hline 0 & I_m \end{array}\right]$, then

I. $TA - FT = DH$,
II. $L = \hat{T}^{-1}$.

Proof. We see that Condition A is the definition that L is a left inverse of T while Condition B is the definition of a right inverse of T. Since for square matrices the existence of a right or left inverse is equivalent to nonsingularity, Conditions A and B are equivalent and either implies

$$L = \hat{T}^{-1}$$

Using the definitions of F and D we have

$$TA - FT = TA(I - PT)$$
$$DH = TA(VH)$$

But as

$$(I - PT) = VH$$

from Condition A, then

$$TA - FT = DH$$

In the main body of Section 4, it can be seen that any relation involving the error-covariance matrix C can be converted using Conditions A and B to one involving the known matrices A, H, R, and Q, and the unknown matrix V. Hence it is sufficient to consider V alone in designing the observer. It should be noted however that V (as well as C) is unconstrained. From Condition B we have

$$HV = I_m \tag{B3}$$

where H is given.

Appendix C. Computation of $\Delta\Gamma(i)$ (Section 6)

From (140) and (150),

$$\begin{aligned}\Delta\Gamma_{11}(i+1) = \Delta\hat{\Gamma}_{11}(i) &+ (\hat{\Gamma}^*_{11}(i)\, M'_{i+1}\hat{\Xi}^{-1}_{i+1}M_{i+1}\,\hat{\Gamma}^*_{11}(i) - \hat{\Gamma}_{11}(i)\, M'_{i+1} \\ &\times \hat{\Xi}^{-1}_{i+1}M_{i+1}\,\hat{\Gamma}_{11}(i)) \\ &+ [\hat{\Gamma}^*_{11}(i)\, M'_{i+1}\hat{\Xi}^{-1}_{i+1}N_{i+1}\,\hat{\Gamma}^{*\prime}_{12}(i) - \hat{\Gamma}_{11}(i)\, M'_{i+1}\hat{\Xi}^{-1}_{i+1}N_{i+1} \\ &\times (S_i + \Phi_i\, \Gamma_{12}(i)\, \Psi_i{}')']\end{aligned}$$

$$
\begin{aligned}
&+ [\hat{\Gamma}_{12}^*(i)\, N_{i+1}' \hat{\Xi}_{i+1}^{-1} M_{i+1}\, \hat{\Gamma}_{11}^*(i) - (S_i + \Phi_i\, \Gamma_{12}(i)\, \Psi_i')N_{i+1}' \\
&\times \hat{\Xi}_{i+1}^{-1} M_{i+1}\, \hat{\Gamma}_{11}(i)] \\
&+ \hat{\Gamma}_{12}^*(i)\, M_{i+1}' \hat{\Xi}_{i+1}^{-1} N_{i+1}\, \Gamma_{12}^*(i)' \\
&+ \hat{\Gamma}_{11}(i)\, M_{i+1}' \hat{\Xi}_{i+1}^{-1} \delta_{i+1} \hat{\Xi}_{i+1}^{-1} M_{i+1}\, \hat{\Gamma}_{11}(i) - (M_{i+1}\, \hat{\Gamma}_{11}^*(i) \\
&+ N_{i+1}\, \hat{\Gamma}_{12}^*(i))' \\
&\times \hat{\Xi}_{i+1}^{-1} \Delta_{i+1} \hat{\Xi}_{i+1} (M_{i+1}\, \hat{\Gamma}_{11}^*(i) + N_{i+1}\, \hat{\Gamma}_{12}^{*\prime}(i))
\end{aligned}
$$

$$
\begin{aligned}
\doteqdot\ & \Delta\hat{\Gamma}_{11}(i) - \Delta\hat{\Gamma}_{11}(i)\, M_{i+1}' \hat{\Xi}_{i+1}^{-1} M_{i+1}\, \hat{\Gamma}_{11}^*(i) \\
&- \hat{\Gamma}_{11}^*(i)\, M_{i+1}' \hat{\Xi}_{i+1}^{-1} M_{i+1}\, \Delta\hat{\Gamma}_{11}(i) \\
&- \hat{\Gamma}_{11}^*(i)\, M_{i+1}' \hat{\Xi}_{i+1}^{-1} N_{i+1} (\Phi_i\, \Delta\Gamma_{12}(i)\, \Psi_i')' \\
&- \Delta\hat{\Gamma}_{11}(i)\, M_{i+1}' \hat{\Xi}_{i+1}^{-1} N_{i+1} (S_i + \Phi_i\, \Gamma_{12}^*(i)\, \Psi_i')' \\
&- (\Phi_i\, \Delta\Gamma_{12}(i)\, \Psi_i') N_{i+1}' \hat{\Xi}_{i+1}^{-1} M_{i+1}\, \hat{\Gamma}_{11}^*(i) \\
&- (S_i + \Phi_i\, \Gamma_{12}(i)\, \Psi_i) N_{i+1}' \hat{\Xi}_{i+1}^{-1} M_{i+1}\, \Delta\hat{\Gamma}_{11}(i) \\
&+ \hat{\Gamma}_{12}^*(i)\, N_{i+1}' \hat{\Xi}_{i+1}^{-1} N_{i+1}\, \hat{\Gamma}_{12}^{*\prime}(i) \\
&+ \hat{\Gamma}_{11}^*(i)\, M_{i+1}' \hat{\Xi}_{i+1}^{-1} \delta_{i+1} \hat{\Xi}_{i+1}^{-1} M_{i+1}\, \hat{\Gamma}_{11}^*(i) \\
&- \Lambda_1{}^*(i)'\, \hat{\Xi}_{i+1}^{-1} \Delta_{i+1} \hat{\Xi}_{i+1}^{-1}\, \Lambda_1{}^*(i)
\end{aligned}
$$

We drop subscripts from now on:

$$
\begin{aligned}
\Delta\Gamma_{12}(i+1) &= \Delta\hat{\Gamma}_{12}(i) + [\hat{\Gamma}_{11}^* M' \hat{\Xi}^{-1} M \hat{\Gamma}_{12}^* - \hat{\Gamma}_{11} M' \hat{\Xi}^{-1} M \hat{\Gamma}_{12}] \\
&\quad + \hat{\Gamma}_{12}^* N' \hat{\Xi}^{-1} M \hat{\Gamma}_{12}^* + [\hat{\Gamma}_{11}^* M' \hat{\Xi}^{-1} N \hat{\Gamma}_{22}^* - \hat{\Gamma}_{11} M' \Xi^{-1} N R] \\
&\quad + (\hat{\Gamma}_{12}^* N' \hat{\Xi}^{-1} N \hat{\Gamma}_{22}^* - \hat{\Gamma}_{12} N' \hat{\Xi}^{-1} N R) \\
&\quad + \hat{\Gamma}_{11} M' \Xi^{-1} N (R - \hat{\Gamma}_{22}) + \hat{\Gamma}_{11}^* M' \hat{\Xi}^{-1} \delta \hat{\Xi}^{-1} N R \\
&\quad - (\hat{\Gamma}_{11}^* M' + \hat{\Gamma}_{12}^* N') \hat{\Xi}^{-1}\, \Delta\hat{\Xi}^{-1} (M \hat{\Gamma}_{12}^* + N \hat{\Gamma}_{22}^*) \\
&= \Delta\hat{\Gamma}_{12}(i) - \Delta\hat{\Gamma}_{11}(i)\, M' \hat{\Xi}^{-1} M \hat{\Gamma}_{12}^* - \hat{\Gamma}_{11}^* M' \hat{\Xi}^{*-1} M\, \Delta\hat{\Gamma}_{12} \\
&\quad + \hat{\Gamma}_{11}^* M' \hat{\Xi}^{-1} N \Psi_i \Gamma_{22}^* \Psi_i{}' - \Delta\hat{\Gamma}_{11}\, M' \hat{\Xi}^{-1} N R \\
&\quad + \Gamma_{12}^* N' \hat{\Xi}^{-1} N \Psi_i \Gamma_{22}^* \Psi_i{}' - \Delta\hat{\Gamma}_{12}\, N' \hat{\Xi}^{-1} N R + \hat{\Gamma}_{12}^* N' \hat{\Xi}^{-1} M \hat{\Gamma}_{12}^* \\
&\quad - \hat{\Gamma}_{11}^* M' \hat{\Xi}^{-1} N \Psi_i \Gamma_{22}^* \Psi_i{}' - \Delta\hat{\Gamma}_{11}\, M' \hat{\Xi}^{-1} N \Psi_i \Gamma_{22} \Psi_i' \\
&\quad - \hat{\Gamma}_{11}^* M' \hat{\Xi}^{-1} N \Psi_i\, \Delta\Gamma_{22}\, \Psi_i{}' + \hat{\Gamma}_{11}^* M' \hat{\Xi}^{-1} \delta \hat{\Xi}^{-1} N R \\
&\quad - (\hat{\Gamma}_{11}^* M' + \hat{\Gamma}_{12}^* N') \hat{\Xi}^{-1}\, \Delta\hat{\Xi}^{-1} (M \hat{\Gamma}_{12}^* + N \hat{\Gamma}_{22}^*)
\end{aligned}
$$

$$
\begin{aligned}
\Delta\Gamma_{22}(i+1) = {} & \Delta\hat{\Gamma}_{22}(i) + (\hat{\Gamma}_{22}^{*}N'\hat{\Xi}^{-1}M\hat{\Gamma}_{12}^{*} - RN'\hat{\Xi}^{-1}M\hat{\Gamma}_{12}) \\
& + (\hat{\Gamma}_{22}^{*}N'\hat{\Xi}^{-1}N\hat{\Gamma}_{22}^{*} - RN'\hat{\Xi}^{-1}N\hat{\Gamma}_{22}) \\
& + (\hat{\Gamma}_{12}^{*\prime}M'\hat{\Xi}^{-1}N\hat{\Gamma}_{22}^{*} - \hat{\Gamma}_{12}'M'\hat{\Xi}^{-1}NR) \\
& + \hat{\Gamma}_{12}^{*}M'\hat{\Xi}^{-1}M\hat{\Gamma}_{12}^{*} \\
& + RN'\hat{\Xi}^{-1}NR - \hat{\Gamma}_{22}N'\hat{\Xi}^{-1}NR \\
& + RN'\hat{\Xi}^{-1}\delta\hat{\Xi}^{-1}NR - (\hat{\Gamma}_{12}^{*\prime}M' + \hat{\Gamma}_{22}^{*}N')\hat{\Xi}^{-1}\Delta^{-1}\hat{\Xi}^{-1} \\
& \times (M\hat{\Gamma}_{12}^{*} + N\hat{\Gamma}_{22}^{*}) \\
= {} & \Delta\hat{\Gamma}_{22}(i) - RN'\hat{\Xi}^{-1}M\,\Delta\hat{\Gamma}_{12} + \Psi_i R_i \Psi_i' N'\hat{\Xi}^{-1}M\hat{\Gamma}_{12}^{*} \\
& - RN\hat{\Xi}^{-1}N\Psi_i\,\Delta\Gamma_{22}\,\Psi_i - \Delta\hat{\Gamma}_{12}'\,M'\hat{\Xi}^{-1}NR \\
& + \hat{\Gamma}_{12}^{*}M'\hat{\Xi}^{-1}M\hat{\Gamma}_{12}^{*} - \Delta\hat{\Gamma}_{22}\,N'\hat{\Xi}^{-1}NR \\
& + RN'\hat{\Xi}^{-1}\delta\hat{\Xi}^{-1}NR - (\hat{\Gamma}_{12}^{*\prime}M' + \hat{\Gamma}_{22}^{*}N')\hat{\Xi}^{-1} \\
& \times \Delta\hat{\Xi}^{-1}(M\hat{\Gamma}_{12}^{*} + N\hat{\Gamma}_{22}^{*}) - \Psi_i\Gamma_{22}^{*}\Psi_i'N'\hat{\Xi}^{-1}NR
\end{aligned}
$$

Chapter VIII

Stochastic Stability

1. Introduction

We consider the question of stability of discrete-time stochastic systems via Lyapunov functions in this chapter.* This topic is not only important in its own right but also provides an example of the classes of engineering problems where the theory of martingales introduced in Chapter VI can be fruitfully applied. It is well known that natures of stability of deterministic dynamical systems can be answered if we can construct Lyapunov functions with certain specified properties. See, for example, La Salle and Lefschetz,[99] Hahn,[70] or Krasovskii.[93] Also see Refs. 141a, 143 for other methods.

Generally speaking, given a dynamical system with the state vector x, the stability of the equilibrium point of a dynamical system (which is taken to be the origin without loss of generality) can be shown by constructing a positive definite continuous function of x, $V(x)$, called a Lyapunov function, such that its time derivative $dV(x)/dt$ along a system trajectory is nonpositive definite. A monotonically decreasing behavior of $V(x)$ along the trajectory implies a similar behavior for the norm of the state vector x, $\| x \|$, i.e., $\| x \| \to 0$ as $t \to \infty$, which is in correspondence with our intuitive notion that the origin is asymptotically stable.

For a discrete-time system with the trajectory $\{x_n, \ n = 0, 1, \ldots\}$,

* For discussions of stability of continuous time stochastic systems see, for example, Samuels,[121–123] Kozin,[94] Bogdanoff,[34] Caughey,[37] and Caughey and Dienes.[38] See also Ref. 61a.

the stability of the origin is implied by the behavior of $V(x)$ such that, for any set of i discrete sampling points in time, $0 \leqslant n_1 < n_2 < \cdots < n_i$,

$$V(x_{n_1}) \geqslant V(x_{n_2}) \geqslant \cdots \geqslant V(x_{n_i}) \tag{1}$$

This behavior of $V(x)$ may be intuitively understood by interpreting $V(x)$ as a "generalized" energy of the system which must not increase with time for stable dynamical systems.

Now consider a discrete-time stochastic dynamical system described by

$$x_{k+1} = D_k(x_k, \xi_k), \qquad k = 0, 1,... \tag{2}$$

where x_k is the n-dimensional state vector and ξ_k is a random variable (generally a vector). A control system described by

$$x_{k+1} = F_k(x_k, u_k, \xi_k), \qquad k = 0, 1,... \tag{3}$$

can be regarded as a dynamical system described by (2) for a given control policy, say $u_k = \phi_k(x_k)$, where ϕ_k is a known function of x_k:

$$\begin{aligned} x_{k+1} &= F_k(x_k, \phi_k(x_k), \xi_k) \\ &\triangleq D_k(x_k, \xi_k) \end{aligned}$$

Only one trajectory results from a given initial state x_0, for a deterministic system. A collection of trajectories is possible from a given x_0 for a stochastic system, depending on realizations of the stochastic process $\{\xi_k\}$.

Using the same intuitive arguments as before, consider a positive definite continuous function of x, $V(x)$, which may be regarded again as representing the system's generalized energy. Because $\{x_n\}$ is now a stochastic process, one must now consider the behavior of $V(x)$ for the class of all possible realizations of trajectories. One may, for example, replace Condition (1) for the behavior of Lyapunov functions of deterministic systems by

$$E\,V(x_{n_1}) \geqslant E\,V(x_{n_2}) \geqslant \cdots \geqslant E\,V(x_{n_i}) \tag{4}$$

for any given set of i time instants, $0 \leqslant n_1 < n_2 < \cdots < n_i$. Namely, (4) requires that the average behavior of $V(x)$ over possible realizations of trajectories behaves like the Lyapunov function of a deterministic system.

Intuitively speaking, stable stochastic systems should be such that $E(V(x_n))$ remains bounded. In terms of $\{x_n\}$, stable stochastic systems should be such that, for the majority of sample sequences $\{x_n\}$, i.e., for the set of sample sequences with probability arbitrarily close to 1, $\| x_n \|$ remains bounded.

For an asymptotically stable stochastic system not only should $E(V(x_n))$ remain bounded for all n but actually $E(V(x_n))$ should decrease monotonically to zero with probability 1.

Equation (4) is implied by the relation that, given any particular realization of $x_0, x_2, \ldots, x_n$, $V(x)$ satisfies the inequality

$$E(V(x_n) \mid x_0, x_1, \ldots, x_{n-1}) \leqslant V(x_{n-1}) \tag{5}$$

since $E(V(x_n)) = E(E(V(x_n) \mid x_0, x_1, \ldots, x_{n-1}))$, where the outer E refers to the expectation operation over possible x_0 $x_1, \ldots, x_{n-1}$. Inequality (5) can be interpreted to mean that the behavior of $\{x_n\}$ is such that, given past behavior of $V(x)$ for a realized (sample) trajectory $x_0, x_1, \ldots, x_{n-1}$, the expected value of $V(x)$ at the next time instant, $E(V(x_n) \mid x_0, \ldots, x_{n-1})$, is not greater than the last value of $V(x)$, $V(x_{n-1})$.

Then the system can be regarded as stable in some stochastic sense, since the conditional expected generalized energy is not increasing with time. Inequality (5) is precisely the definition that $V(x_n)$, $n = 0, 1, \ldots$, is an expectation-decreasing martingale or a supermartingale (also known as a lower semimartingale).

The idea of discussing stability of stochastic systems by suitably extending the deterministic Lyapunov theory seems to have appeared first in the papers by Bertram and Sarachik[25] and Kats and Krasovskii.[90] The realization that such stochastic Lyapunov functions are supermartingales seems to be due to Bucy[36] and Kushner.[96,97]

In the next section, we will make precise the statements made in this section and discuss the problems of stability of stochastic systems. The exposition is based in part on Bucy and Kushner.

2. Stochastic Lyapunov Functions as Semimartingales

We consider a stochastic system described by (2) such that

$$D_k(0, \xi_k) = 0 \qquad \text{for all} \quad k \tag{6}$$

i.e., the origin is taken to be the equilibrium point of the system. The solution of (2) is denoted by x_k, $k = 0, 1, \ldots$, or by

$$x(k, x_0), \qquad k = 0, 1, \ldots$$

when it is desired to indicate the dependence of the solution on the initial state vector x_0. Note that x_0 is generally a random variable.

We now give definitions of stability and asymptotic stability in a way which parallels the definitions for deterministic systems.

Definition of stability. The origin is stable with probability 1 if and only if, for any $\delta > 0$ and $\epsilon > 0$, there is a $\rho(\delta, \epsilon) > 0$ such that, if $\| x_0 \| \leqslant \rho(\delta, \epsilon)$, then

$$\Pr[\sup_n \| x_n \| \geqslant \epsilon] \leqslant \delta$$

Definition of asymptotic stability. The origin is asymptotically stable with probability 1 if and only if it is stable with probability 1 and

$$\| x(n, x_0)\| \to 0 \quad \text{with probability 1 as} \quad n \to \infty \tag{7}$$

for x_0 in some neighborhood of the origin.

If (7) is true for all x_0 in the state space, then we say that the origin is asymptotically stable in the large. Let us now indicate how we prove the stability of a stochastic system if a positive definite continuous scalar function $V(\cdot)$ is defined on the space of state vectors such that $\{V(x(n, x_0))\}$ is an expectation-decreasing martingale in some region about the origin.

Such a proof can be made to depend essentially on the semimartingale inequality[47a]: for any $\lambda > 0$,

$$\Pr[\sup_n V(x_n) \geqslant \lambda] \leqslant E\, V(x_0)/\lambda \tag{8}$$

See Appendix A at the end of this chapter for proof. See also Appendix I at the end of this book.

To simplify the arguments, we show the proof for positive definite scalar function $V(x_n)$ which forms an expectation-decreasing martingale in the whole state vector space. It is a minor technical complication to extend the arguments to include $\{V(x_n)\}$ which is an expectation-decreasing martingale only in some region about the origin. We assume that

$$E\, V(x_0) < \infty$$

Consider a positive definite continuous function of n-dimensional vector x, $V(x)$, such that $V(0) = 0$, $V(x)$ finite for any finite $\| x \|$, and $V(x) \to \infty$ as $\| x \| \to \infty$, and suppose that the sequence $\{V(x(n, x_0))\}$ is an expectation-decreasing martingale for all x_0. Then we will show that the origin is stable. From (8), for any $\epsilon > 0$,

$$\Pr[\sup_n V(x_n) \geqslant \epsilon] \leqslant E\, V(x_0)/\epsilon \tag{9}$$

Given such a scalar-valued function $V(x)$, it is always possible to find continuous positive nondecreasing functions α and β of real variables such that

$$\alpha(0) = 0, \qquad \beta(0) = 0$$

$$\alpha(\| x \|) \to \infty, \qquad \beta(\| x \|) \to \infty \qquad \text{as} \quad \| x \| \to \infty$$

and

$$\alpha(\| x \|) \leqslant V(x) \leqslant \beta(\| x \|)$$

For example, such α and β can be constructed by

$$\beta(\| x \|) \triangleq \max_{\| y \| \leqslant \| x \|} V(y)$$

and

$$\alpha(\| x \|) \triangleq \min_{y} V(y)$$

where

$$\| x \| \leqslant \| y \| \leqslant b(c(\| x \|))$$

where

$$c(\| x \|) \triangleq \min_{\| y \| = \| x \|} V(y)$$

and where the function b is chosen so that, for any $a > 0$,

$$V(x) > a \qquad \text{for} \quad \| x \| > b(a)$$

Since $V(x) \to \infty$ as $\| x \| \to \infty$, it is always possible to choose such $b(a)$. Choose $\rho(\delta, \epsilon)$ such that if

$$\| x_0 \| \leqslant \rho(\delta, \epsilon)$$

then

$$EV(x_0) \leqslant E\, \beta(\| x_0 \|) \leqslant \epsilon\delta \tag{10}$$

From (9) and (10),

$$\Pr[\sup_n V(x_n) \geqslant \epsilon] \leqslant \delta \tag{11}$$

Since

$$\Pr[\sup_n \alpha(\| x \|) \geqslant \epsilon] \leqslant \Pr[\sup_n V(x_n) \geqslant \epsilon]$$

and since $\alpha(\cdot)$ has a unique inverse in the neighborhood of the origin, the origin is stable with probability 1.

Condition (10) can be satisfied in other ways. For example, if x_0 is the random variable such that

$$\Pr[\| x_0 \| \leqslant M] = 1$$

for some finite $M > 0$, then

$$E\,V(\|x_0\|) \leqslant \beta(a)\,[1 - \Pr(\|x_0\| \geqslant a)] + \beta(M)\Pr(\|x_0\| \geqslant a)$$

or

$$\Pr[\|x_0\| \geqslant a] \leqslant (EV(\|x_0\|) - \beta(a))/\beta(M)$$

Choose $\rho(\delta, \epsilon) > 0$ sufficiently small so that $\beta(\rho) + \rho\beta(M) \leqslant \epsilon\delta$. Then for x_0 satisfying $\Pr(\|x_0\| \geqslant \rho) \leqslant \rho$ we have

$$E\,V(\|x_0\|) \leqslant \epsilon\delta$$

From this inequality and (9), (11) follows.

Thus we have proved the stability with a slightly different definition of stability that the origin is stable if and only if, for any $\delta > 0$ and $\epsilon > 0$, there exists a $\rho(\delta, \epsilon) > 0$ such that for every x_0 satisfying $\Pr(\|x_0\| \geqslant \rho) \leqslant \rho$, and $\Pr(\|x_0\| \leqslant M) = 1$, (11) holds.

The criterion for asymptotic stability is given by the following.

Suppose that there exists a continuous nonnegative function $\gamma(\cdot)$ of real numbers such that it vanishes only at zero and

$$E[V(x(n, x_0)) \mid x_0, ..., x_{n-1}] - V(x(n-1, x_0)) \leqslant -\gamma(\|x(n-1, x_0)\|) < 0 \quad (12)$$

for all x_0. Then the origin is asymptotically stable with probability 1. As commented earlier in connection with the definition of the asymptotic stability, in order to show the asymptotic stability it is necessary to show $E\,V(x_n) \to 0$ as $n \to \infty$. Letting

$$V_n \triangleq V(x_n)$$

and

$$\gamma_n \triangleq \gamma(\|x_n\|)$$

(12) is written as

$$E(V_n \mid x_0, x_1, ..., x_{n-1}) \leqslant V_{n-1} - \gamma_{n-1}$$

Taking the expectation of this with respect to the random variables $x_0, ..., x_{n-1}$,

$$E(V_n) \leqslant EV_{n-1} - E\gamma_{n-}$$

or

$$EV_{n+1} - EV_0 \leqslant -\sum_{i=0}^{n} E\gamma_i < 0$$

or

$$0 \leqslant \sum_{i=0}^{n} E\gamma_i \leqslant EV_0 \leqslant E\beta_0 < \infty \tag{13}$$

for every n. (13) implies that

$$E\gamma_n \to 0 \qquad \text{as} \quad n \to \infty$$

Thus, $\gamma_n \to 0$ in probability.*

Since it is possible to pick a subsequence of $\{\gamma_n\}$ such that the subsequence converges almost surely, let $\{\gamma_{n_i}\}$ be such a subsequence.* Then, since γ is continuous and vanishes only at zero, we have $\| x(n_i, x_0) \| \to 0$ with probability 1.

Since $0 \leqslant EV_n \leqslant EV_0 < \infty$ by the semimartingale convergence theorem (see Doob, p. 324),[47a]

$$\lim_{n\to\infty} V_n \triangleq V_\infty$$

exists with probability 1. But

$$0 \leqslant V_n \leqslant \beta_n \tag{14}$$

Then taking the limit of (14) on the subsequence $\{\beta_{n_i}\}$,

$$0 \leqslant V_\infty \leqslant \beta(0) = 0$$

Therefore,

$$V_\infty = 0 \quad \text{with probability 1}$$

or

$$\overline{\lim}\, \alpha_n = \alpha(\overline{\lim}\, \| x(n, x_0)\|) = 0$$

hence,

$$\| x(n, x_0)\| \to 0 \quad \text{with probability} \quad 1$$

3. Examples

The following examples are taken from Kushner.[97]

Consider a scalar system

$$x_{k+1} = (a + \xi_k)x_k \tag{15}$$

---

* See Appendix I for discussion of convergence in probability and convergence with probability 1 or almost sure convergence.

where the ξ_n are independent and identically distributed with

$$E\xi_n = 0, \qquad E\xi_n{}^2 = \sigma^2 \tag{16}$$

Choose

$$V(x) = x^2 \tag{17}$$

Then

$$E(V_n \mid x_0, ..., x_{n-1}) = (a^2 + \sigma^2)x_{n-1}^2$$

Therefore, if $(a^2 + \sigma^2) < 1$, then

$$E(V_n \mid x_0, ..., x_{n-1}) - V_{n-1} = x_{n-1}^2(a^2 + \sigma^2 - 1) < 0 \tag{18}$$

hence the origin is asymptotically stable. This example can be extended to systems described by vector difference equation immediately.

From the basic semimartingale inequality (8),

$$c \Pr[\sup_n V_n \geqslant c] \leqslant \int V_0 = Ex_0{}^2$$

or (19)

$$\Pr[\sup_n \mid x_n \mid < c^{1/2}] > 1 - Ex_0{}^2/c$$

gives a useful probability expression on the magnitude of x_n. Now for the same system, if $V(x)$ is chosen to be

$$V(x) = x^{2r} \tag{20}$$

for some positive integer $r > 1$, then

$$E(V_n \mid x_0, ..., x_{n-1}) = x_{n-1}^{2r}[E(a + \xi_0)^{2r} - 1]$$

Thus, for those positive integers r such that

$$E(a + \xi_0)^{2r} < 1 \tag{21}$$

$\{x_n^{2r}\}$ is still an expectation-decreasing martingale and is still asymptotically stable. Now, instead of Eq. (19), one has

$$\Pr[\sup_n x_n^{2r} \geqslant c] \leqslant Ex_0^{2r}/c$$

or

$$\Pr[\sup_n \mid x_n \mid \geqslant c^{1/2r}] \geqslant Ex_0^{2r}/c \tag{22}$$

Another inequality which is sometimes useful is:

$$\Pr\left[\max_{i\leqslant j\leqslant n}\left|\sum_{i=1}^{j} z_i\right| \geqslant \lambda\right] \leqslant \frac{1}{\lambda^2}\sum_{i=1}^{n} \operatorname{var} z_i$$

where z's are independent random variables with mean zero and finite variances.

Appendix. Semimartingale Inequality[47a]

Let $\{z_i, \mathscr{B}_i, i = 0, 1, 2, \ldots\}$ be an expectation-decreasing martingale where $\mathscr{B}_i$ is the σ field associated with z_i. Define, for any nonnegative c,

$$\sigma(\omega) = \inf\{k \mid z_k(\omega) \geqslant c\} \cup \{0\}$$

That is, σ is k such that $z_k \geqslant c$ for the first time. If no such k exists, $k = 0, 1, 2, \ldots$, then σ is set equal to 0 by definition. Now $\{z_0, z_\sigma, \mathscr{B}_0, \mathscr{B}_\sigma\}$ is a two-member expectation-decreasing martingale. Therefore,

$$Ez_0 \geqslant Ez_\sigma = \int_B z_\sigma \, dP + \int_{\bar{B}} z_\sigma \, dP \tag{A1}$$

where

$$B \triangleq [\sup_k z_k \geqslant c]$$

and where $\bar{B}$ is the complement of B. Since for $\omega \in \bar{B}$, $\sup_k z_k(\omega) < c$, hence $\sigma = 0$:

$$\int_{\bar{B}} z_\sigma \, dP = \int_{\bar{B}} z_0 \, dP \tag{A2}$$

Therefore, from Eqs. (A1) and (A2),

$$\int_B z_0 \, dP \geqslant \int_B z_\sigma \, dP \geqslant c \Pr B$$

Therefore,

$$\Pr B \leqslant \frac{1}{c}\int_B z_0 \, dP \leqslant \frac{1}{c} E \mid z_0 \mid$$

Chapter IX

Miscellany

1. Probability as a Performance Criterion

In most parts of this book we have used criterion functions which are explicit functions of state vectors and/or control vectors. There are problems, however, where it is more realistic to use implicit functions of state vectors and/or control vectors as criterion functions. A time optimal control problem[6] is a good example of this. Another example of problems where the criterion functions are implicit functions is given by a final-value control problem where the probability that the terminal error exceeds a specified value is used as a criterion of performance.

Although it is sometimes possible to obtain approximately equivalent criterion functions which are explicit functions of state and control vectors for some problems with implicit criterion functions,* for most problems with implicit criterion functions such approximations are not possible.

We will discuss in this section yet another example of a control system with an implicit criterion function where the probability of the maximum system deviation exceeding a given value is used as the criterion of performance. The development of this section is based in part on Odanaka[108] and Aoki.[7]

* For example, the probability of the terminal error can be approximated by a quadratic function of x_N, i.e., by an explicit criterion function of x_N in some cases (see Pfeiffer[113]), where x_N is the system state vector at the terminal time N.

A. PROBLEM FORMULATION

The derivation of an optimal control policy with this criterion function is illustrated for a two-dimensional system described by

$$\begin{aligned} x_1(i+1) &= x_1(i) + f_1(x_1(i), x_2(i)) \\ x_2(i+1) &= x_2(i) + f_2(x_1(i), x_2(i)) + u_i + \xi_i, \qquad i = 0, 1, ..., N-1 \end{aligned} \tag{1}$$

where $x_j(i)$ is the jth component of the state vector at time i, $j = 1, 2$, u_i is a scalar control variable at time i, and ξ's are independent random noise with known probability density functions. They are taken to be identically distributed with the density function $p(\xi)$ for the sake of simplicity. Later we will indicate how this assumption can be dropped and how the method can be extended to certain other classes of nonlinear systems. ξ_i is the scalar value of the noise at time i.

In this section x_1 and x_2 are assumed to be observable without error. The function f_1 is assumed to be such that $(x_1 + f_1(x_1, x_2))^2 < D^2$ whenever $x_1^2 + x_2^2 < D^2$, where D is a given constant. $2x_1f_1 + f_1^2 < x_2^2$ is one sufficient condition for this.

The admissible set of control is taken to be the whole real line. The extension to the case of bounded control variable $|u_i| \leqslant m_i$, m_i given, will also be indicated at the end of this section.

Assume that the origin ($x_1 = 0$, $x_2 = 0$) is an unstable equilibrium point of this system. The random disturbances in (1) will tend to move the state vector away from the origin. It is desired to keep the system state vector in the neighborhood of the origin in the face of random disturbances by appropriate control actions.

We take the duration of the control to be finite, N. The criterion function is taken to be the probability that the maximum of the current and all future deviations exceeds a predetermined value, D.

Define

$$P_k(c_1, c_2) = \min_{u_k,...,u_{N-1}} \Pr[\max_{k \leqslant i \leqslant N} (x_1(i)^2 + x_2(i)^2) \geqslant D^2] \tag{2}$$

where

$$x_1(k) = c_1 \quad \text{and} \quad x_2(k) = c_2$$

Namely, $P_k(c_1, c_2)$ is the probability that the maximum of the current and the future deviations of the system exceeds the value D, when the system starts from the state vector (c_1, c_2) and an optimal control policy is employed.

Clearly,

$$\begin{aligned} P_k(c_1, c_2) = 1 \qquad \text{if} \quad c_1^2 + c_2^2 \geqslant D^2 \\ k = 0, 1, ..., N \end{aligned} \tag{3}$$

Also

$$P_N(c_1, c_2) = 0 \quad \text{if} \quad c_1^2 + c_2^2 < D^2 \tag{4}$$

The recurrence relation for P_k is given by

$$P_k(c_1, c_2) = \begin{cases} 1, & c_1^2 + c_2^2 \geqslant D^2 \\ \min\limits_{u_k} \int P_{k+1}(c_1', c_2')\, p(\xi_k)\, d\xi_k, & c_1^2 + c_2^2 < D^2 \end{cases} \tag{5}$$

where

$$\begin{aligned} c_1' &= c_1 + f_1(c_1, c_2) \\ c_2' &= c_2 + f_2(c_1, c_2) + u_k + \xi_k \end{aligned} \tag{6}$$

for $c_1 = x_1(k)$ and $c_2 = x_2(k)$.

B. Derivation of Optimal Control Policy

Suppose that the probability density function $p(\xi)$ satisfies the following assumptions:

(i) $p(\xi)$ is differentiable and unimodal;

(ii) $0 < \int_{a-b}^{a-b} p(\xi)\, d\xi$ for any finite $a, b > 0$.

From (3) and (4), $P_N(c_1, c_2)$ is given for all c_1 and c_2. From (5),

$$P_{N-1}(c_1, c_2) = \min_{u_{N-1}} \int P_N(c_1', c_2')\, p(\xi)\, d\xi \tag{7}$$

where (c_1', c_2') is related to (c_1, c_2) by (6).

From (3) and (4) the integrand P_N in (7) is one whenever

$$c_1'^2 + c_2'^2 \geqslant D^2 \tag{8}$$

and zero otherwise.

From (6) the set of ξ_{N-1} values for which (8) is satisfied is obtained by solving the inequality

$$(c_1 + f_1(c_1, c_2))^2 + (c_2 + f_2(c_1, c_2) + u_{N-1} + \xi_{N-1})^2 \geqslant D^2$$

where

$$c_1 = x_1(N-1) \quad \text{and} \quad c_2 = x_2(N-1)$$

This inequality for ξ_{N-1} can be solved explicitly and the situation of (8) is true for ξ_{N-1} satisfying the inequalities

$$\xi_{N-1} < \xi^1_{N-1} \qquad \text{or} \qquad \xi_{N-1} > \xi^2_{N-1}$$

where

$$\begin{aligned} \xi^1_{N-1} &\triangleq -u_{N-1} - \alpha_{N-1} - \beta_{N-1} \\ \xi^2_{N-1} &\triangleq -u_{N-1} - \alpha_{N-1} + \beta_{N-1} \end{aligned} \tag{9}$$

and where

$$\begin{aligned} \alpha_i &\triangleq x_2(i) + f_2(x_1(i), x_2(i)) \\ \beta_i &\triangleq \{D^2 - [x_1(i) + f_1(x_1(i), x_2(i))]^2\}^{1/2}, \qquad 0 \leqslant i \leqslant N-1 \end{aligned} \tag{10}$$

Note that $D^2 > (c_1 + f_1(c_1, c_2))^2$ whenever $c_1{}^2 + c_2{}^2 < D^2$ by the assumption on f_1.

Define $G_{N-1}(u_{N-1})$ by

$$G_{N-1}(u_{N-1}) = \int P_N(c_1', c_2')\, p(\xi_{N-1})\, d\xi_{N-1}$$

Then, from (9),

$$G_{N-1}(u_{N-1}) = \int_{-\infty}^{-u_{N-1}-\alpha_{N-1}-\beta_{N-1}} p(\xi_{N-1})\, d\xi_{N-1} + \int_{-u_{N-1}-\alpha_{N-1}+\beta_{N-1}}^{\infty} p(\xi_{N-1})\, d\xi_{N-1} \tag{11}$$

The optimal control at time $N-1$, u^*_{N-1}, is the control which minimizes G_{N-1}. Since G_{N-1} is differentiable with respect to u_{N-1},

$$G'_{N-1}(u^*_{N-1}) = 0$$

From (10) and (11),

$$\begin{aligned} G_{N-1}(u_{N-1}) &= -p(-u_{N-1} - \alpha_{N-1} - \beta_{N-1}) + p(-u_{N-1} - \alpha_{N-1} + \beta_{N-1}) \\ &= \int_{-u_{N-1}-\alpha_{N-1}-\beta_{N-1}}^{-u_{N-1}-\alpha_{N-1}+\beta_{N-1}} p'(\xi_{N-1})\, d\xi_{N-1} \end{aligned} \tag{12}$$

where p' exists by assumption.

Equation (11) can be written as

$$G_{N-1}(u_{N-1}) = \int_{-\infty}^{\infty} \phi_{N-1}(\xi + u_{N-1})\, p'(\xi)\, d\xi \tag{13}$$

where

$$\phi_{N-1}(\xi + u_{N-1}) \triangleq \begin{cases} 1, & -\alpha_{N-1} - \beta_{N-1} \leqslant \xi \leqslant -\alpha_{N-1} + \beta_{N-1} \\ 0, & \text{otherwise} \end{cases}$$

Since $\phi_{N-1} \geqslant 0$ and $p'(x)$ changes its sign from plus to minus once somewhere on the real axis because $p(x)$ is unimodal by assumption, G'_{N-1} changes its sign from minus to plus once as u_{N-1} varies from $-\infty$ to $+\infty$.

Therefore, there is a unique u^*_{N-1} at which G'_{N-1} is zero. From (7) and (11), p_{N-1} is obtained as

$$P_{N-1}(x_1(N-1), x_2(N-1))$$
$$= \begin{cases} 1, & x_1^2(N-1) + x_2^2(N-1) \geqslant D^2 \\ 1 - \int_{-u^*_{N-1}-\alpha_{N-1}-\beta_{N-1}}^{-u^*_{N-1}-\alpha_{N-1}+\beta_{N-1}} p(\xi)\, d\xi, & x_1^2(N-1) + x_2^2(N-1) < D^2 \end{cases} \tag{14}$$

Let us next derive $P_{N-2}(x_1, x_2)$. From (5) and (14),

$$P_{N-2}(c_1, c_2) = \begin{cases} 1 & \text{for } c_1^2 + c_2^2 \geqslant D^2 \\ \min\limits_{u_{N-2}} \int P_{N-1}(c_1', c_2')\, p(\xi)\, d\xi & \text{for } c_1^2 + c_2^2 < D^2 \end{cases} \tag{15}$$

Define

$$G_{N-2}(u_{N-2}) = \int P_{N-1}(c_1', c_2')\, p(\xi)\, d\xi \tag{16}$$

Noting again that $(c_1')^2 + (c_2')^2 > D^2$ for certain ξ values, (16) can be written as

$$G_{N-2}(u_{N-2}) = \int_{-\infty}^{-u_{N-2}-\alpha_{N-2}-\beta_{N-2}} p(\xi)\, d\xi + \int_{-u_{N-2}-\alpha_{N-2}+\beta_{N-2}}^{\infty} p(\xi)\, d\xi$$
$$+ \int_{-u_{N-2}-\alpha_{N-2}-\beta_{N-2}}^{-u_{N-2}-\alpha_{N-2}+\beta_{N-2}} P_{N-1}(c_1', c_2')\, p(\xi)\, d\xi \tag{17}$$

where α_{N-2} and β_{N-2} are defined by (10).

Differentiating (17) with respect to u_{N-2},

$$G'_{N-2}(u_{N-2}) = -p(-u_{N-2} - \alpha_{N-2} - \beta_{N-2}) + p(-u_{N-2} - \alpha_{N-2} + \beta_{N-2})$$
$$- P_{N-1}(\bar{c}_1', \bar{c}_2')\, p(-u_{N-2} - \alpha_{N-2} + \beta_{N-2})$$
$$+ P_{N-1}(\tilde{c}_1', \tilde{c}_2')\, p(-u_{N-2} - \alpha_{N-2} - \beta_{N-2})$$
$$+ \int_{-u_{N-2}-\alpha_{N-2}-\beta_{N-2}}^{-u_{N-2}-\alpha_{N-2}+\beta_{N-2}} \frac{\partial P_{N-1}}{\partial u_{N-1}}\, p(\xi)\, d\xi \tag{18}$$

where $\bar{c}_1'$ and $\bar{c}_2'$ are c_1' and c_2' with ξ given by the upper limit of the integration. $\tilde{c}_1'$ and $\tilde{c}_2'$ are similarly defined with ξ given by the lower limit of the integration.

Since u and ξ enter into the arguments of P_{N-1} symmetrically, i.e., since

$$\frac{\partial P_{N-1}}{\partial u_{N-1}} = \frac{\partial P_{N-1}}{\partial \xi_{N-1}}$$

we have

$$\int_\gamma^\delta \frac{\partial P_{N-1}}{\partial u_{N-1}} p(\xi)\, d\xi = P_{N-1}\, p(\xi) \Big|_\gamma^\delta - \int_\gamma^\delta P_{N-1}\, p'(\xi)\, d\xi \tag{19}$$

for any γ and δ. From (18) and (19),

$$\begin{aligned} G'_{N-2} &= -p(-u_{N-2} - \alpha_{N-2} - \beta_{N-2}) + p(-u_{N-2} - \alpha_{N-2} + \beta_{N-2}) \\ &\quad - \int_{-u_{N-2}-\alpha_{N-2}-\beta_{N-2}}^{-u_{N-2}-\alpha_{N-2}+\beta_{N-2}} P_{N-1}(c_1', c_2')\, p'(\xi)\, d\xi \\ &= \int_{-\infty}^{\infty} \phi_{N-2}(u_{N-2} + \xi)\, p'(\xi)\, d\xi \end{aligned} \tag{20}$$

where

$$\phi_{N-2}(\xi + u_{N-2}) \triangleq \begin{cases} 1 - P_{N-1}(c_1', c_2'), & -\alpha_{N-2} - \beta_{N-2} \leqslant \xi \leqslant -\alpha_{N-2} + \beta_{N-2} \\ 0, & \text{otherwise} \end{cases} \tag{21}$$

By arguments paralleling those used in establishing the existence of the unique u_{N-1}^*, G_{N-2}' vanishes for the unique u_{N-2}^*.*

From (15), (16), and (17),

$$P_{N-2}(c_1, c_2) = \begin{cases} 1, & c_1^2 + c_2^2 \geqslant D^2 \\ 1 - \displaystyle\int_{-u_{N-2}^*-\alpha_{N-2}-\beta_{N-2}}^{-u_{N-2}^*-\alpha_{N-2}+\beta_{N-2}} P_{N-1}(c_1', c_2')\, p(\xi)\, d\xi, & c_1^2 + c_2^2 < D^2 \end{cases} \tag{22}$$

where u_{N-2}^* is the zero of (20) and where $c_1 = x_1(N-2)$, $c_2 = x_2(N-2)$, and c_1' and c_2' are related to c_1 and c_2 by (6).

* See, for example, Ref. 89b.

It is now clear that $P_k(c_1, c_2)$ can be expressed quite analogously to (14) or (22) where the optimal control u_k^* is determined as the unique zero of

$$G_k'(u_k) = \int_{-\infty}^{\infty} \phi_k(u_k + \xi)\, p'(\xi)\, d\xi \tag{23}$$

where

$$\phi_k(\xi + u_k) \triangleq \begin{cases} 1 - P_{k+1}(c_1', c_2') \geqslant 0, & -\alpha_k - \beta_k \leqslant \xi \leqslant -\alpha_k + \beta_k \\ 0, & \text{otherwise} \end{cases} \tag{24}$$

C. Extensions

Certain extensions of the results in Section B are almost immediate. The assumption of identically distributed random variables can be dropped by using $p_k(\xi_k)$ instead of $p(\xi_k)$ in (23), where $p_k(\cdot)$ is the probability density function of ξ_k.

The control variable u_k can be taken to be constrained $|u_k| \leqslant m_k$. Then, $G_k'(u_k)$ may not become zero for any $|u_k| \leqslant m_k$. Denote the zero of G_k' by $\bar{u}_k$.

We now have the optimal control given by

$$u_k^* = \begin{cases} m_k, & m_k < \bar{u}_k \\ \bar{u}_k, & |\bar{u}_k| \leqslant m_k \\ -m_k, & \bar{u}_k < -m_k \end{cases}$$

As for the expression of P_k we have, instead of (22),

$$P_k(c_1, c_2) = 1 \qquad \text{for} \quad c_1^2 + c_2^2 > D^2$$

$$P_k(c_1, c_2) = 1 - \int_{-m_k-\alpha_k-\beta_k}^{-m_k-\alpha_k+\beta_k} [1 - P_{k+1}(c_1', c_2 + f_2(c_1, c_2) + m_k + \xi)]\, p(\xi)\, d\xi$$

$$\text{for} \quad c_1^2 + c_2^2 < D^2, \quad m_k < \bar{u}_k$$

$$P_k(c_1, c_2) = 1 - \int_{-\bar{u}_k-\alpha_k-\beta_k}^{-\bar{u}_k-\alpha_k+\beta_k} [1 - P_{k+1}(c_1', c_2 + f_2(c_1, c_2) + \bar{u}_k + \xi)]\, p(\xi)\, d\xi$$

$$\text{for} \quad c_1^2 + c_2^2 < D^2, \quad |\bar{u}_k| < m_k$$

$$P_k(c_1, c_2) = 1 - \int_{m_k-\alpha_k-\beta_k}^{m_k-\alpha_k+\beta_k} [1 - P_{k+1}(c_1', c_2 + f_2(c_1, c_2) - m_k + \xi)]\, p(\xi)\, d\xi$$

$$\text{for} \quad c_1^2 + c_2^2 < D, \quad \bar{u}_k < -m_k$$

where $c_1 = x_1(k)$, $c_2 = x_2(k)$, c_1' and c_2' are given by (6), and α_k, β_k are given by (10).

The development in Section B allows us to see that a similar recursion equation for P_k is possible when the probability density function for ξ contains an unknown parameter. Because of the perfect observation assumption, we need only to replace $p(\xi)$ in the equations for P_k and G_k' by

$$\int p(\xi \mid \theta)\, p(\theta \mid x^{k-1})\, d\theta$$

It is also easy to see that the plant equation need not be given by (1), nor need the system be two-dimensional.

The properties of (1) that have been used are:

(i) $\| x(i+1) \|^2 \geqslant D^2$ can be solved for $\xi(i)$ so that the probability of ξ satisfying the inequality can be evaluated from $p(\xi)$, where $\| \cdot \|$ is the Euclidean norm;

(ii) $\partial P_{k+1}/\partial u_k$ and $\partial P_{k+1}/\partial \xi_k$ are related by a simple equation.

These two conditions are met by a large variety of linear and nonlinear equations.

Other implicit criterion functions are possible for this type of problem, such as the maximum expected deviation. A computational work with this criterion function has been carried out by M. Aoki for a system satisfying Van der Pol equations for both purely stochastic and adaptive systems.[7]

2. Min-Max Control Policies

A priori probability distribution functions must be known or assumed before Bayes' optimal control policies can be obtained for problems with unknown or random parameters. For some problems the assumption of such a priori distribution functions is not valid. Even if valid, such a priori distribution functions may not be available and choice of a priori distribution functions may be arbitrary. The empirical Bayes approach[118] or other considerations[79] mentioned in Chapter VI eliminate this arbitrariness to some degree but not completely.

In such cases, we may want to use control policies which do not assume any a priori distribution functions for the unknown parameter θ of the problems. The class of control policies known as min-max control policies does not require any assumption on the distribution functions of θ on the parameter space Θ. In Example 8 of Section 2,I of Chapter I, we have already encountered one min-max control policy.

In this section, we gather a few facts on min-max control policies when the probability distribution functions for the random noises in the plant equations contain unknown parameters θ. For more detailed exposition of the subject, the reader is referred to Blackwell and Girshick,[29] Ferguson,[58a] and Sworder.[133,134]

A. Equalizer Control Policies

Given a criterion function J, it can be regarded as a function of the random variables $\xi_0, \ldots, \xi_{N-1}$ and of a control policy ϕ.

Define

$$H(\phi, \theta) = E\ J(x^N, u^{N-1})$$

where the expectation is taken with respect to ξ^{N-1} and x_0, and where ϕ is a member of the admissible class of controls, Φ. The detailed structure of this admissible set differs depending on the types of control policies being considered such as open-loop or closed-loop control policies. The fact EJ is a functional of ϕ and θ does not change. It is assumed throughout this section that $H(\phi, \theta)$ is a convex in ϕ for every $\theta \in \Theta$.

Denote the set of all probability distribution functions (including the degenerate distribution functions which assign probability 1 to a point in Θ) of θ over Θ by $\Theta^{\#}$. An element of $\Theta^{\#}$ is denoted by $\theta^{\#}$.[*] In a similar manner, the class of randomized control policies is denoted by $\Phi^{\#}$ and its element by $\phi^{\#}$.

Define

$$H(\phi^{\#}, \theta^{\#}) = E_{\phi,\theta}\, H(\phi, \theta)$$

where the expectation operation is with respect to ϕ and θ with the distribution functions $\phi^{\#}$ and $\theta^{\#}$, respectively.

Define the max-cost of a randomized control $\phi^{\#}$ by

$$\sup_{\theta^{\#} \in \Theta^{\#}} H(\phi^{\#}, \theta^{\#})$$

Min-Max Control Policy. If there exists a control policy $\phi_0^{\#} \in \Phi^{\#}$ such that

$$\sup_{\theta^{\#} \in \Theta^{\#}} H(\phi_0^{\#}, \theta^{\#}) = \inf_{\phi^{\#} \in \Phi^{\#}} \sup_{\theta^{\#} \in \Theta^{\#}} H(\phi^{\#}, \theta^{\#})$$

then $\phi_0^{\#}$ is called a min-max control policy.

---

* Since we have used an asterisk to indicate optimality such as u_i^* being the optimal control at time i, we use a somewhat unconventional symbol, #.

Bayes Control Policy. In terms of this set of notations, a randomized optimal Bayes control policy $\phi_0^{\#}$, if it exists, is given by

$$H(\phi_0^{\#}, \theta^{\#}) = \inf_{\phi^{\#}} H(\phi^{\#}, \theta^{\#})$$

where $\theta^{\#}$ is the assumed (or known) probability distribution function for θ. If, for every $\epsilon > 0$, there exists $\theta_\epsilon^{\#} \in \Theta^{\#}$ such that a given control policy $\phi_0^{\#}$ comes within ϵ of $\inf H(\phi^{\#}, \theta_\epsilon^{\#})$, then $\phi_0^{\#}$ is called an extended Bayes or ϵ-Bayes control policy.[29]

Equalizer Control Policy. If there exists a control policy $\phi^{\#}$ such that

$$H(\phi^{\#}, \theta) = \text{constant}$$

for all $\theta \in \Theta$, then it is called an equalizer control policy.

The usefulness of equalizer policies may be illustrated by the following theorem.

Theorem. If $\phi_0^{\#} \in \Phi^{\#}$ is an equalizer policy and is extended Bayes, then it is a min-max control policy.

If Θ contains only a finite number of elements θ_i, $i = 1,..., M$, then, by considering the convex set $\{H(\phi^{\#}, \theta_i), i = 1,..., M, \phi^{\#} \in \Phi^{\#}\}$, a stronger result can be obtained.

Theorem. If Θ contains a finite element, then there always exists a least-favorable (worst case) distribution function $\theta^{\#}$ and a min-max control policy $\phi^{\#} \in \Phi^{\#}$ exists which is a Bayes control policy with respect to $\theta^{\#}$. (See Ferguson[58a] or Sworder[133] for proof.)

3. Extensions and Future Problems

We have suggested in several places of this book problems requiring further investigations. Some of the suggested problems are such that they can be treated by minor extensions or modifications of the techniques developed in this book. Optimal control of plants with delay, of systems with intermittent observations, or of systems with delay in the observation mechanisms are of such a type and are discussed to some extent in Section 4 of Chapter II.

Random errors in the control actuations have not been discussed explicitly as such. What we have studied in this regard is the optimal control problems where the gains of the control variables are assumed to be random variables or unknown constants.

It is clear, however, that the same approach can be utilized to study the effects of random actuation errors (perhaps with unknown statistics). For example, when the plant equation is originally given by a linear difference equation $x_{i+1} = A_i x_i + B_i u_i$, both the fixed component of the actuation error and the component of the actuation error proportional to control can be considered by modifying the plant equation to

$$x_{i+1} = A_i x_i + (B_i + \Delta B_i) u_i + \xi_i$$

where ξ_i and ΔB_i are independent random variables. The random variable ξ_i represents the fixed actuation error and $\Delta B_i u_i$ gives rise to the proportional actuation error. Also see Orford[109]

Another problem in this class is the optimal control problem of systems where system parameters may change randomly at random times.[16,75] This problem is sketched in Section A. The extreme cases where parameter values may change at each time instant (either independently or in some dependent manner) and where the parameter values remain constant throughout the control periods have already been discussed. See, for example, Section 2 of Chapter II, and Chapters III and IV.

There are other problems, however, which seem to require considerable extensions or modifications of the method presented in this book.

For control processes that run indefinitely, the criterion function we have used in this book, $J = \sum_1^N W_i(x_i, u_{i-1})$, may be meaningless without additional assumptions on W_i, such as the incorporation of the future discount factor or time-averaging factors. Also, the method of deriving optimal control policies developed in this book is not suitable for processes of infinite duration.* Some results for this class of problems can be found in Baum,[19] Bellman,[20] Blackwell,[32] Drenick and Shaw,[48] Eaton and Zadeh,[52] Howard,[74a] and Strauch,[131] for example.

Consider, as another example, control problems where the terminations of control depend on random events. For such problems, the control durations are also random.

Stochastic version of time optimal problems, pursuit and rendezvous problems in noisy environments, are typical of this class of problems with random control durations. See also Dubins and Savage,[50] Eaton and Zadeh.[52]

In discussing optimal control of such problems, we may take a criterion function to be

$$J = \sum_{i=1}^{N} W_i(x_i, u_{i-1}; N)$$

* Instead of the usual backward dynamic programming, a forward dynamic programming method may be used.

where it is now assumed that N is a random variable and the cost of control at stage i depends not only on x_i and u_{i-1} but also on N.

For example, in a final-value problem where a cost is associated only to a final state, the cost at stage i will definitely be a function of N. Some preliminary investigation of this problem has been made by R. A. Baker, and will be the subject of Section B.

A. Systems with Parameters which Change Randomly at Random Times

In Chapters II–IV, we have discussed the method of deriving optimal control policies for systems where system parameters appearing in plant and observation equations and statistics of the probability distribution functions are constant (may be unknown) or random variables for each time constant.

In this section, we will indicate how the method can be extended to derive optimal control policies for systems whose parameters may change their values randomly at random times. An example of such a system is given by the system which obeys the equations

$$x_{i+1} = Ax_i + Bu_i$$
$$y_i = Hx_i + \eta_i$$

where B and H are known and the noise η has a known probability distribution and where it is assumed that the matrix A is unknown and is such that it may change its value at some random time during the control. A special case where A is an independent random variable for each time instant with common distribution function has been discussed in Chapter II. Another special case is discussed by Rosenbrock[120] where the measurements are exact, where there are two possible values for A, and where A is known to change its value exactly once during the control period.

Howard[75] discussed similar problems for memoryless systems, i.e., for systems without dynamics where the underlying statistical parameters of the process may change from time to time.

We will illustrate the method to derive optimal control policies for systems described by

$$x_{i+1} = F_i(x_i, u_i, \xi_i, \alpha_i)$$
$$y_i = G_i(x_i, \eta_i)$$
$$J = \sum_i^N W_i(x_i, u_{i-1}), \qquad W_i \geqslant 0$$

where the same set of symbols is used as before. The plant parameter α is assumed to be the parameter which may change randomly from time to time.

It is assumed that there are no other parameters in the problem and that the noise processes $\{\xi_i\}$ and $\{\eta_i\}$ are all assumed to have known probability distribution functions.

The only additional piece of information we need in deriving optimal control policies is the description of the $\{\alpha\}$-process. Assume that α undergoes random changes at discrete time instants $0 < n_1 < n_2 < \cdots < n_{\mu_N} \leqslant N$ such that the intervals between the successive changes are independently and identically distributed random variables with common known probability distribution, $P(\tau)$.*

Define

$$\begin{aligned} \tau_0 &= n_1 > 0 \\ \tau_i &= n_{i+1} - n_i\,, \qquad 1 \leqslant i \leqslant \mu_N - 1 \end{aligned}$$

where μ_k is the total number of parameter value changes in k time instants, $\mu_k \leqslant k$. The new parameter value after each change is assumed to be chosen independently from the common known distribution, $p(\alpha)$.

The main recursion equations remain unchanged:

$$\gamma_i^* = \min_{u_{i-1}}[\lambda_i + E(\gamma_{i+1}^* \mid y^{i-1}, u^{i-1})]$$

where

$$\lambda_i = E(W_i \mid y^{i-1}, u^{i-1}), \qquad i = 1,\ldots, N$$

The auxiliary recursion equations to generate $p(x_i\,, \alpha_i \mid y^i)$ and $p(y_{i+1} \mid y_i\,, u_i)$ must now be modified to include the possibility that α may change. Since the pattern of the parameter change intervals τ^{μ_i-1} completely specifies the possible changes in α up to time i, and since $p(\alpha^i \mid \tau^{\mu_i-1})$ is computable by the independence assumption of α values after parameter value changes occur, $P(\tau^{\mu_i-1} \mid y^i, u^i)$ is the only new probability expression needed in computing $p(x_i\,, \alpha_i \mid y^i)$. The reader is invited to derive it for himself. The detail is found in Aoki.[16]

B. Optimal Control Systems with Random Stopping Times

a. *Statement of the Problem*

Consider a system described by the system and observation equations

$$\begin{aligned} x_{i+1} &= F_i(x_i\,, u_i\,, \xi_i) \\ y_i &= G_i(x_i\,, \eta_i) \end{aligned}$$

---

* The random variable τ takes only integer values.

The $\{\alpha\}$-process is a special case of a general stochastic process known as a semi-Markov process.[114a]

where y_i is an observable and u_i a control. Assume that this system operates from $i = 0$ to $i = N$, where N is a random variable. The cost is a function of x^i, u^{i-1}, and N, and may be expressed as

$$J = \sum_{i=1}^{N} W_{i,N}(x_i , u_{i-1})$$

We wish to find the control policy that will minimize the expected cost of J.

We shall assume that we know the distributions of all of the random variables, x_0, ξ_i, η_i, and N. In particular, we know the conditional distribution of N, conditioned on $N > i$, the observable vectors y^i, and an auxiliary observable γ_i. To simplify notation, we shall write

$$\Pr(N = j \mid N > i, y^i, \zeta_i) = P_{j/i}$$

We shall restrict our problem to the following two special cases:

Case A. $\Pr(N > M) = 0$ for some fixed M;

Case B. $\Pr(N = j \mid \zeta_i , y^i, N > i) = \Pr(N = j \mid N > i)$.

In Case A, we shall find a general procedure following the approach of this book. In Case B, we show that the problem can be transformed into one in which there is an infinite running time and a new cost function J', which is not a function of stopping time. If the plant and observation equations are linear, with the only random variables (besides stopping time) being additive noise, and if the cost function is quadratic, that is if

$$\begin{aligned} x_{i+1} &= A_i x_i + B_i u_i + \xi_i \\ y_i &= C_i x_i + \eta_i \\ W_{i,N} &= (u_{i-1} , G_{N,i} u_{i-1}) + (x_i , H_{N,i} x_i) \end{aligned}$$

where A_i, B_i, and C_i are known and ξ_i and η_i are independent random variables with known distributions, then we can, formally, write a solution to the optimal problem.

b. *Case A* [$Pr(N > M) = 0$]

Suppose the system has survived through $i = M - 1$ steps. Then we know that we have exactly one more step to go. The problem is then the same as the case of a known stopping time and we have already solved that problem. Hence there is an explicit expression for u_{M-1} as a function of u^{M-2} and y^{M-1} that will minimize the expected cost.

Now suppose we have survived $M - 2$ steps. Now there are two possibilities: either the stopping time is $N = M - 1$ with probability $P_{M-1/M-2}$, or $N = M$ with probability $P_{N/M-2}$. If the former holds, the additional cost will be $W_{M-1,M-1}$; in the latter case it will be $W_{M-1,M} + W_{M,M}$. Hence, taking the conditional expectation with respect to stopping time, the conditional expectation of the last two-stage cost ΔJ is given by

$$E_N[\Delta J \mid \zeta_{M-2}] = P_{M-1/M-2}W_{M-1,M-1} + P_{M/M-2}W_{M-1,M} + P_{M/M-2}W_{M,M}$$

$W_{M,M}$ is a function of x_M, u_{M-1}; u_{M-1} is a function of y^{M-1}, u^{M-2}; x_M is a function of x_{M-1}, u_{M-1}, ξ_{M-1} and hence a function of x_{M-1}, y^{M-1}, u^{M-2}, ξ_{M-1}. Hence $E_N \Delta J$ is a function of ζ_{M-2} (because P is a function of ζ_{M-2}), y^{M-2}, u^{M-3}, which are observables, plus y_{M-1}, ξ_{M-1}, x_{M-1}, which are not observables, and also, of course, u_{M-2}. In principle, we can find the probability distribution

$$p(y_{M-1}, \xi_{M-1}, x_{M-1} \mid y^{M-2}, u^{M-2})$$

and hence

$$E_{N,y_{M-1},\xi_{M-1},x_{M-1}}[\Delta J \mid y^{M-2}, u^{M-2}, \zeta_{M-2}]$$

Then the optimal policy is to choose u_{M-2} to minimize this conditional expectation. Now we see that this u_{M-2} is a function of y^{M-2}, u^{M-3}, and ζ_{M-2}.

Going back another step, we have

$$\begin{aligned} E_N(\Delta J \mid \zeta_{M-3}) = {} & P_{M-2/M-3}W_{M-2,M-2} + P_{M-1/M-3}W_{M-2,M-1} \\ & + P_{M/M-3}W_{M-2,M} + P_{M-1/M-3}W_{M-1,M-1} + P_{M/M-3}W_{M-1,M} \\ & + P_{M/M-3}W_{M,M} \end{aligned}$$

This expression is a function of the observables ζ_{M-3}, y^{M-3}, u^{M-4}, the nonobservables y_{M-2}, y_{M-1}, ξ_{M-2}, ξ_{M-1}, x_{M-2}; and on u_{M-3}. Again we find the conditional probabilities of the nonobservables conditioned on the observables and u_{M-3}. Then we find the conditional expectation of the additional cost after $M - 3$ stages conditioned on the same variables. Again, we choose u_{M-3} to minimize this conditional expectation. We see again that the control u_{M-3} is a function of the observables y^{M-3}, u^{M-4}, and ζ_{M-3}.

The process continues with the general expression

$$E_N[\Delta J \mid \zeta_i] = \sum_{j=i+1}^{M} P_{j/i} W_{i+1,j} + \sum_{j=i+2}^{M} P_{j/i} W_{i+2,j} + \cdots$$

$$+ P_{M/i} W_{M,M}$$

$$= \sum_{k=1}^{M-1} \sum_{j=i+k}^{M} P_{j/i} W_{i+k,j}$$

which is a function of the observables y^i, u^{i-1}, ζ_i, the nonobservables $y_{i+1}, y_{i+2}, \ldots, y_{M-1}, \xi_i, \xi_{i+1}, \ldots, \xi_{M-1}, \zeta_{i+1}, \zeta_{i+2}, \ldots, \zeta_{M-1}, x_i$, and the control u_i. The conditional expectation of ΔJ, conditioned on the observables and u_i, is found and u_i chosen to minimize this expectation.

As in the case of known stopping times, the practical problem is finding the conditional probabilities required. The process is only slightly more difficult by the inclusion of the extra variable ζ, which determines the conditional distribution of stopping times.

c. *Case B*

Now let us consider the special case where the only additional information about the stopping time we have at the ith step over what we know at the first step is that the stopping time is greater than i.

That is, ζ_i disappears for this problem and we have

$$\Pr(N = j \mid y^i, N > i) = \Pr(N = j \mid N > i)$$

$$= \begin{cases} \dfrac{\Pr(N = j)}{\Pr(N > i)} & \text{if } j > i \\ 0 & \text{otherwise} \end{cases}$$

Now, if we examine $E_N[\Delta J \mid N > n]$ and where $\Delta J =$ cost from n on, we have

$$E_N[\Delta J \mid N > n] = \frac{1}{\Pr(N > n)} \Big[\sum_{i=n+1} \Pr(i = N)\, W_{n+1,i}$$

$$+ \sum_{i=n+2} \Pr(i = N)\, W_{n+2,i} + \cdots \Big]$$

$$= \frac{1}{\Pr(N > n)} \sum_{k=1} \sum_{i=n+k} \Pr(i = N)\, W_{N-k,i}$$

If we multiplied all of the cost by a constant, we would change nothing. Hence, once we get to the nth stage, we can use

$$E_N[\Delta J' \mid N > n] = \sum_{k=1} \sum_{i=n+k} \Pr(i = N)\, W_{n+k,i}$$

But then

$$E_N[\Delta J] = E_N[\Delta J' \mid N > n]$$

That is, the expression for the expected cost function from n on is the same as from time zero.

This shows us that we can use a single equivalent cost function in which the implicit dependence on the random stopping time disappears. That is, we note that

$$E_N[J] = \sum_{k=1} \sum_{i=k} \Pr(i = N)\, W_{k,i} = \sum_{k=1} W_k'$$

where

$$W_k' = \sum_{i=k} \Pr(i = N)\, W_{k,i}$$

Note that we have left off the upper limits of summation in all cases. We can let this upper limit go to infinity.

Now our optimal control policy is that policy which is optimal for the system given and a cost function of

$$J' = \sum_{k-1}^{\infty} W_k'(x_k\,,\, u_{k-1})$$

As an example, suppose $W_{k,i} = x_i^2 \delta_{k,i}$ (that is least squares in the final state). Then

$$W_k' = \sum_{i-k}^{\infty} P(i = N)\, W_{k,i} - \sum_{i=k}^{\infty} P(i = N)\, x_k^2 \delta_{k,i}$$

$$= P(k = N)\, x_k^2$$

or, if

$$W_{k,i} = \lambda x_k^2 \delta_{k,i} + u_{k-1}^2$$

then

$$W_k' = \sum_{i=k}^{\infty} P(i = N)\, \lambda x_i^2 \delta_{k,i} + \sum_{i=k}^{\infty} (P = i)\, u_{k-1}^2$$

$$= \lambda\, P(k = N)\, x_k^2 + P(N \geqslant k)\, u_{k-1}^2$$

Now, the obvious difficulty is that we have an equivalent system with an infinite time duration. This precludes the possibility of going to the last stage and working back.

If we have linear plant and observation equations with additive independent noise and a quadratic cost function, the problem is solvable. This is because we know the optimal policy is the same as in the deterministic case except we use $E[x_n \mid y^n]$ instead of x_n. The deterministic linear system of infinite duration can be solved by variational techniques and hence our problem can be solved.[20]

Even in this special case, we may not be able to find explicit expressions for $E(x_n \mid y^n)$. If the observation equation is noise free, or if the system is noise free and the observation noise is Gaussian, we can solve the problem in principle.

Appendix I

Some Useful Definitions, Facts, and Theorems from Probability Theory

In order to facilitate the reading of this book (especially of Chapters VI and VIII) several facts and theorems from the theory of probability are collected here together with some of their intuitive explanations. For more detailed and systematic accounts see, for example, Doob[47a] or Loève.[102]

PROBABILITY TRIPLE

In order to be able to discuss probabilities of certain events, three things must be specified. They are.

(i) the sample space, Ω;

(ii) the class of events to which probabilities can be assigned, $\mathscr{F}$. Events in the class $\mathscr{F}$ are certain subsets of the sample space Ω;

(iii) probability measure P (defined on $\mathscr{F}$) so that, to any event A in the class $\mathscr{F}$, a real nonnegative number PA, $0 \leqslant PA \leqslant 1$, is assigned, with $P\Omega = 1$.

These three things are collectively referred to as a probability triple $(\Omega, \mathscr{F}, P)$.

Since each event in $\mathscr{F}$ must have a probability assigned to it unambiguously, $\mathscr{F}$ cannot be any arbitrary collection of subset of Ω but must have a certain structure.

For example, in a single coin tossing, the sample space Ω is composed of two points: H (for head) and T (for tail). The class $\mathscr{F}$ consists of four subsets, $\{(\phi), (H), (T), (H, T)\}$, where ϕ denotes a null set. When we say a coin is fair, we mean that

$$PH = PT = \tfrac{1}{2}$$

Intuitively, $\mathscr{F}$ includes all the events to which probabilities can be assigned. If an event A has a probability p, then one also wants to talk about the probability of $\bar{A}$ (the event that A does not occur) $1 - p$; i.e., if $A \in \mathscr{F}$, then $\mathscr{F}$ must be such that $\bar{A} \in \mathscr{F}$. If A_1 and A_2 are in $\mathscr{F}$, then one wants to discuss the event $A_1 \cap A_2$ (the event that A_1 and A_2 occur simultaneously), the event $A_1 \cup A_2$ (the event that at least one of A_1 and A_2 occur), etc. Namely, if $A_1, A_2 \in \mathscr{F}$, then $\mathscr{F}$ must be such that $\mathscr{F}$ contains $A_i \cup A_j$, $A_i \cap A_j$, $\bar{A}_i \cup A_j$, $\bar{A}_i \cap A_j$, $\bar{A}_i \cup \bar{A}_j$, and $\bar{A}_i \cap \bar{A}_j$, $i, j = 1, 2$.

Such a class is known as a field. Since we also want to discuss probabilities of events which are limits of certain other events such as $\lim_{n\to\infty} \bigcup_1^n A_i$ and $\lim_{n\to\infty} \bigcap_1^n A_i$, $A_i \in \mathscr{F}$, $i = 1, 2, \ldots$, $\mathscr{F}$ is usually taken to be a σ field.

Example. Given a set $A \subset \Omega$, $\mathscr{F} = \{\phi, A, \Omega - A, \Omega\}$ is the minimal σ field containing A (i.e., the smallest σ field containing A).

Random Variables

A random variable X (abbreviated as r.v. X) is a mapping from Ω to the extended real line $\bar{R}$ (the real line plus $\pm\infty$) such that

$$X^{-1}A \in \mathscr{F}$$

for all $A \in$ Borel field (σ field on $\bar{R}$) where X^{-1} is the inverse mapping of X; i.e., $X^{-1}A = \{\omega; X(\omega) \in A, \omega \in \Omega\}$. Such an X is called $\mathscr{F}$ measurable.

We denote by $\sigma(X) = X^{-1}$ (Borel field) the smallest σ field of subsets of Ω with respect to which X is measurable.

Independence

Let $\Sigma_1, \Sigma_2, \ldots, \Sigma_n$ be sub-σ-fields of $\mathscr{F}$, i.e., Σ_i is a σ field such that $\Sigma_i \subset \mathscr{F}$, $1 \leqslant i \leqslant n$.

They are called independent if and only if

$$P\left(\bigcap_1^n A_i\right) = \prod_1^n P(A_i) \qquad \text{for arbitrary} \quad A_i \in \Sigma_i, \quad 1 \leqslant i \leqslant n$$

A sequence of sub-σ-fields of $\mathscr{F}$, Σ_i, $i = 1, \ldots$, is independent if $\Sigma_1, \ldots, \Sigma_n$ are independent for all $n = 1, 2, \ldots$. Random variables $X_1, X_2, \ldots$ are independent if and only if $\sigma(X_1), \sigma(X_2), \ldots$ are independent.

EXPECTATION

An indicator function (also called a set indicator) I_A is defined to be

$$I_A(\omega) = \begin{cases} 1, & \omega \in A \\ 0, & \omega \notin A \end{cases}$$

The expectation of I_A is defined to be

$$EI_A = PA$$

A finite linear combination of indicator functions is called a simple function. If

$$X = \sum_{i=1}^{m} a_i I_{A_i} = \sum_{i=1}^{n} b_j I_{B_i}$$

where A_i and B_j are measurable, i.e., A_i, $B_j \in \mathscr{F}$, then the expectation of X is defined to be

$$EX = \sum_{1}^{m} a_i PA_i = \sum_{1}^{n} b_j PB_j$$

If X is a nonnegative random variable, and if $\{X_n\}$ and $\{Y_n\}$ are two sequences of measurable simple functions such that $X_n \uparrow X$ and $Y_n \uparrow Y$ ($X_n \uparrow X$ means that $X_n \leqslant X_{n+1}$ and $\lim_n X_n(\omega) = X(\omega)$, for all $\omega \in \Omega$), then

$$\lim EX_n = \lim EY_n$$

and this common value is defined to be EX (the expectation of X).

The expectation of a random variable X on $(\Omega, \mathscr{F}, P)$ is defined to be

$$EX = EX^+ - EX^-$$

where

$$X^+ = \max(X, 0), \qquad X^- = \max(0, -X)$$

when the right-hand side is meaningful.

EX is also written as

$$EX = \int X \, dP.$$

Absolute Continuity

Let us suppose that two probabilities P and Q are available for the same $(\Omega, \mathscr{F})$.

We say P is absolutely continuous with respect to Q, written as $P \ll Q$, if $Q(A) = 0$ implies $P(A) = 0$.

Radon–Nikodym Theorem. $P \ll Q$ if and only if there exists a measurable function f (written as dP/dQ) such that

(i) $f \geqslant 0$, Q almost everywhere;

(ii) $PA = \int f\, dQ$ for arbitrary $A \in \mathscr{F}$, $\int f\, dQ < \infty$;

(iii) unique Q almost everywhere.

(That is, functions with Properties (i) and (ii) differ at most on a set whose probability is zero computed according to the probability measure Q.)

Example. Consider $(\Omega, \mathscr{F}, P)$ such that Ω is partitioned into four mutually exclusive subsets A_i, $1 \leqslant i \leqslant 4$, $\Omega = \bigcup_{i=1}^4 A_i$, $A_i \cap A_j = \phi$, $i \neq j$:

A_1	A_2
A_3	A_4

Let $\mathscr{F}$ be the σ field generated by this partition. Let P be such that

$$PA_i = p_i > 0, \qquad \sum_{i=1}^{4} p_i = 1$$

Let Q be such that

$$QA_i = q_i > 0, \qquad \sum_1^4 q_i = 1$$

$P \ll Q$ means $\sum_I q_i = 0 \Rightarrow \sum_I p_i = 0$ where I is a subset of $\{1, 2, 3, 4\}$. Since $q_i > 0$, $p_i > 0$ for all i, $1 \leqslant i \leqslant 4$, in the above example, $P \ll Q$ as well as $Q \ll P$ and $dP/dQ = p_i/q_i$ on set A_i, $1 \leqslant i \leqslant 4$.

Conditional Expectation

Let $(\Omega, \mathscr{F}, P)$ be a given probability triple, Σ be a sub-σ-field of $\mathscr{F}$ and X be a random variable such that

$$\int |X|\, dP < \infty \qquad \text{(such an } X \text{ is denoted by } X \in L^1(P))$$

It can be shown by the Radon–Nikodym theorem that there exists a function h such that

(i) h is Σ measurable,

(ii) $\int_A h\, dP = \int_A X\, dP$ for all $A \in \Sigma$,

(iii) h is unique P almost everywhere.

This function h is written as $E(X \mid \Sigma)$ and is called the conditional expectation of X with respect to Σ.

Note that, if $\mathcal{A}$ and $\mathcal{B}$ are two sub-σ-fields of $\mathcal{F}$ such that $\mathcal{A} \subset \mathcal{B}$, then $\int_A E(X \mid \mathcal{A})\, dP = \int_A E(X) \mid \mathcal{B})\, dP$ for all $A \in \mathcal{A}$.

Given two r.v. X and Y, $E(X \mid Y)$ is to be interpreted as

$$E(X \mid \sigma(Y))$$

Martingales

Let $(\Omega, \mathcal{F}, P)$ be a probability triple. Let T be an ordered set (e.g., T is a time axis $T = \{t, t \geqslant 0\}$ or $T = \{0, 1, 2, 3, \ldots\}$). For each $t \in T$, $\mathcal{F}_t$ is a sub-σ-field of $\mathcal{F}$ such that $\mathcal{F}_t \subset \mathcal{F}_s$, $t < s$. Let X_t be a r.v. such that

(i) $E \mid X_t \mid < \infty$,

(ii) X_t is $\mathcal{F}_t$ measurable,

(iii) $\int_A X_t\, dP = \int_A X_s\, dP$ for all $A \in \mathcal{F}_t$, $t < s$.

This can also be stated as

$$E(X_s \mid \mathcal{F}_t) = X_t \qquad P \text{ almost everywhere (a.e.)}$$

When the nondecreasing sequence of σ fields $\{\mathcal{F}_t, t \in T\}$ is not specified, take $\mathcal{F}_t = \sigma(X_t, T \leqslant t)$.

Such $\{X_t, \mathcal{F}_t, t \in T\}$ is called a martingale.

In (iii) if the equality sign is replaced by an inequality sign $\leqslant (\geqslant)$, then $\{X_t, \mathcal{F}_t, t \in T\}$ is called an expectation-increasing (decreasing) martingale or semimartingale.

Examples

Let us consider a fair gambling situation and denote by X_n the capital after n plays. Thus, X_0 is the initial capital. By a "fair" gambling situation we mean

$$E(X_m \mid X_0, \ldots, X_n) = X_n, \qquad m > n$$

where the abbreviated notation of the conditional expectations is used for

$$E(X_m \mid \sigma(X_0, \ldots, X_n))$$

That is, a game is considered fair if the expected capital after m plays, conditioned on the wins and losses of the past n plays ($m > n$), is the same as the current capital X_n. Thus one's capital in a fair gambling situation is a martingale.

As another example of a similar nature, consider

$$X_n = \sum_1^n Y_i$$

where the Y_i are independent, $i \geqslant 1$, with $EY_i = 0$, $i = 1, 2, \ldots$.

Then, for $i < j$, $A \in \sigma(X_0, \ldots, X_i)$,

$$\int_A X_j \, dP = \int_A X_i \, dP$$

since

$$\int_A Y_k \, dP = PA \cdot EY_k = 0, \qquad k = i + 1, \ldots, j.$$

As a final example of martingales, consider a situation where Σ_n is a nondecreasing sequence of sub-σ-fields, $(\Omega, \mathscr{F}, P)$ given. Let $X \in L^1$. Let

$$T = \{1, 2, \ldots, z, z + 1\}$$

where

$$\mathscr{F}_t \triangleq \Sigma_t, \qquad t < z$$

$$\mathscr{F}_z \triangleq \vee_n \mathscr{F}_n \triangleq \sigma\left(\bigcup_n \mathscr{F}_n\right)$$

$$\mathscr{F}_{z+1} \triangleq \mathscr{F}$$

Let

$$X_t = E(X \mid \mathscr{F}_t)$$

Then $\{X_t, \mathscr{F}_t, T\}$ is a martingale.

Subsequences of Martingales

Take $T = \{1, 2, \ldots, N\}$ and assume that $\{(X_i, \mathscr{F}_i), 1 \leqslant i \leqslant N\}$ is a martingale.

A random time τ is called admissible if and only if

$$P(\tau = 1, 2, \ldots, N) = 1, \qquad [\omega : \tau(\omega) = n] \in \mathscr{F}_n$$

Sometimes the set $[\omega: \tau(\omega) = n]$ is written in an abbreviated form as $(\tau = n)$.

Define

$$\mathscr{F}_t = \{A : A \in \mathscr{F}, A \cap (\tau = n) \in \mathscr{F}_n\}$$

Let $\tau_1 \leqslant \tau_2 \leqslant \cdots \leqslant \tau_k \leqslant N$ be admissible, then $(X_{\tau_1}, \mathscr{F}_{\tau_1}),\ldots, (X_{\tau_k}, \mathscr{F}_{\tau_k})$ is a martingale.

Convex Functions of Martingales

Let $(X_t, \mathscr{F}_t, T)$ be a martingale on $(\Omega, \mathscr{F}, P)$.

Let ϕ be a convex function (nondecreasing).

If $\phi(X_{t^*}) \in L^1$, then $\{\phi(X_t), \mathscr{F}_t, t \in T, t \leqslant t^*\}$ is an expectation-increasing martingale.

Inequalities

Chebychev Inequality. Let $X \geqslant 0$, $EX < \infty$, then

$$\Pr[X \geqslant \lambda] \leqslant (1/\lambda)EX.$$

Martingale Inequality. Let $\{X_i, \mathscr{F}_i, 0 \leqslant i \leqslant n\}$ be an expectation-decreasing martingale, where $X_i \geqslant 0$. Then, for $\lambda > 0$,

$$\Pr[\max_{0 \leqslant j \leqslant n} X_j \geqslant \lambda] \leqslant \frac{1}{\lambda} EX_0$$

Let $(X_0, \mathscr{F}_0),\ldots, (X_n, \mathscr{F}_n)$ be an expectation-increasing martingale on $(\Omega, \mathscr{F}, P)$. Let $\lambda > 0$. Then,

$$\Pr[\max_{0 \leqslant j \leqslant n} X_j \geqslant \lambda] \leqslant \frac{1}{\lambda} E \mid X_n \mid$$

(Compare these with the Chebychev inequality.)

Let $\{(X_i, \mathscr{F}_i), i = 0, 1,\ldots\}$ be a martingale on $(\Omega, \mathscr{F}, P)$ such that

$$EX_i^2 < \infty, \qquad i = 0, 1,\ldots$$

Then,

$$\Pr[\max_{0 \leqslant j \leqslant n} \mid X_j \mid \geqslant \lambda) \leqslant \frac{1}{\lambda^2} EX_n^2$$

Convergence

Convergence in probability: A sequence of r.v. $\{X_n\}$ is said to converge to a r.v. X in probability if, for every $\epsilon > 0$, there exists $\delta > 0$ and $N(\delta, \epsilon)$ such that

$$\Pr[\mid X_n - X \mid \geqslant \epsilon] < \delta \qquad \text{for} \quad n \geqslant N(\epsilon, \delta)$$

Convergence with probability one: A sequence of r.v. $\{X_n\}$ is said to converge with probability one to a r.v. X if $\Pr[X_n \to X] = 1$, i.e., for every $\epsilon > 0$,

$$\Pr\left[\bigcap_n \bigcup_m | X_{n+m} - X | \geqslant \epsilon\right] = 0$$

or, equivalently,

$$\Pr\left[\bigcup_m [| X_{n+m} - X | \geqslant \epsilon]\right] \to 0, \qquad n \to \infty$$

Convergence in L^1: A sequence of r.v. $\{X_n\}$, $X_n \in L^1$, $n = 1,...,$ converges to a r.v. X in L^1 if

$$EX_n \to EX, \qquad n \to \infty$$

Examples

Convergence in probability does not imply convergence with probability one.

Let X_n be independent such that

$$\Pr[X_n = 0] = 1 - 1/n, \qquad \Pr[X_n = 1] = 1/n$$

Then, $X_n \to 0$ in probability one but not with probability one. As a matter of fact, the set of ω such that $\{X_n(\omega)\}$ will be one infinitely often has the probability one.

Convergence with probability one does not imply convergence in L^1.

Let X_n be independent, $EX_n < \infty$ with

$$\Pr[X_n = 0] = 1 - 1/n^2, \qquad \Pr[X_n = n^2] = 1/n^2$$

Then $X_n \to 0$ with probability one but

$$EX_n = 1 \not\to EX = 0$$

Some Convergence Theorems

Monotone Convergence Theorem. Consider a r.v. X and a sequence of r.v. X_n such that $X_n \uparrow X$. Then $EX = \lim_n EX_n$.

Martingale Convergence Theorem. Let $\{X_i, \mathscr{F}_i, i = 1, 2,...\}$ be a martingale on $(\Omega, \mathscr{F}, P)$.

If $E|X_n| \leqslant k < \infty$, then

$$\lim_n X_n = X_\infty \quad \text{exists a.e., and} \quad E|X_\infty| \leqslant k$$

Given $(\Omega, \mathscr{F}, P)$, let $X \in L^1$ and $\mathscr{F}_n$ be nondecreasing σ fields. Then

$$E(X \mid \mathscr{F}_n) \to E(X \mid \vee_n \mathscr{F}_n) \quad \text{a.e. and} \quad L^1$$

Appendix II

Pseudoinverse

Introduction

There are many situations where it is necessary to solve an algebraic equation such as

$$Ax = y \tag{1}$$

where A is an $m \times n$ matrix, x is an n vector, and y is an m vector. If A is square and nonsingular, i.e., if $m = n =$ rank A, then (1) can be solved as $x = X^{-1}y$. Even when A^{-1} does not exist, it is desirable to solve (1) in some approximate sense. For example, if $m > n =$ rank A, then we may be interested in $x = (A'A)^{-1}A'y$ as a solution to (1) in some cases.

We have seen one example in Chapter II, Section 2, where it is necessary to minimize a quadratic expression

$$[(u, Su) + 2(u, Tx)] \tag{2}$$

with respect to u even when S^{-1} is not defined. In (2), as shown in Appendix A of Chapter II, the desired u is obtained by solving the linear equation

$$Su + Tx = 0 \tag{3}$$

when S^{-1} exists.

Even if S^{-1} does not exist and (3) cannot be solved for u, one is still interested in finding u which minimizes the quadratic form (2). This minimizing u satisfies (3) in an approximate sense, to be described below.

The concept of pseudoinverses of matrices is introduced as an extension of the concept of the inverses to provide the method of solving the equation such as (1) or (3) approximately in such a way that, when the inverses of appropriate matrices exist, these two concepts coincide.[65,110,111]

There are several ways to introduce and derive properties of pseudoinverses.[27,47,142] Here, the starting point is taken to be the minimization of a quadratic form. Namely, the problem of solving (1) for x is transformed into that of minimizing a quadratic form

$$\| Ax - y \|^2 = (Ax - y, Ax - y) \tag{4}$$

with respect to x. After all, this is the way the pseudoinverses appeared in our problem in Chapter II, Section 2.

The minimizing x of (4) may not be unique. Then, let us agree to pick that x with the smallest norm $\| x \|$ as our solution. This seems quite reasonable for (2), for example, since one is usually interested in minimizing the performance index (2) with the smallest fuel, energy, etc., which may be interpreted as u having the smallest norm. For further discussions of quadratic programming problems to select unique solutions by successive use of various criteria, see Mortensen.[107]

Denote x with these properties by

$$x = A^+ y \tag{5}$$

where A^+ is called the pseudoinverse of A. Note that when A^{-1} exists, $x = A^{-1}y$ satisfies the conditions of uniquely minimizing $\| Ax - y \|^2$.

Construction of the Pseudoinverse

The development of the pseudoinverses presented here is based on the properties of finite-dimensional Hermitian matrices.[107] See Beutler[27] for similar treatments of pseudoinverses in more general spaces.

Let A be an $m \times n$ matrix with rank r, C^n an n-dimensional complex Euclidean vector space, $\mathscr{R}(A)$ the range space of A, $\mathscr{N}(A)$ the null space of A, and A^* the complex conjugate transpose of A. Vectors are column vectors. Vectors with asterisk are, therefore, row vectors with complex conjugate components.

Our construction of A^+ is based on the polar decomposition of A:

$$A = \sum_{i=1}^{r} \lambda_i f_i g_i^* \tag{6}$$

where $r = \text{rank } A$, and where f_i and g_i are column vectors, $f_i \in C^m$, $g_i \in C^n$, such that

$$f_i^* f_j = \delta_{ij}, \qquad g_i^* g_j = \delta_{ij}, \qquad 1 \leqslant i, j \leqslant r$$

and where

$$\lambda_i > 0$$

is defined later by (15).

In (6), $f_i g_j{}^*$ is a dyad ($m \times n$ matrix of rank one) and $f_i{}^* f_j$ is complex inner product.

Then it will be shown that A^+ with the desired property is obtained as

$$A^+ = \sum_{i=1}^{r} \lambda_i^{-1} g_i f_i{}^* \tag{7}$$

First, (6) is derived. Let x_i, $i = 1, \ldots, n$, be an orthonormal basis in C^n.

Then one can write

$$x = \sum_{i=1}^{n} \alpha_i x_i \qquad \text{for all} \quad x \in C^n$$

where

$$\alpha_i = x_i{}^* x$$

Now

$$Ax = \sum_{i=1}^{n} \alpha_i A x_i$$

where

$$A x_i \in C^m, \qquad i = 1, \ldots, n$$

since A is a linear mapping from C^n to C^m. Since rank $A = r$, let $y_1, \ldots, y_r$ be the orthonormal basis of $\mathscr{R}(A) \subset C^m$.

Then, generally,

$$A x_i = \sum_{j=1}^{r} \beta_{ij} y_j \tag{8}$$

By suitable choices of bases in C^m and C^n, β_{ij} in (8) can be made quite simple.

To find such suitable bases, consider A^*A, an $(n \times n)$ matrix. It is a Hermitian linear transformation on C_n, hence it has n nonnegative real eigenvalues, and its matrix representation can be made diagonal by a proper choice of a basis in C^n.

Since

$$r = \text{rank } A = \text{rank } A^*A$$

exactly r of the n eigenvalues are nonzero. Let ρ_i be such positive eigenvalues with eigenvector z_i, $1 \leqslant i \leqslant r$,

$$A^*Az_i = \rho_i z_i, \qquad \rho_i > 0, \quad z_i \in C^n, \quad i = 1,..., r \tag{9}$$

Multiplying (9) by A from left yields

$$AA^*(Az_i) = \rho_i(Az_i), \qquad i = 1,..., r \tag{10}$$

This shows that, if z_i is an eigenvalue of A^*A, with the eigenvalue ρ_i, then the Az_i are eigenvectors of AA^* with the same eigenvalue ρ_i.

Since AA^* has exactly r positive eigenvalues, rank (AA^*) = rank $(A^*A) = r$, hence A^*A and AA^* have ρ_i, $i = 1,..., r$, as their common eigenvalues.

Orthonormalize the eigenvectors for A^*A and denote them by $\{g_i, i = 1, ..., r\}$:

$$A^*Ag_i = \rho_i g_i, \qquad i = 1,..., r$$

We have seen in (10) that Ag_i are eigenvectors for AA^*. Choose the eigenvectors for AA^* $\{f_i, i = 1,..., r\}$ by

$$Ag_i = \beta_i f_i, \qquad i = 1,..., r$$

Since

$$g_i{}^*A^*Ag_j = \rho_j g_i{}^*g_j = \bar{\beta}_i\beta_j f_i{}^*f_j$$

$\{f_i, i = 1,..., r\}$ is also orthonormal if $\beta_i = (\rho_i)^{1/2}$, $i = 1,..., r$. Thus

$$Ag_i = \rho_i^{1/2} f_i \tag{11}$$

It is known that[142]

$$C^n = \mathscr{R}(A^*A) \oplus \mathscr{N}(A^*A), \qquad C^m = \mathscr{R}(AA^*) \oplus \mathscr{N}(AA^*)$$

Since $\mathscr{R}(A^*A) \subset C^n$, complete an orthonormal basis for C^n by adding $g_{r+1},..., g_n$ to $\{g_i, i = 1,..., r\}$. Similarly, $\mathscr{R}(AA^*) \subset C^m$ and an orthonormal basis for C^m is obtained by augmenting $\{f_i, i = 1,..., r\}$ by $\{f_{r+1},..., f_m\}$. Then $\{g_{r+1}, ..., g_n\}$ spans $\mathscr{N}(A^*A)$ and $\{f_{r+1},..., f_m\}$ spans $\mathscr{N}(AA^*)$.

It is also true[142] that $\mathscr{R}(A) \perp \mathscr{N}(A^*)$ and $\mathscr{R}(A^*) \perp \mathscr{N}(A)$. Thus

$$A^*Ax = 0 \Leftrightarrow Ax = 0, \qquad AA^*x = 0 \Leftrightarrow A^*x = 0$$

Hence, from $A^*Ag_j = 0$,

$$Ag_j = 0, \qquad j = r + 1,..., n$$

and from $AA^*f_j = 0$, (12)

$$A^*f_j = 0, \qquad j = r+1, \ldots, m$$

From (11) and (12),

$$\begin{aligned} A^*f_i &= \rho_i^{1/2} g_i, \qquad & i &= 1, \ldots, r \\ A^*f_i &= 0, & i &= r+1, \ldots, m \end{aligned} \tag{13}$$

Since $\{g_1, \ldots, g_n\}$ is a basis in C^n, given any $x \in C^n$,

$$x = \sum_1^n \alpha_i g_i$$

where

$$\alpha_i = g_i{}^* x$$

and

$$Ax = \sum_1^n \alpha_i A g_i = \sum_1^r \alpha_i \rho_i^{1/2} f_i \tag{14}$$

or

$$A = \sum_1^r \lambda_i f_i g_i{}^* \qquad \text{where} \quad \lambda_i = \rho_i^{1/2} \tag{15}$$

where ρ_i is a positive eigenvalue of A^*A, $1 \leqslant i \leqslant r$. Equation (14) is the simplified form of (8). Thus $\mathscr{R}(A)$ is spanned by f_i, $i = 1, \ldots, r$.

Now we consider Problem (4) with $x \in C^n$. Write

$$y = v + w \qquad \text{with} \quad v \in \mathscr{R}(A)$$

Then v has the expansion

$$v = \sum_1^r \gamma_i f_i \qquad \text{with} \quad \gamma_i = f_i{}^* v \tag{16}$$

Now consider a vector related to x by

$$\hat{x} = \sum_1^r \frac{\alpha_i}{\rho_i^{1/2}} g_i + \sum_{r+1}^n \alpha_j g_j$$

Then, from (14),

$$A\hat{x} = v$$

and therefore

$$\| A\hat{x} - y \|^2 \leqslant \| Ax - y \|^2 \qquad \text{for all} \quad x \in C^n$$

Also

$$\| \hat{x} \|^2 = \left\| \sum_1^r \frac{\alpha_i}{\rho_i^{1/2}} g_i \right\|^2 + \left\| \sum_{r+1}^n \alpha_j g_j \right\|^2 \geqslant \sum_1^r \frac{\alpha_i^2}{\rho_i}$$

Therefore, one sees that A^+ is defined by

$$A^+ v = \sum_1^r \frac{\alpha_i}{\rho_i^{1/2}} g_i = \sum_1^r g_i \frac{f_i^* v}{\rho_i^{1/2}}$$

or

$$A^+ = \sum_1^r \lambda_i^{-1} g_i f_i^* \tag{17}$$

where λ_i is given by (15). From (15),

$$A^* = \sum_1^r \lambda_i g_i f_i^*$$

and

$$(A^*)^+ = \sum_1^r \lambda_i^{-1} f_i g_i^* \tag{18}$$

From (17) and (18), one can readily obtain useful identities:

(i) $AA^+A = A$
(ii) $A^+AA^+ = A^+$
(iii) $(A^+)^* = (A^*)^+$
(iv) $(A^+)^+ = A$

For example, (i) is obtained from (15) and (17);

$$\begin{aligned} AA^+A &= \left(\sum_1^r \lambda_i f_i g_i^*\right)\left(\sum_1^r \lambda_j^{-1} g_j f_j^*\right)\left(\sum_1^r \lambda_k f_k g_k^*\right) \\ &= \sum_{i,j,k} \lambda_i \lambda_j^{-1} \lambda_k f_i g_i^* g_j f_j^* f_k g_k^* \\ &= \sum_i \lambda_i f_i g_i^* = A \end{aligned}$$

since

$$g_i^* g_j = \delta_{ij}, \qquad f_i^* f_k = \delta_{jk}$$

Expressions such as (17) and (18) can be put in to matrix forms. Define

$$F = \{f_1, \ldots, f_m\}: \qquad m \times m \quad \text{matrix}$$
$$G = \{g_1, \ldots, g_n\}: \qquad n \times n \quad \text{matrix}$$

and

$$R = \left(\begin{array}{ccc:c} \lambda_1 & & 0 & \\ & \ddots & & 0 \\ 0 & & \lambda_r & \\ \hdashline 0 & & & 0 \end{array}\right): \qquad m \times n \quad \text{matrix}$$

The orthonormalities of f's and g's imply

$$FF^* = F^*F = I_m$$

where I_m is the m-dimensional identity matrix. Similarly,

$$GG^* = G^*G = I_n$$

From (15) and (17),

$$A = FRG^*$$

and

$$A^+ = GR^+F^*$$

where

$$R^+ = \left(\begin{array}{ccc:c} \lambda_1^{-1} & & & \\ & \ddots & & 0 \\ & & \lambda_r^{-1} & \\ \hdashline & 0 & & 0 \end{array}\right)$$

Similarly,

$$A^* = GR'F^*$$

$$(A^*)^+ = F(R^+)'G^*$$

where ['] means a transpose.

Appendix III

Multidimensional Normal Distributions

In this section certain useful facts on multidimensional normal distributions are listed for easy reference. An attempt has been made to give a logical self-contained presentation wherever deemed possible without unduly lengthening the material presented in the appendix. Most of the proofs are omitted. For a more complete discussion of the material, the reader is referred to Cramèr[39] and Miller.[106]

Random Matrices and Random Vectors

Definition 1. A random $(m \times n)$ matrix Z is a matrix

$$Z = (z_{ij}), \qquad i = 1, 2, ..., m, \quad j = 1, 2, ..., n$$

of random variables $z_{11}, z_{12}, ..., z_{mn}$.

Definition 2.

$$EZ = (Ez_{ij})$$

Lemma 1. Let Z be an $(m \times n)$ random matrix. Let A be a $(l \times m)$ matrix, B an $(n \times q)$ matrix, and C a $(l \times q)$ matrix. Then

$$E(AZB + C) = A(EZ)B + C$$

Example 1. Let X be an n-dimensional random vector with mean μ, i.e.,

$$EX = \mu$$

Then $(X - \mu)(X - \mu)'$ is an $(n \times n)$ random matrix and

$$\Lambda \triangleq E[(X - \mu)(X - \mu)']$$

is defined as a covariance matrix of the random vector X. Thus, by definition, Λ is a symmetric positive matrix (i.e., either positive definite or positive semidefinite).

Characteristic Functions and Probability Density Functions

Definition 3. The characteristic function (abbreviated ch.f.) of an n-dimensional random vector X is

$$\phi(t) \triangleq E\, e^{it'X}$$

for every real n-dimensional vector t.

When $n = 1$, this definition reduces to the usual definition of the ch.f. of a random variable.

Theorem 1. Given two distribution functions F_1 and F_2 on the real line, if the corresponding ch.f. is such that $\phi_1(t) \equiv \phi_2(t)$, then $F_1 \equiv F_2$. The inversion formula

$$\lim_{T \to \infty} \frac{1}{2\pi} \int_{-T}^{T} \frac{e^{-ita} - e^{-itb}}{it} \phi(t)\, dt$$

exists and is equal to $F(b) - F(a)$, where a and b are any continuity points of F.

This theorem has the corresponding generalization to n-dimensional Euclidean space.

Definition 4. When an n-dimensional random vector X has the ch.f.

$$\phi(t) = \exp[it'm - \tfrac{1}{2}t'\Lambda t]$$

where m is an n vector and Λ is a positive $(n \times n)$ matrix, then the corresponding distribution function is called normal (n-dimensional normal distribution) and is denoted by $N(m, \Lambda)$.

The parameters of the distribution function m and Λ are the mean and the covariance matrix of X, respectively.

Lemma 2. The ch.f. of the marginal distribution of any k components of an n-dimensional vector, say $x_1, x_2, \ldots, x_k$, is obtained from $\phi(t)$ by putting $t_i = 0$, $k + 1 \leqslant i \leqslant n$.

Notice that normal distributions are specified as soon as m and Λ are specified, in other words as soon as the mean and covariance matrices of the random vector X are specified. From (1), (2), and (5),

$$E(X) = m, \qquad E(X - m)(X - m)' = CC' = \Lambda \tag{7}$$

Partition of Random Vectors

Let X be an n-dimensional random vector with $N(m, \Lambda)$. Assume that Λ is nonsingular. Partition X into two vectors X_1 and X_2 of k and $(n - k)$ dimensions each. Define

$$\begin{aligned} \Lambda_{11} &= E(X_1 - m_1)(X_1 - m_1)', & m_1 &= E(X_1) \\ \Lambda_{22} &= E(X_2 - m_2)(X_2 - m_2)', & m_2 &= E(X_2) \\ \Lambda_{12} &= E(X_1 - m_1)(X_2 - m_2)' \end{aligned} \tag{8}$$

If $\Lambda_{12} = 0$, then

$$|\Lambda| = |\Lambda_{11}|\,|\Lambda_{22}|$$

$$\Lambda^{-1} = \begin{pmatrix} \Lambda_{11}^{-1} & 0 \\ 0 & \Lambda_{22}^{-1} \end{pmatrix}$$

and the density function of x becomes, from Eq. (6),

$$\begin{aligned} f(X_1, X_2) &= \frac{1}{(2\pi)^{k/2}\,|\Lambda_{11}|^{1/2}} \exp(-\{\tfrac{1}{2}(X_1 - m_1)'\Lambda_{11}^{-1}(X_1 - m_1)\}) \\ &\quad \times \frac{1}{(2\pi)^{(n-k)/2}\,|\Lambda_{22}|^{1/2}} \exp(-\{\tfrac{1}{2}(X^2 - m^2)'\Lambda_{22}^{-1}(X^2 - m^2)\}) \end{aligned} \tag{9}$$

Therefore when $\Lambda_{12} = 0$, X_1 and X_2 are independent and are distributed according to $N(m_1, \Lambda_{11})$ and $N(m_2, \Lambda_{22})$, respectively. Thus, we have

Lemma 4. Two uncorrelated normally distributed random vectors are independent.

Conditional Distributions

Generally,

$$\Lambda_{12} \neq 0$$

In this case, introduce random vectors Y_1 and Y_2 of k and $(n - k)$ dimensions each by

$$Y_1 = X_1 - DX_2$$
$$Y_2 = X_2$$

where D is a $(k \times (n - k))$ matrix to be specified in a moment. Then

$$E[(Y_1 - EY_1)(Y_2 - EY_2)'] = \Lambda_{12} - D\Lambda_{22}$$

If D is chosen to be

$$D = \Lambda_{12}\Lambda_{22}^{-1}$$

then Y_1 and Y_2 are uncorrelated normally distributed random vectors, hence independent from Lemma 4.

Since Y_1 and Y_2 are normally distributed, their distributions are specified by computing their means μ_1 and μ_2 and covariance matrices Σ_1 and Σ_2 where

$$\mu_1 = EY_1 = m_1 - \Lambda_{12}\Lambda_{22}^{-1}m_2$$
$$\mu_2 = EY_2 = m_2$$
$$\Sigma_1 = E[(Y_1 - EY_1)(Y_1 - EY_1)']$$
$$= \Lambda_{11} - \Lambda_{12}\Lambda_{22}^{-1}\Lambda_{21}$$

and

$$\Sigma_2 = E[(Y_2 - EY_2)(Y_2 - EY_2)']$$
$$= \Lambda_{22}$$

Then the joint density function of (X_1, X_2) when $\Lambda_{12} \neq 0$ is given by

$$f(X_1, X_2) = g(Y_1) \cdot g(Y_2) \mid J \mid$$

where

$$J = \left| \frac{\partial y_i}{\partial x_j} \right|, \qquad 1 \leqslant i, j \leqslant n$$

Then the conditional probability density function of X_1 on X is obtained from

$$f(X_1 \mid X_2) = \frac{f(X_1, X_2)}{f(X_2)}$$

This has the normal distribution law

$$N(m_1 + \Lambda_{12}\Lambda_{22}^{-1}(X_2 - m_2), \Sigma_1) \tag{10}$$

Thus the conditional mean of a normally distributed random vector is linear in the conditioning vector X_2 :

$$E(X_1 \mid X_2) = E(X_1) + \Lambda_{12}\Lambda_{22}^{-1}(X_2 - E(X_2))$$

Singular Distributions

When a covariance matrix Λ is positive semidefinite, then Λ^{-1} does not exist and the density function cannot be obtained from the inversion formula as has been done in previous sections.

The function $\phi(t)$ of Definition 3, however, is still a ch.f. Therefore, there exists a corresponding d.f. even when Λ^{-1} does not exist. (For necessary and sufficient condition for $\phi(t)$ to be a ch.f. see, for example, Cramèr).

This d.f. can be obtained as a limit of a d.f. with nonsingular $\Lambda_k \to \Lambda$. For example, let

$$\Lambda_k = \Lambda + \epsilon_k t' t, \qquad \epsilon_k > 0$$

Λ_k^{-1} now exists and the corresponding d.f. F_k can be found. As $\epsilon_k \to 0$, a ch.f. with Λ_k converges at every t.

Then it can be shown that there exists a d.f. F with $\phi(t)$ as its ch.f. to which F_k converges at every continuity point of F. This limit d.f. is called a singular normal distribution.

Let

$$\text{rank } \Lambda = r < n$$

Consider a linear transformation

$$Y = C(X - m) \tag{11}$$

Then the covariance matrix M of y is given by

$$M = E(YY') = C\Lambda C'.$$

Choose C as an orthogonal matrix such that Λ is diagonalized. Since

$$\text{rank } M = \text{rank } \Lambda = r$$

only r diagonal elements of M are positive, the rest are all zero. Therefore,

$$E(y_i^2) > 0, \qquad 1 \leqslant i \leqslant r$$
$$E(y_j^2) = 0, \qquad r + 1 \leqslant j \leqslant n$$

by rearranging components of y, if necessary.

This implies

$$y_j = 0 \qquad \text{with probability 1,} \quad r + 1 \leqslant j \leqslant n$$

Then, from Eq. (11),

$$X = m + C'Y$$

It is seen therefore that random variables $x_1, \ldots, x_n$, with probability 1, can be expressed as linear combinations of r uncorrelated random variables $y_1, \ldots, y_r$. Since each y_i, $1 \leqslant i \leqslant r$, is a linear combination of $x_1, \ldots, x_n$, each y_i, $1 \leqslant i \leqslant r$, is normally distributed and is independent.

Theorem 2. If n random variables are distributed normally with the covariance matrix of rank r, then they can be expressed as linear combinations of r independent and normally distributed random variables with probability 1.

Appendix IV

Sufficient Statistics

INTRODUCTION

We have discussed in some detail, in Chapters II–IV, optimal control problems for a class of dynamical systems involving some random variables in the description of their environments, plants, and observation schemes. We have obtained optimal control policies for these problems by first computing γ's, the conditional expected values of the criterion function, conditioned on the currently available information about the system and on the utilized control variables, then minimizing γ's over the class of admissible control variables.

In order to compute γ_k we needed the conditional probability density functions $p(x_k \mid y^{k-1}, u^{k-1})$ or $p(x_{k-1} \mid y^{k-1}, u^{k-1})$. Also, in Chapter IV, we needed expressions for $p(\mu_k \mid \nu^k)$ and $p(\nu_k \mid \nu^{k-1})$ in computing γ_k, where μ_k and ν_k are the unobserved and observed portions of the Markov process $\{\zeta_k\}$, $\zeta_k = (\mu_k, \nu_k)$.

Generally, expressions for $p(x_k \mid y^k, u^k)$, $p(\mu_k \mid \nu^k)$, and $p(\nu_k \mid \nu^k)$ are rather complicated functions of the observed data and employed controls. An optimal controller must remember all past observations and past controls ν^k or y^k and u^k in order to synthesize the optimal control vector at time $k + 1$. Thus, the optimal controller generally needs a memory which grows with time.

For certain classes of systems, however, we have seen that it is possible to compute these conditional probability densities by knowing only a fixed and finite number of quantities $t_k(y^k, u^{k-1})$ of fixed dimensions. They are functions of the observed data (y^k, u^{k-1}); i.e., for some problems, optimal control policies can be synthesized by knowing values of only a finite fixed number of functions of the observed data thus eliminating the need for a growing memory.

Random variables which are functions of observed realizations (i.e., samples) of another random variable are called statistics.

When statistics carry with them all information about the probability distribution function that can possibly be extracted by studying observed data, they are called sufficient statistics.[73]

Thus, we can realize optimal control policies with controllers of finite memory capacity if sufficient statistics exist for the problems. See, for example, Section 3 of Chapter II, Section 5 of Chapter III, and Section 2,B of Chapter IV.

Sufficient Statistics

A formal definition of sufficient statistics for random variables with probability density functions is as follows.[73]

Let z^n be a random sample with the probability density function $p(z^n; \theta)$ which depends on a parameter $\theta \in \Theta$. A statistic $T_1 = t_1(z^n)$ (a real-valued function) is called a sufficient statistic for θ if and only if, for any other real-valued statistics $T_2, ..., T_n$ such that the Jacobian is not identically zero, the conditional probability density function $p(t_2, ..., t_n \mid t_1)$ of $T_2, ..., T_n$ given $T_1 = t_1$ is independent of θ. Namely, not only does θ not appear in $p(t_2, ..., t_n \mid t_1)$ but also the domain of $p(t_2, ..., t_n \mid t_1)$ does not depend on θ.

A vector-valued sufficient statistic is similarly defined as a finite collection of real-valued sufficient statistics. The above definition is somewhat inconvenient to apply, since one must test conditional density functions of all statistics for the dependence on θ. We have a criterion called the Fisher–Neyman criterion or factorization theorem which is much more convenient in practice to test if given statistics are sufficient or not. We state the theorem when the probability density function exists and when its domain is independent of θ.

Factorization Theorem. T is a sufficient statistic for θ if and only if it is possible to factor the joint probability density function as

$$p(z^n; \theta) = g(z^n)\, h(T, \theta)$$

where g does not involve θ.

Therefore, when a sufficient statistic T exists, an optimal controller needs to remember only T, and the problem of growing memories does not arise.

We will now consider an example to illustrate the above discussion. In Section 4, the implications of the existence of sufficient statistics on controller memory requirements are further considered.

EXAMPLES[73]

Consider a sample of size 2, $z^2 = (z_1, z_2)$ where z_1 and z_2 are independent Gaussian random variables with unknown mean θ and known variance 1.

Then

$$t_1 = z_1 + z_2$$

is a sufficient statistic for θ.

This can be seen, for example, by directly applying the definition.

Consider any statistic $t_2 = f(z_1, z_2)$ such that z_1 and z_2 are expressed by

$$z_1 = k_1(t_1, t_2)$$
$$z_2 = k_2(t_1, t_2)$$

and the Jacobian is nonzero.

Then, by writing the density function for z^2,

$$p(t_1, t_2; \theta) = p(k_1(t_1, t_2), k_2(t_1, t_2)) \mid J \mid$$
$$= \frac{\mid J \mid}{2\pi} \exp\left(-\frac{1}{2}\left[\frac{(t_1 - 2\theta)^2}{2} + \frac{t_1^2 \quad 4\, k_1(t_1, t_2)\, k_2(t_1, t_2)}{2}\right]\right)$$

where J is independent of θ.

Since

$$p(t_1; \theta) = \frac{1}{(2\pi)^{1/2}} \exp(-\tfrac{1}{4}(t_1 - 2\theta)^2)$$

the conditional density of t_2 given t_1 becomes

$$p(t_2 \mid t_1; \theta) = \frac{J}{(2\pi)^{1/2}} \exp\left(-\frac{t_1^2 - 4k_1k_2}{4}\right)$$

which is independent of θ. Therefore t_1 is a sufficient statistic for θ. Actually, that t_1 is a sufficient statistic for θ can be seen much more directly by applying the Fisher–Neyman criterion, by writing

$$p(z_1, z_2; \theta) = g(t_1, \theta)\, h(z_1, z_2)$$

where

$$g(t_1, \theta) = \frac{1}{(2\pi)^{1/2}} \exp\left(-\frac{(t_1 - 2\theta)^2}{4}\right)$$

$$h(z_1, z_2) = \frac{1}{(2\pi)^{1/2}} \exp\left(-\frac{(z_1 - z_2)^2}{4}\right)$$

Other examples are found in Hogg and Craig.[73]

Self-Reproducing Distribution Function

One of the extraordinary features of Gaussian random variables is that the transformations of a priori probability distribution functions by the Bayes rule into a posteriori distributions turn out to preserve the normal forms of the probability distribution functions when the plant and the observation equations are linear in the random variables. A normal distribution function is completely specified by its mean and covariance matrix. See, for example, Appendix III. This is the reason why the controllers need remember at any time i only two quantities, μ_i and Γ_i, in the examples of Section 4, Chapter II, and the controllers can compute the next set of numbers μ_{i+1} and Γ_{i+1} given a new set of data y_{i+1} and u_i. Unfortunately not all probability distribution functions share this property of "reproducing" the form of the a priori distribution function in the a posteriori distribution function form.

If the a posteriori distribution functions have the same form as the a priori distribution functions, then only a set of parameter values need be determined to specify the particular distribution function.

Since it is infinitely easier to specify a set of numbers than a function, one sees the advantage of choosing a priori probability distribution functions which reproduce in Bayesian optimization of control problems. See Spragins[128,129] for detail.

We have already mentioned that normal distributions have the self-reproducing property.

As another example, consider random variables y such that

$$y_i = \begin{cases} 1 & \text{with probability } \theta \\ 0 & \text{with probability } 1 - \theta \end{cases}$$

and where

$$p_0(\theta) = \frac{\Gamma(a + b + 2)}{\Gamma(a + 1)\,\Gamma(b + 1)}\,\theta^a(1 - \theta)^b, \qquad 0 < \theta < 1$$

which is a Beta distribution.

Then in the sequence of n independent observations $(y_0, \dots, y_{n-1})$, if 1 is observed r times, then

$$p(\theta \mid y^{n-1}) = \frac{\Gamma(n + a + b + 2)}{\Gamma(a + r + 1)\,\Gamma(n + b - r + 1)}\,\theta^{a+r}(1 - \theta)^{n+b-r} \tag{1}$$

which is also a Beta distribution.

As already mentioned, what makes this class of probability distribution functions very attractive in adaptive control system analysis is the fact that the effect of learning can be summarized by a finite number of parameter values, and the a posteriori distributions are determined by specifying the parameter values; for example, by $a + r$ and $n + b - r$ in (1). If $p_0(\theta)$ is of the nonreproducing type, then the form of distributions is not preserved by the Bayes rules and actual implementation or computation of the learning process may become very elaborate and not feasible because the record of all past observations must be carried to obtain the a posteriori distributions.

In the reproducing-type distributions, the effect of past observations is expressed compactly as the parameter values of the a posteriori distribution where functional forms remain the same as the a priori distribution. Thus, the amount of data needed by the system to specify the a posteriori distributions remains constant and does not grow with the number of observations. Therefore, in obtaining a posteriori distributions, it is not necessary to retain all past observations. It suffices to obtain only a certain fixed number of functions of the observations as parameter values. Thus, the parameter values in the a posteriori distribution is equivalent to the past observations.

One suspects, therefore, that there must be a close connection between the class of distribution functions with the self-reproducing property and the existence of a finite number of sufficient statistics for such distribution functions because sufficient statistics, when they exist, serve to pick a particular distribution out of the class and any member of the class of self-reproducing distribution functions is specified by a set of parameters.

Spragins[128] showed that, under certain assumptions, distribution functions $F(x \mid \theta)$ reproduce themselves if and only if a sufficient statistic for θ of fixed dimension exists. We now present heuristic arguments for this fact.

Let $y_0, \ldots, y_n$ be a set of observations, and let them have a joint density function with the unknown parameter θ with $p_0(\theta)$ as its a priori density function.

By the Bayes rule,

$$p(\theta \mid y^n) = \frac{p_0(\theta)\, p(y^n \mid \theta)}{\int d\theta\, p_0(\theta)\, p(y^n \mid \theta)}$$

$$= \frac{p(y^n \mid \theta)}{\int p(y^n \mid \theta)\, d\theta} \cdot \frac{p_0(\theta)}{\int p_0(\theta) \left[\dfrac{p(y^n \mid \theta)}{\int p(y^n \mid \theta)\, d\theta} \right] d\theta} \tag{2}$$

Note that the choice of an a priori distribution has effects only on the second factor of (2). Let a parameter t_n be a sufficient statistic. Then the joint density can be written as

$$p(y^n \mid \theta) = g(y^n)\, h(t_n, \theta) \tag{3}$$

The first factor of (2) then has the form

$$\frac{p(y^n \mid \theta)}{\int d\theta\, p(y^n \mid \theta)} = \frac{h(t_n, \theta)}{\int d\theta\, h(t_n, \theta)}$$

which has the same form for all n and only the value t_n differs for each n. Thus, in (2),

$$p(\theta \mid y^n) = \frac{h(t_n, \theta)}{\int d\theta\, h(t_n, \theta)} \cdot \frac{p_0(\theta)}{\int d\theta \dfrac{p_0(\theta)\, h(t_n, \theta)}{\int d\theta\, h(t_n, \theta)}}$$

The normalized likelihood function

$$q(\theta \mid y^n) \triangleq \frac{p(y^n \mid \theta)}{\int d\theta\, p(y^n \mid \theta)} = \frac{h(t_n, \theta)}{\int h(t_n, \theta)\, d\theta} \tag{4}$$

reproduces itself under Bayes' rule.

On the other hand, assume that the normalized likelihood is of the reproducing type. Then it has the form

$$q(\theta \mid y^n) = f(\theta, s_n(y^n))$$

where s_n is the parameter value through which q depends on the observations. Then, from (4),

$$\begin{aligned} p(y^n \mid \theta) &= q(\theta, s_n) \int p(y^n \mid \theta)\, d\theta \\ &= q(\theta, s_n)\, k(y^n) \end{aligned}$$

where

$$k(y^n) = \int p(y^n \mid \theta)\, d\theta$$

which shows by the factorization theorem of sufficient statistics that s_n is a sufficient statistic.

Therefore the class of self-reproducing probability distribution is the class of distributions with sufficient statistics.

Lastly, let us note that in the discussions of various convergence questions in Bayesian optimization problems involving incompletely known stochastic processes, if a priori distribution functions with the self-reproducing property are assumed for these stochastic processes, then the question of a posteriori distributions for the stochastic processes converging to the true distribution is equivalent to that of sufficient statistics in a posteriori distributions for the unknown parameters converging to the true values of these parameters (with probability one).

Bibliography

ARIS, R., "Discrete Dynamic Programming." Random House (Blaisdell), New York, 1964.

BELLMAN, R., "Introduction to Matrix Analysis." McGraw-Hill, New York, 1960.

CHUNG, K. L., "Markov Chains with Stationary Transition Probabilities." Springer-Verlag, Berlin, 1960.

FEL'DBAUM, A. A., "Optimal Control Systems." Academic Press, New York, 1966.

HALMOS, P., "Finite Dimensional Vector Spaces." Van Nostrand, Princeton, New Jersey, 1958.

KEMENY, J. G., SNELL, J. L., and KNAPP, A. W., "Denumerable Markov Chains." Van Nostrand, Princeton, New Jersey, 1966.

TOU, J. T., "Modern Control Theory." McGraw-Hill, New York, 1965.

VARGA, R. S., "Matrix Iterative Analysis." Prentice-Hall, Englewood Cliffs, New Jersey, 1962.

WILDE, D. J., "Optimum Seeking Methods." Prentice-Hall, Englewood Cliffs, New Jersey, 1964.

REFERENCES

1. AITCHISON, J., and BROWN, J. A. C., "The Lognormal Distribution." Cambridge Univ. Press, London and New York, 1957.
2. ASTROM, K. J., Optimal control of Markov processes with incomplete state information. *J. Math. Anal. Appl.* **10**, 174–205 (1965).
3. AOKI, M., On the application of dynamic programming and numerical experimentation as applied to adaptive control systems. Tech. Rep. No. 60-16, Dep. of Eng., Univ. of California, Los Angeles (November 1959).
4. AOKI, M., On the optimal and suboptimal policies in the choice of control variables for final value control systems. *IRE Intern. Conv. Record*, Part IV, 15–22 (1960).
5. AOKI, M., Dynamic programming approach to the final value control system with a random variable having an unknown distribution function. *IRE Trans. Auto. Control* **5**, No. 4, 270–282 (1960).
6. AOKI, M., Stochastic time-optimal control systems. *Trans. Amer. Inst. Elec. Engrs.* **80**, Part II, 41–46 (1961).
7. AOKI, M., On minimum of maximum expected deviation from an unstable equilibrium position of a randomly perturbed control system. *IRE PGAC*, *AC*-7, 1–12 (1962).
8. AOKI, M., Successive approximations in solving some control system optimization problems, II. *J. Math. Anal. Appl.* **5**, No. 3, 418–434 (December 1962).
9. AOKI, M., On a successive approximation technique in solving some control system optimization problems, I. *Trans. ASME Ser. D. J. Basic Eng.* **85**, 177–180 (June 1963).
10. AOKI, M., On the approximation of trajectories and its application to control systems optimization problems. *J. Math. Anal. Appl.* **9**, No. 1, 23–41 (August 1964).
11. AOKI, M., On optimal and suboptimal control policies in control systems, "Advances in Control Systems," Vol. 1, Chap. 1, C. T. Leondes, ed. Academic Press, New York, 1964.

12. Aoki, M,, On performance losses in some adaptive control systems, I. *Trans. ASME Ser. D. J. Basic Eng.* **87**, No. 1, 90–94 (March 1965).
13. Aoki, M., On some convergence questions in Bayesian optimization problems. *IEEE Trans. Auto. Control*, **10**, No. 2, 180–182 (April 1965).
14. Aoki, M., Optimal Bayesian and min.-max. control of class of stochastic and adaptive dynamic systems. Proc. IFAC Symposium System Engineering for Control System Design, 77–84, Tokyo (August 1965).
15. Aoki, M., Optimal control of partially observable Markovian control systems. *J. Franklin Inst.* **280**, No. 5, 367–386 (November 1965).
16. Aoki, M., Optimal control policies for dynamical systems whose characteristics change randomly at random times. Presented at Third Congress IFAC, London (June 1966).
17. Aoki, M., and Huddle, J. R., On estimation of the state vector of a stochastic system using a minimal order observer. Proc. Joint Auto. Control Conf. 694–702, Univ. Washington, Seattle (August 1966).
18. Balakrishnan, A. V., A general theory of nonlinear estimation problems in control systems. *J. Math. Anal. Appl.* **8**, No. 1, 4–30 (February 1964).
19. Baum, E. K., Optimal control of long running stochastic systems. Res. Rep. No. PIBMRI-1220-1964, Polytech. Inst. of Brooklyn (June 1964).
20. Bellman, R., "Dynamic Programming." Princeton Univ. Press, Princeton, New Jersey, 1957.
21. Bellman, R, and Kalaba, R., Dynamic programming and adaptive processes, mathematical foundation. *IRE Trans. Auto. Control* **5**, 5–10 (January 1960).
22. Bellman, R., "Adaptive Control Processes: A Guided Tour." Princeton Univ. Press, Princeton, New Jersey, 1961.
23. Bellman, R., and Dreyfus, S., "Applied Dynamic Programming." Princeton Univ. Press, Princeton, New Jersey, 1962.
24. Bellman, R. E., Kagiwada, H. H., Kalaba, R. E., and Sridhar, R., Invariant imbedding and nonlinear filtering Theory. RAND, RM-4374-PR (December 1964).
25. Bertram, J. E., and Sarachik, P. E., On the stability of circuits with randomly varying parameters. *IRE Trans. Inform. Theory* **5**, 260–270 (1959).
26. Bertram, J. E., Control by stochastic adjustment. Amer. Inst. Elec. Engrs. Paper 59-1156, Application and Industry (1959).
27. Beutler, F. J., The operator theory of the pseudo-inverse; 1, Bounded operators. *J. Math. Anal. Appl.* **10**, 1–11 (1965).
28. Bharucha-Reid, A. T., On the theory of random equations. *Proc. Symp. Appl. Math.* **14**, 40–69 (1964).
29. Blackwell, D., and Girshick, M. A., "Theory of Games and Statistical Decisions." Wiley, New York, 1954.
30. Blackwell, D., On the functional equation of dynamic programming. *J. Math. Anal. Appl.* **2**, 273–276 (1961).
31. Blackwell, D., and Dubins, L., Merging of opinions with increasing information. *Ann. Math. Statist.* **33**, No. 3, 882-886 (September 1962).
32. Blackwell, D., Discounted dynamic programming. *Ann. Math. Statist.* **36**, 226–235 (1965).
33. Breakwell, J. V., A doubly singular problem in optimal interplanetary guidance. *J. Soc. Ind. Appl. Math., Ser. A. Control* **3**, No. 1, 71–77 (1965).
33a. Bryson, A. E., and Johansen, D. E., Linear filtering for time-varying systems using measurements containing colored noise. *IEEE Trans. Auto. Control* **10**, No. 1, 4–10 (Jan. 1965).

34. Bogdanoff, J. L., and Kozin, F., Moments of the output of linear random systems. *J. Acoust. Soc. Amer.* **34**, No. 8, 1063–1066 (1962).
35. Bucy, R. S., Nonlinear filtering theory. *IEEE Trans. PGAC* **10**, No. 2, 198 (April 1965).
36. Bucy, R. S., Stability and positive supermartingale. *J. Differential Equations* **1**, No. 2, 151–155 (April 1965).
37. Caughey, T. K., Commets on: On the Stability of Random Systems. *J. Acoust. Soc. Amer.* **32**, No. 10, 1356 (1960).
38. Caughey, T. K., and Dienes, J. K., The behavior of systems with random parametric excitation. *J. Math. Phys.* **41**, No. 4, 300–318 (1962).
39. Cramèr, H., "Mathematical Method of Statistics." Princeton Univ. Press, Princeton, New Jersey, 1946.
40. Cox, H., On the estimation of state variables and parameters for noisy dynamic systems. *IEEE Trans. Auto. Control* **9**, No. 1, 5–12 (January 1964).
41. Cox, H., Estimation of state variables via dynamic programming. Conference Paper, Proc. Joint Auto. Control Conf., 376–381, Stanford, California (1964).
42. Daly, R. F., Adaptive binary detectors. Tech. Rep. No. 2003-2, Stanford Electronics Labs. Stanford, California (June 1961).
43. Daly, R. F., The adaptive binary-detection problem on the real line. Tech. Rep. No. 2003-3, Stanford Electronics Labs., Stanford, California (February 1962).
44. Davenport, W. B., Jr., and Root, W. L., "An Introduction to the Theory of Random Signals and Noise." McGraw-Hill, New York, 1958.
45. Deley, G. W., and Franklin, G. F., Optimal bounded control of linear sampled-data systems with quadratic loss. *Trans. ASME Ser. D. J. Basic Eng.* **87**, No. 1, 135–141 (March 1965).
46. Detchmendy, D. M., and Sridhar, R., Sequential estimation of states and parameters in noisy nonlinear dynamical systems. Proc. Joint Auto. Control Conf., 56–63, Troy, New York (1965).
47. Desoer, C. A., and Whalen, B. H., A note on pseudo-inverses. *J. Soc. Anal. Appl. Math.* **11**, No. 2, 442–447 (June 1963).
47a. Doob, J. L., "Stochastic Processes." Wiley, New York, 1953.
48. Drenick, R. F., and Shaw, L., Optimal control of linear plants with random parameters. *IEEE Trans. Auto. Control* **9**, No. 3, 236–244 (July 1964).
49. Dreyfus, S. E., Some types of optimal control of stochastic systems. *J. Soc. Ind. Appl. Math. Ser. A. Control* **2**, No. 1, 120–134 (1964).
50. Dubins, L. E., and Savage, L. J., "How to Gamble if You Must, Inequalities for Stochastic Processes." McGraw-Hill, New York, 1965.
51. Dvoretzky, A., On stochastic approximation. Proc. Third Berkeley Symposium on Mathematical Statistics and Probability **1**, 39–55, Univ. of California Press, Berkeley, California (1956).
51a. Dynkin, E. B., Controlled random sequences. *Theor. Probability Appl.* **10**, No. 1, 1–14 (1965).
52. Eaton, J. H., and Zadeh, L. A., Optimal pursuit strategies in discrete state probabilistic systems. *Trans. ASME Ser. D. J. Basic Eng.* **84**, 23–29 (1961)
53. Eaton, J. H., Discrete-time interrupted stochastic control processes. *J. Math. Anal. Appl.* **5**, 287–305 (1962).
54. Farrison, J. B., Identification and control of random-parameter discrete systems. Tech. Rep. No. 6302-4, System Theory Lab., Stanford Electronics Labs., Stanford, California (January 1964).
55. Fel'dbaum, A. A., Theory of dual control, I, II, III, IV. *Automat. Remote Control* **21**,

No. 9, 1240-49, No. 11, 1453-64 (1960); **22**, No. 1, 3–16, No. 2, 129–143 (1961).

56. Fel'dbaum, A. A., On the optimal control of Markov objects. *Automat. Remote Control* **23**, No. 8, 993–1007 (1962).
57. Fel'dbaum, A. A., Optimal systems, "Disciplines and Techniques of System Control," Chap. VII, J. Peschon, ed. Random House (Blaisdell), New York, 1965.
58. Feller, W., "An Introduction to Probability Theory and its Application," Vol. I, 2nd ed. Wiley, New York, 1957.
58a. Ferguson, T., "Statistical Inference." Academic Press, New York, to appear in 1966.
59. Fitzgerald, R. J., A gradient method for optimizing stochastic systems. Paper presented at IEEE-OSA Symposium on Recent Advances in Optimization Techniques, Carnegie Inst. Tech., Pittsburgh, Pennsylvania (April 1965).
60. Florentin, J. J., Optimal control of continuous time Markov stochastic systems. *J. Electron. Control* **10**, No. 6, 473–488 (1961).
61. Florentin, J. J., "Partial Observability and Optimal Control," *J. Electron. Control* **11**, 263–279 (1962).
61a. Friedland, B., Than, F. E., and Sarachik, P. E., Stability problems in randomly excited dynamic systems. Proc. Joint Auto. Control Conf. 848–861, Univ. Washington, Seattle (August 1966).
62. Fukao, T., Some fundamental properties of adaptive control processes, I. *Bull. Electrotech. Lab.* **28**, No. 1, 1–19 (in Japanese) (January 1964) (*Tokyo*).
62a. Fukao, T. System identification by Bayesian learning processes, I and II. *Bull. Electrotech. Lab.* **29**, No. 5, 364–380 (1960).
63. Galtieri, C. A., Problems of estimation in discrete-time processes. Res. Paper RJ-315, IBM San Jose Res. Lab., San Jose, California (August 1964).
63a. Gantmacher, F. R., "The Theory of Matrices," Vol. 1. Chelsea, New York, 1960.
64. Gardner, L. A., Jr., "Adaptive Predictors." Trans. Third Prague Conference on Information Theory, Statistical Decision Function, Random Processes, 123–192, Publishing House of the Czechoslovak Academy of Sciences, Prague, 1964.
65. Greville, T. N. E., Some applications of the pseudo-inverse of a matrix. *Ind. Appl. Math. Rev.* **2**, No. 1, 15–22 (1960).
66. Grishin, V. P., On a calculation method related to a process of automatic adaptation. *Automat. Remote Control* **23**, No. 12, 1502–1509 (1962).
67. Gunckel, T. L., III, and Franklin, G. F., A general solution for linear sampled-data control. *Trans. ASME Ser. D. J. Basic Eng.* **85**, 197–201 (1963).
68. Hadley, G., "Linear Programming." Addison-Wesley, Reading, Massachusetts, 1962.
69. Hadley, G., Nonlinear and dynamic programming, "Stochastic Programming," Chap. 5. Addison-Wesley, Reading, Massachusetts, 1964.
70. Hahn, W., "Theory and Application of Liapunov's Direct Method, Translated by S. H. Lehnigk and H. H. Hosenthien. Prentice-Hall, Englewood Cliffs, New Jersey, 1963.
71. Hans, O., "Random Fixed Point Theorems," Trans. Prague Conference on Information Theory, Statistical Decision Function, 105–125, Prague Czechoslovak Academy of Sciences, Prague, 1956.
71a. Ho, Y. C., The method of least squares and optimal Filtering theory. RM-3329-PR, RAND Corporation, Santa Monica, California, (October 1962).
72. Ho, Y. C., and Lee, R. C. K., A Bayesian approach to problems in stochastic estimation and control. Proc. Joint Auto. Control Conf., 382–387, Stanford Univ., Stanford, California (June 1964).

72a. Ho, Y. C., and Whalen, B. H. An approach to the identification and control of linear dynamic systems with unknown parameters.
72b. Ho, Y. C., and Lee, R. C. K., Identification of linear dynamic systems. *Inform. Control* **8**, 93–110 (1965).
73. Hogg, R. V., and Craig, A. T., "Introduction to Mathematical Statistics." Macmillan, New York, 1959.
73a. Horowitz, E., Some suboptimal control policies in optimal stochastic control systems. M. S. Thesis, Dep. of Eng., Univ. of California, Los Angeles (June 1966).
74. Householder, A. S., "Principle of Numerical Analysis." McGraw-Hill, N.Y., 1953.
74a. Howard, R., "Dynamic Programming and Markov processes." Wiley, N.Y., 1960.
75. Howard, R. A., Dynamic inference. Tech. Rep. No. 10, Operations Res. Center, MIT, Cambridge, Massachusetts (December 1964).
76. Hsu, J. C., and Meserve, W. E., Decision-making in adaptive control systems. *IRE Trans. Auto. Control* **7**, 24–32 (January 1962).
77. Jaynes, E. T., New engineering applications of information theory. Proc. 1960 Random Function Theory Symposium, 163–203, J. L. Bogdanoff and F. Kozin, eds. Held at Purdue University in 1960, Wiley, New York, 1963.
78. Johansen, D. E., Optimal control of linear stochastic systems with complexity constraints. Tech. Rep., Appl. Res. Lab., Sylvania Electronic Systems, Division of Sylvania Electric Products, Ind., Waltham, Massachusetts.
79. Johns, M. V., Non-parametric Bayes procedures. *Ann. Math. Statist* **28**, No. 3, 649–669 (September 1957).
80. Joseph, P. D., and Tou, J. T., On a linear control theory. *Trans. Amer. Inst. Elec. Engrs.* **80**, Part II, 193–196 (September 1961).
81. Joseph, P. D., Suboptimal linear filtering. Tech. Rep., Space Technology Labs., Inc. (December 1963).
82. Joseph, P. D., On board navigation for rendez-vous missions. Lecture Note for 2-wk Summer Course, Univ. of California Los Angeles, Engineering Extension, Los Angeles, California (1964).
83. Kallianpur, G., A problem in optimum filtering with finite data. *Ann. Math. Statist.* **30**, 659–669 (1959).
84. Kalman, R. E., New methods and results in linear prediction and filtering theory. Tech. Rep. No. 61-1, RIAS, Baltimore, Maryland (1960).
85. Kalman, R. E., A new approach to linear filtering and prediction problems. *Trans. ASME Ser. D. J.* Basic Eng. **82**, 35–45 (1960).
86. Kalman, R. E., and Bucy, R. S., New results in linear filtering and prediction theory. *Trans. ASME Ser. D, J. Basic Eng.* **83**, 95–108 (March 1961).
87. Kalman, R. E., On the general theory of control systems. Proc. First IFAC Congress, Butterworth, London and Washington, D. C. (1961).
88. Kalman, R. E., Englar, T. S., and Bucy, R. S., Fundamental study of adaptive control systems. Tech. Rep. No. ASD-TR-61-27, Vol. 1, RIAS (April 1962).
89. Kalman, R. E., Ho, Y. C., and Narendra, K. S., Controllability of linear dynamical systems. *Contributions to Differential Equations* **1**, No. 2, 189–213 (1963).
89a. Kalman, R. E., Contribution to the theory of optimal control. *Bol. Socieda Matematica Mexicana*, 102–119 (1960).
89b. Karlin, S., Pólya type distributions, II. *Ann. Mat. Stat.* **28**, 281–308 (1957).
90. Kats, I. I., and Krasovskii, N. N., On the stability of systems with random parameters. *Appl. Math. Mech.* (*PMM*) **24**, 809–823 (1960).
91. Kolmogorov, A. N., and Fomin, S. V., "Functional Analysis": Vol. 1, "Metric

and Normal Spaces," Vol. 2, "Measure, Lebesgue Integral, Hilbert Space," English translation. Graylock Press, Rochester, New York, 1957.

91a. Koopmans, T. C., Rubin, H., and Leipnik, R. B., Measuring the equation systems of dynamic economics, *in* "Statistical Inference in Dynamic Economic Models" (T. C. Koopmans, ed.), Chap. II. Wiley, New York, 1950.

92. Krasovskii, N. N., and Lidskii, E. A., Analytical design of controls in systems with random properties, I, II, III. *Automat. Remote Control* **22**, No. 9, 1021-1025, No. 11, 1289–1294, No. 10, 1141–1146 (1961).

93. Krasovskii, N. N., Application of Liapunov's second method to differential systems and equations with delay, "Stability of motion," Translated by J. L. Brenner. Stanford Univ. Press, Stanford, California, 1963.

94. Kozin, F., On almost sure stability of linear systems with random coefficients. *J. Math. Phys.* **42**, No. 1, 59–67 (1963).

95. Kushner, H. J., On the optimum timing of observations for linear control systems with unknown initial state. *IEEE Trans. Auto. Control* **4**, No. 2, 144–150 (April 1964).

96. Kushner, H. J., On the stability of stochastic dynamical systems. *Proc. Nat. Acad. Sci. U.S.A.* **53**, No. 1, 8–12 (January 1965).

97. Kushner, H. J., New theorems and examples in the Liapunov theory of stochastic stability. Proc. Joint Auto. Control Conf., 613–619, Rensselaer Polytech. Inst., Troy, New York, 1965.

98. Laning, J. H., Jr., and Battin, R. H., "Random Processes in Automatic Control." McGraw-Hill, New York, 1956.

99. La Salle, J., and Lefschetz, S., "Stability by Liapunov's Direct Method with Applications." Academic Press, New York, 1961.

100. Lee, R. C. K., Optimal estimation, identification and control. Research Monograph No. 28, MIT Press, Cambridge, Massachusetts (1964).

100a. Lefschetz, S., "Stability of Nonlinear Control Systems." Academic Press, New York, 1965.

101. Linnik, Y. V., "Method of Least Squares and Principles of the Theory of Observations," English translation. Pergamon Press, New York, 1961.

102. Loève, M., "*Probability Theory*." Van Nostrand, Princeton, New Jersey, 1960.

103. Luenberger, D. G., Observing the state of a linear system. *IEEE Trans. Military Electron.* **8**, No. 2, 74–80 (April 1964).

104. Meditch, J. S., Suboptimal linear filtering for continuous dynamic processes. Tech. Rep., Aerospace Corp. Contract No. AFO4(695)-469 (July 15, 1964).

104a. Meditch, J. S., A class of suboptimal linear controls. Proc. Joint Auto. Control Conf. 776–782, Univ. Washington, Seattle (August 1966).

104b. Merriam, C. W., III, "Optimization Theory of the Design of Feedback Control Systems." McGraw-Hill, New York, 1964.

105. Magill, D. T., Optimal adaptive estimation of sampled stochastic processes. *IEEE Trans. Auto. Control* **10**, No. 4, 434–439 (October 1965).

105a. Meier, L, III, Combined optimum control and estimation theory. Tech. Rep. No. NAS2-2457, Stanford Res. Inst., Menlo Park, California (October 1965).

106. Miller. K. S., "Multidimensional Gaussian Distributions," SIAM Series in Applied Mathematics. Wiley, New York, 1964.

107. Mortensen, R. E., A note on polar decomposition and the generalized inverse of an arbitrary matrix, Notes on System Theory," Vol. VI. Electronics Res. Lab., Univ. of California, Berkeley, California, April 1964.

108. Odanaka, T., Minimization of the probability of the maximum deviation, in

Japanese. Proc. 7th Joint Auto. Control Conf. of Japan, Univ. of Nagoya, Japan (October 1964).

109. ORFORD, R. J., Optimal stochastic control systems. *J. Math. Anal. Appl.* **6**, 419–429 (1963).

109a. ORR, R. E., Optimal linear discrete filtering. M. S. Thesis, Dep. of Eng., Univ. of California, Los Angeles (1964).

109b. PAPOULIS. A. "Probability, Random Variables and Stochastic Processes." McGraw-. Hill, New York, 1965.

109c. PESCHON, J., MEIER, L., III, LARSON, R. E., FOY, W. H., Jr., and DAWSON, C. H. Information requirements for guidance and control systems. Tech. Rep, No. NAS2-2457, Stanford Res. Inst., Menlo Park, California (November 1965),

110. PENROSE, R., A generalized inverse for matrices. *Proc. Cambridge Phil. Soc.* **51**. 406–413 (1955).

111. PENROSE, R., On best approximate solution of linear matrix equations. *Proc. Cambridge Phil. Soc.* **52**, 17–19 (1956).

112. PENTECOST, E. E., and STUBBRUD, A. R., Synthesis of computationally efficient sequential linear estimators. To appear in *IEEE Trans. Aerospace Electron. Systems.*

113. PFEIFFER, C. G., A dynamic programming analysis of multiple guidance corrections of a trajectory. *A.I.A.A. Journal* **3**, No. 9, 1674–1681 (September 1965).

114. PONTRYAGIN, L.S., *et al.*, "The Mathematical Theory of Optimal Processes," English translation. Wiley (Interscience), New York, 1962.

114a. PYKE, R., Stationary probabilities for a semi-Markov process with finitely many states (abstract). *Ann. Math. Statist.* **31**, No. 1, 240 (March 1960).

115. RAIFFA, M., and SCHLAIFER, R., "*Applied Statistical Decision Theory.*" Harvard Business School, Boston, Massachusetts, 1961.

116. RAVIV, J., Decision making in incompleted known stochastic systems. Rep. 64–25, Electronic Res. Lab., Univ. of California, Berkeley, California (July 1964).

117. ROBBINS, H., An empirical Bayes approach to statistics. Proc. Third Berkeley Symposium on Math. Statist, Prob. 1, 157–164, Univ. of California, Berkeley, California (1955).

118. Robbins, H., The empirical Bayes approach to statistical decision problems. *Ann. Math. Statist.* **35**, No. 1, 1–20 (March 1964).

119. ROSENBROCK, H. H., The foundation of optimal control, with an application to large systems. *Automatica* **1**, 263–288 (December 1963).

120. ROSENBROCK, H. H., An example of optimal adaptive control. *J. Electron. Control* **13**, 557–567 (1964).

121. SAMUELS, J. C., On the mean square stability of random linear systems. *IRE Trans. Inform. Theory* **5**, 248–259 (May 1959).

122. SAMUELS, J. C., and ERINGEN, A. C., On stochastic linear systems. *J. Math. Phys.* **38**, No. 2, 83–103 (1959).

123. SAMUELS, J. C., On the stability of random systems and the stabilization of deterministic systems with random noise. *J. Acoust. Soc. Amer.* **32**, No. 5, 594–601 (1960).

124. SCHULTZ, P. R., An optimal control problem with state vector measurement error, "Advances in Control Systems," Chap. V, Vol. 1, C. T. Leondes, ed. Academic Press, New York, 1964.

125. SORENSON, H. W., On the controllability and observability of optimal stochastic linear control systems. Tech. Memorandum, LAS-3329, A. C. Electronics Division, General Motors (January 1966).

125a. SORENSON, H. W., Nonlinear perturbation theory for estimation and control of time discrete stochastic systems. Ph. D. Thesis, Dept. of Eng. Univ. of California, Los Angeles (1966).

126. Spang, H. A., III, Optimum control of an unknown linear plant using Bayesian estimation of the error. *Proc. Nat. Electron. Conf.* **20**, 620–625 (1964).

127. Spang, H. A., III, The effects of estimation of error on the control of an unknown linear plant. Rep. No. 65-RL-3907E, General Electric Res. Lab., Schenectady, New York (April 1965).

128. Spragins, J. D., Reproducing distributions for machine learning. TR 6103-7, Stanford Electronics Labs., Stanford, California (November 1963).

129. Spragins, J. D., A note on the iterative application of Bayes' rule. *IEEE Trans. Inform. Theory* **11**, No. 4, 544–549 (October 1965).

130. Stratonovich, R. L., Conditional Markov processes. *Theor. Probability Appl.* **5**, No. 2, 156–178 (1960).

131. Strauch, R. E., Negative dynamic programming. Ph. D. Thesis in Statistics, Univ. of California, Berkeley, California (1965).

132. Sussman, R., Optimal control of systems with stochastic disturbances. Rep. AF-AFOSR 139–63, Electronics Res. Lab. Univ. of California, Berkeley, California (November 1963).

133. Sworder, D. D., Synthesis of optimal, discrete time, adaptive control systems. Ph. D. Thesis, Dep. of Eng., Univ. of California, Los Angeles, California (June 1964).

134. Sworder, D. D., Minmax control of discrete time stochastic systems. *Soc. Ind. Appl. Math. Ser. A. Control* **2**, No. 3, 433–449 (1964).

135. Sworder, D. D., Control of a linear system with a Markov property. *IEEE Trans. Auto. Control* **10**, No. 3, 294–300 (July 1965).

135a. Sworder, D. D., A study of the relationship between identification and optimization in adaptive control problems. *J. Franklin Inst.* **281**, No. 3, 198-213 (March 1966).

136. Sworder, D. D. and Aoki, M., On the control system equivalents of some decision theoretic theorems. *J. Math. Anal. Appl.* **10**, No. 2, 424–438 (1965).

136a. Theil, H., A note on certainty equivalence in dynamic planning. *Econometrics* **25**, No. 2, 346–349 (April 1957).

137. Truxal, J. G., and Padalino, J. J., Decision theory, "Adaptive Control Systems," Chap. 15, Mishkin and Braun, eds. McGraw-Hill, New York, 1961.

138. Ula, N., and Kim, M., An empirical Bayes approach to adaptive control. *J. Franklin Inst.* **280**, No. 3, 189–204 (September 1965).

139. Vajda, S., "Mathematical Programming." Addison-Wesley, Reading, Massachusetts, 1961.

140. Watanabe, S., Information theoretic aspects of inductive and deductive inference. *IBM J. Res. Develop.*, 208–2310 (April 1960).

141. Wonham, W. M., Stochastic problems in optimal control. RIAS Tech. Rep., 63–14 (May 1963).

141a. Yakubovitch, V. A., The matrix inequality method in the theory of nonlinear control systems, I. *Autom. Remote Control* **25**, No. 7, 1017–1029 (July 1964).

142. Zadeh, L. A., and Desoer, C. A., "Linear System Theory: The State Space Approach." McGraw-Hill, New York, 1963.

143. Zames, G., On the stability of nonlinear time-varying feedback systems. *Proc. Natl. Election. Conf.* **20**, 725 (October 1964).

LIST OF SYMBOLS

A^+	Pseudoinverse of A
$A > B$	$A - B$ is positive definite
$A \geqslant B$	$(A - B)$ is nonnegative definite
A_k, F_k	Plant matrix
B_k, G_k	Control matrix
c_k	Actual output of a system
d_k	Desired output of a system
$d(x, y)$	$= dx\,dy$
e_k	In general, denotes error vector
$E(\cdot)$	Expectation of
H_k	Observation matrix
J	Criterion function
J_k	Criterion function of estimation problems
$\lvert J_\xi \rvert$, $\lvert J_\eta \rvert$	Jacobian determinants
K_i	Gain of Kalman filter
$\mathscr{L}(\cdot)$	Distribution function
N	Total duration of control process
$N(\theta, \sigma^2)$	Normal distribution function with mean θ and variance σ^2
$\mathscr{N}(\cdot)$	Null space
$p(\cdot)$	Probability density function
$p(\cdot \mid \cdot)$	Conditional probability density function
$P(\cdot)$	Probability
R_k	$= E(W_k)$
$\mathscr{R}(\cdot)$	Range space
s_k, t_k	Sufficient statistics
$\mathrm{tr}(\cdot)$	Trace of a matrix

u_i	Control variable at ith time instant
u^i	$= (u_0, u_1, \ldots, u_i)$
U_i	Admissible set of control at ith time instant
$\mathrm{Var}(\cdot)$	Variance of
$W_k(x_k, u_{k-1})$	Contribution to J from kth time instant
x_i	State variable of a system at ith time instant
x^i	$= (x_0, x_1, \ldots, x_i)$
x_i^*	$= E(x_i \mid y^i)$
$\tilde{x}_i$	$= x_i - x_i^*$
$\hat{x}_i$	$= E(x_i \mid y^{i-1})$
X_k, ζ_k	Augmented state vector
y_i	Observed value of x_i
y^i	$= (y_0, \ldots, y_i)$
Y_i	The set on which the observed value is taken at ith time instant
α	Unknown or random parameter in the system plant equation
β	Unknown or random parameter in the system observation equation
γ_k	$= \lambda_k + \int \gamma_{k+1}^* p(y_k \mid y^{k-1}, u^{k-1})\, dy_k$
Γ_i	Covariance matrix associated with μ_i
Γ_i, Σ_i, P_i, Q_i, R_i, S_i, Λ_i	Usually refer to covariance matrices

η_i	Random disturbance in the observation equation at ith time instant
θ	Mean of random variable or random parameters
$\Theta, \Theta_1, \Theta_\alpha$, etc.	Known parameter spaces
λ_k	$= E(W_k \mid y^{k-1}, u^{k-2})$
μ_i	$= E(x_i \mid y^i)$
ξ_i	Random disturbance in the plant equation at ith time instant
$\rho_i(u_i)$	$= p(u_i \mid y^i, u^{i-1})$
σ^2	Variance of a random variable
ϕ^i	$= (\phi_0, \ldots, \phi_i)$
Φ_k	Plant matrix of augmented system
Ψ_k	Gain matrix of augmented system
$*$	Used as a superscript, the asterisk generally indicates optimality in the sense of the context
$\hat{}$	A caret over a symbol generally indicates the estimated value
$\bar{}$	A bar over a symbol generally indicates the expected value
$\triangleq$	Equality by definition
$\Vert \cdot \Vert_V$	$= (\cdot, V \cdot)$
$'$	A prime indicates the transpose of a vector or a matrix
$\Vert \cdot \Vert$	Euclidean norm of a vector
$(\cdot, \cdot)$	Inner product
$\langle \cdot \rangle_k$	$= E(\cdot \mid \theta_k)$
$\oplus$	Direct sum

Author Index

Numbers in parentheses are reference numbers and indicate that an author's work is referred to although his name is not cited in the text. Numbers in italic show the page on which the complete reference is listed.

Subject Index

116/-